ADVANCED STRUCTURAL ANALYSIS

SIDNEY F. BORG, Dr.Eng. *AND* JOSEPH J. GENNARO, M.S.

*Professor and Head
of Civil Engineering
Stevens Institute of Technology*

*Assistant Professor
of Civil Engineering
Stevens Institute of Technology*

D. VAN NOSTRAND COMPANY, INC.

PRINCETON, NEW JERSEY

TORONTO

NEW YORK

LONDON

D. VAN NOSTRAND COMPANY, INC.

120 Alexander St., Princeton, New Jersey *(Principal office)*
24 West 40th Street, New York 18, New York

D. VAN NOSTRAND COMPANY, LTD.
358, Kensington High Street, London, W.14, England

D. VAN NOSTRAND COMPANY (Canada) LTD.
25 Hollinger Road, Toronto 16, Canada

First Published April 1959

Reprinted August 1960

PRINTED IN THE UNITED STATES OF AMERICA

PREFACE

The book was written because of the authors' firm conviction that the structural engineer—civil, mechanical, naval, or other—meets in his professional work many topics not generally treated in the usual textbooks of structural design.

For example, the civil engineer of today (and this will probably be even more true in the future) must know the principles of slab and shell analysis. The mechanical, aeronautical, and naval engineers find that temperature analyses enter into their work more and more. Torsion must occasionally be considered in modern civil engineering structural design, and numerical methods are such a powerful tool that they are useful in all fields of applied mechanics, including structural theory. Electronic computer machines enable the structural engineer to solve problems which would otherwise be unsolvable.

These are typical of the advances being made in structural engineering—advances which, the authors feel, have not in general been adequately covered in textbooks on this subject. Thus, a major aim in writing the book was to include a discussion of the newer methods. Equally important was the requirement that the discussions be in a form which would be useful not only to the student, but also to the practicing engineer. This implied a twofold requirement on the form of presentation. First, the basic theoretical treatment must be as complete and as rigorous as possible. Second, the actual engineering application of the theory (which frequently requires more or less modification of the rigorous theory) must also be given—and all must be given in a form that practicing engineers would find useful.

In order that the entire work present a unified coverage and be most coherent, it was decided to present, in the first several chapters, a treatment of those topics generally thought of as "classical" in structural analysis. This material on deflections and statically indeterminate structures is presented in some detail, and the authors attempted to give the energy method portion of this discussion in a more rigorous and complete form than is generally done. The first four chapters comprise a detailed, thorough discussion of the various methods for determining deflections and for solving statically indeterminate structures. They include a fairly complete discussion of moment distribution and slope deflection

iii

methods and, in particular, discuss the frame constant tables of the Portland Cement Association which are so useful in the design of members with variable moments of inertia. It is felt that this first portion of the text can be included in a senior course in civil, aeronautical, or mechanical engineering.

The remainder of the text will probably be more suitable for advanced undergraduate and graduate courses in engineering and will also, it is hoped, prove to be of use to the practicing structural designer.

The theory of arches is covered in considerable detail, particularly with reference to higher-order effects—the so-called "deflection theory"—which incidentally is very closely related to a similar approach in suspension bridge design.

The chapter on numerical and approximate methods of analysis should be useful not only for the indicated applications to the subject matter of the text, but also because these methods are general and find application in all the fields of applied mechanics. It is hoped that the presentation given herein will be a suitable introduction for the graduate student and practicing engineer to this very important field of applied mathematics.

Another chapter is devoted to methods of torsion analysis and the related topics of shear center and unsymmetrical bending. The subject is first approached from the theoretical point of view, following which actual design procedures are discussed.

Plasticity design or ultimate design (limit design)—the subject which bears the same relation to the science of rheology that strength of materials bears to the science of elasticity—is presented in an introductory form, and typical beam applications are discussed. The emphasis here (as in all other parts of the book) is on the engineering applications. Toward this end, the significance of limit design is emphasized insofar as (a) economy of material and (b) simplification of analysis of statically indeterminate structures is concerned.

Because shells are being used more and more commonly in civil engineering structures, the authors thought this topic required some special treatment in a book of this kind. The subject is gone into quite thoroughly—the basic theory and the actual design methods are examined critically. The relation between the various so-called "exact" theories and the different approximate methods is discussed, and illustrative problems are introduced to bring out many of the important features of the different theories. Special attention is given to the American Society of Civil Engineers Design Manual Method, since, in the authors' opinion, this will very probably become the standard method of design for the United States. However, some attention is also given to a procedure in use in England, and the two methods are compared.

Following this a method of temperature analysis is presented which should be useful in many different modern applications—not the least of which would be to the design of nuclear reactor components subject to temperature stresses.

The final chapter presents an introductory treatment of electronic computer machines. These inevitably will find more and more application in structural analysis problems. Following a short descriptive section dealing with the various types of computers, a brief treatment of matrix algebra is presented. One formulation, suitable for digital machine programing, is given of a statically indeterminate problem, and finally a typical rigid frame problem is set up and the machine solution is described in detail.

To clarify and broaden the theoretical coverage, many illustrative examples have been included in the text. In all cases these illustrate the application of the theory under discussion. Also, for student use, it was deemed necessary that assignment problems be included as well. A number of these are given at the end of most chapters.

It is impossible to discuss completely all of the topics considered in this text. Indeed, it is not even possible to include all of the different subjects that are pertinent to the various chapters. To remedy this, the authors have given a fairly comprehensive list of references. It is hoped that these will assist the student or engineer by calling to his attention some of the many reference books in the vast field of structural analysis.

To the best of the authors' knowledge, much of the material given herein has not previously appeared in book form. It is perhaps inevitable that, in a work of this type, errors will occur. The authors will be grateful if these are called to their attention.

The authors wish to thank all those who have assisted in the preparation of this book. Special thanks are due to several graduate students who solved numerous problems included in the text and at the ends of various chapters. In addition, particular thanks are due the authors of standard textbooks and research papers which were liberally referred to in preparing the textual material. Wherever possible acknowledgment for this assistance is made in footnotes.

S. F. BORG
JOSEPH J. GENNARO

Hoboken, N. J.
March 1959

CONTENTS

Chapter 1

DEFLECTIONS

1-1 Introduction

In structural analysis the displacements induced by the applied loads are commonly called deflections. The total deflection of a point can be produced by axial or transverse forces which induce direct bending, shear or torsion stresses, or combinations of these. It may be said that deflections are an indication of the state of stress within a given material and as such furnish a means of correlating stress and strain both theoretically and experimentally. In addition, considerations of deflection (and consequently strain) enable one to set up the compatibility conditions used in solving statically indeterminate structures.

For our purposes, we may say that there are, in general, three different procedures for determining the deflections of engineering structures. All three will be discussed in this chapter. These are:

1. Integration of the deflection differential equation of the beam. This may be accomplished either by straightforward integration or by integration based upon analogies (as in the moment area and conjugate beam methods of Arts. 1-9 and 1-12).

2. The strain energy stored in a structure and the use of the Law of Conservation of Energy permit one to determine deflections of the general engineering structure.

3. Graphical methods can frequently be used to advantage in determining particular deflections—such as in the case of trusses.

Deflections are the visible indications of the response of a structure to load. This response is a function of the frequency, intensity, and duration of loading, as well as of the physical properties of the materials forming the structure. The response is ordinarily quite complex since most actual loads are very variable both as to intensity, duration, direction, and frequency.

Also the physical properties of the material forming a structure are not necessarily uniform. This is apparent if one considers the variations in cross section of a rolled steel section and the multiplicity of materials that constitute the structure of a building. It would appear

1

impossible, therefore, that anything less than a statistical analysis can take into account the possible variations in loading and materials that actually occur in the usual engineering structures.

The foregoing discussion indicates that it is frequently difficult (and perhaps impossible) to determine the exact displacements of engineering structures. However, in engineering-type analyses with which this book is concerned, it is possible to make simplifying assumptions which enable one to solve for displacements, stresses, and other elastic quantities to a sufficiently accurate degree for engineering purposes. A brief discussion of these assumptions follows in the next section.

1-2   Assumptions made in engineering structural analysis

The ordinary methods of structural analysis are based upon the following fundamental assumptions:

1. The material is homogeneous and isotropic.

2. The material is stressed within the elastic limit. This is the usual assumption of elementary structural analysis. In recent years, however, this assumption is occasionally waived, in which case the structure is designed in accordance with inelastic or ultimate design methods. See Chapter 8.

3. Displacements are small enough that stresses, deflections, etc., computed from applied loads assumed acting through the undeflected positions will not materially change as the displacements take place.

4. The surface effects of external loads are negligible.

In most of our analyses, loads are treated as static loads acting upon structures assumed to be at rest. The dynamic factors are then automatically compensated for by using appropriate working stresses, factors of safety, etc., which are determined from previous experience and experimentation. The recent use of more advanced mathematical techniques enables one to depart occasionally from the concept of static loads and structures and to determine analytically the response of a structure to time dependent loads capable of mathematical expression. However, except where otherwise stated, the structures discussed in this book will be considered subject to static loads. The structures will be considered at rest in the deflected position and will be assumed to be made of homogeneous, isotropic, and elastic materials.

1-3   Methods of computing deflections

Several methods of computing deflections have been developed and are commonly used. Some of these methods originate from considerations of forces in equilibrium, others from the Law of the Conservation of Energy. Thus, we may speak of the *equilibrium* approach and of the *energy* approach to the solution of deflection problems. For the beam, the differential equation due to bending is fundamental to both approaches and will be presented next.

1-4 Derivation of the differential equation of bending

The differential equation of bending as developed in ordinary mechanics of materials depends upon the following assumptions in addition to those presented in Art. 1-2:

1. Plane sections before bending remain plane after bending.
2. Each cross section is symmetric about the loading plane.

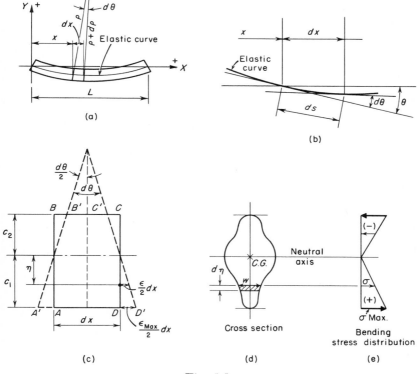

Fig. 1.1

In the theory of elasticity it is shown that assumption 1 is satisfied if the bending moment is either constant or a linear function of distance along the beam.[1]

Fig. 1.1a shows a beam in its deflected position, with the coordinate system selected so that the x axis is along the undeflected axis of the

[1] See S. F. Borg, *An Introduction to Matrix Tensor Methods in Theoretical and Applied Mechanics*, Edwards Bros., Ann Arbor, 1956, Chapter 4.

beam. Thus, the y coordinate of any point of the deflected beam axis is numerically equal to the deflection of the point. It should be noted that the positive and negative directions of the x and y axes have been selected arbitrarily. However, once the choice of axes is made, the mathematical treatment of the problem must be developed consistent with that convention.

Fig. 1.1b shows the relations that exist between the slopes and the locations of two points on the elastic curve a differential distance apart.

From Hooke's Law and the assumption that a plane section before bending remains a plane section after bending, it follows that (see Fig. 1.1c)

$$\frac{\epsilon}{\eta} = \frac{\epsilon_{max}}{\eta_{max}} = \text{constant} = c$$

$$\frac{\sigma}{\epsilon} = \frac{\sigma_{max}}{\epsilon_{max}} = \text{constant} = E \text{ and } \frac{\sigma}{\eta} = cE = \text{constant}$$

where E is the modulus of elasticity of the material, σ is the stress, and ϵ is the unit strain in a fiber located a distance η below the neutral axis. The differential force produced by the normal stresses acting upon a differential strip of area $wd\eta$ located a distance η from the neutral axis (see Fig. 1.1d) is $\sigma wd\eta$, and the moment of this differential force about the neutral axis is $\sigma w\eta d\eta$. By integrating moments over the entire area, one obtains the total moment on the section

$$M = \int_{-c_2}^{c_1} \sigma w\eta d\eta = \int_{-c_2}^{c_1} \frac{\sigma}{\eta} w\eta^2 d\eta = \frac{\sigma}{\eta}\int_{-c_2}^{c_1} w\eta^2 d\eta \qquad (1\text{-}1)$$

The sum of the normal stresses on the cross section must also equal zero. Hence,

$$\int_{-c_2}^{c_1} \sigma w d\eta = 0 = \frac{\sigma}{\eta} \int_{-c_1}^{c_1} w\eta d\eta = 0$$

But $\frac{\sigma}{\eta} \neq 0$; hence,

$$\int_{-c_2}^{c_1} w\eta d\eta = 0$$

a condition satisfied only if η is measured from an axis through the centroid of the cross section. Thus, the neutral axis is also a centroidal axis of the cross section.

Equation (1-1) is equivalent to

$$M = \frac{\sigma}{\eta}\int_{-c_2}^{c_1} w\eta^2 d\eta = \frac{\sigma}{\eta} I = \frac{\sigma_{max}}{c} I \qquad (1\text{-}1a)$$

where I is the moment of inertia of the cross section about the neutral axis. From Fig. 1.1c, by similar triangles,

$$\frac{\frac{1}{2}\epsilon dx}{\eta} = \frac{\frac{1}{2}dx}{\rho} \tag{1-2}$$

where ρ is the instantaneous radius of curvature of the elastic curve. In this problem Hooke's Law takes the form,

$$\frac{\sigma}{\epsilon} = E \tag{1-3}$$

Substituting Equation (1-3) into Equation (1-2) and canceling common factors, we find that

$$\frac{\sigma}{E\eta} = \frac{1}{\rho}$$

But since

$$\frac{\sigma}{\eta} = \frac{M}{I}$$

it follows that

$$\frac{1}{\rho} = \frac{M}{EI} \tag{1-4}$$

$1/\rho$ is the curvature or rate of change of slope of the elastic curve, $d\theta/ds = \dfrac{y''}{(1+y'^2)^{3/2}}$. Hence,

$$\frac{M}{EI} = \frac{1}{\rho} = \frac{d\theta}{ds} = \frac{y''}{(1+y'^2)^{3/2}} \tag{1-5}$$

Equation (1-5) is the fundamental differential equation of bending— the so-called Bernoulli-Euler equation.[2]

For small displacements, $(y')^2$ can be neglected, in comparison to unity, and the differential equation of bending becomes

$$\frac{d^2y}{dx^2} = \frac{M}{EI} \tag{1-6}$$

---

[2] The statement that the curvature of the deflection curve at any point on a bent beam is proportional to the bending moment at that point was first made by Jacob Bernoulli in about 1700. Leonard Euler, in a book published in 1744, extended this and obtained results which are similar in form to those in use today. Hence the name "Bernoulli-Euler" is frequently given to this formula. For a more complete historical discussion of this and other topics in the field of structural engineering, see S. P. Timoshenko, *History of Strength of Materials*, McGraw-Hill Book Company, New York, 1953.

1-5 Solution of the differential equation of bending—method of double integration

Equation (1-6) is a second-order ordinary differential equation. If *EI* is constant and the bending moment *M* is a function of x, this equation can be solved by successive integration. If *EI* is variable, the same general method of solution can be used, provided M/EI is a function of x. Since two successive integrations are required in order to determine the equation of the elastic curve, the procedure is named *the method of double integration*.

The method will be described by solving the illustrative problem shown in Fig. 1.2.

Example: A simple beam is subjected to a uniform load of $(-p)$ lb/ft acting over its entire length (Fig. 1.2a). Determine the slope and deflection of all points on the elastic curve.

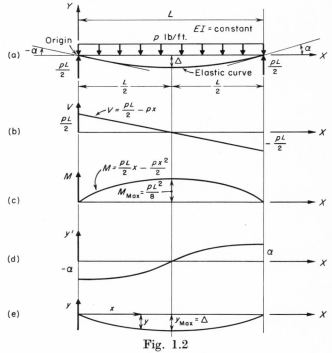

Fig. 1.2

Solution: The reactions are computed and the shear and moment equations obtained and plotted (Figs. 1.2b, 1.2c). In setting up all equations, a common origin of coordinates, arbitrarily selected, is used. With the origin shown, positive angles are counterclockwise, positive moments produce compression in the upper fiber, and positive shears are those whose moments are clockwise about any point within the free body diagram. The moment equation is substituted into the differential Equation (1-6) which now becomes

$$EI \frac{d^2y}{dx^2} = + \left[\frac{pLx}{2} - \frac{px^2}{2} \right] \tag{1-7}$$

The positive sign is used in this case before the brackets since two positive quantities are being equated. The rate of change of slope of the elastic curve d^2y/dx^2 in this case is positive, and the moment equation is also positive for all values of x between O and L. It is necessary to apply this test for signs in all cases before attempting to solve the differential equation of bending.

Successive integrations yield the following:

$$EI \frac{dy}{dx} = + \frac{pLx^2}{4} - \frac{px^3}{6} + C_1 \tag{1-8}$$

$$EI\, y = + \frac{pLx^3}{12} - \frac{px^4}{24} + C_1 x + C_2 \tag{1-9}$$

Equations (1-8) and (1-9) are, respectively, the slope and elastic curve equations. They contain two constants of integration, C_1 and C_2, which must be evaluated. To do this, two boundary conditions relating to the elastic curve must be utilized. These conditions are

(a) at $x=0$, $y=0$
(b) at $x=L$, $y=0$

They may be rewritten as (a), $y(0)=0$; (b), $y(L)=0$. Substituting condition (a) in Equation (1-9), one finds $C_2=0$. If we substitute condition (b) into Equation (1-9), $C_1 = -pL^3/24$; and therefore

$$EI \frac{dy}{dx} = \frac{pLx^2}{4} - \frac{px^3}{6} - \frac{pL^3}{24} \tag{1-10}$$

and

$$EI\, y = \frac{pLx^3}{12} - \frac{px^4}{24} - \frac{pL^3 x}{24} \tag{1-11}$$

are the slope and elastic curve equations that completely define the rotation and deflection of every point on the elastic curve.

The maximum slopes occur at $x=0$, $x=L$, and are

$$y'(0) = -\frac{pL^3}{24\,EI} \qquad\qquad y'(L) = +\frac{pL^3}{24\,EI}$$

The maximum deflection occurs at $L/2$ and is

$$y_{max} = \Delta = -\frac{5}{384} \frac{pL^4}{EI}$$

1-6   Double integration method for beams with discontinuous moment equations

If the loads on the beam are discontinuous, such as a partial uniform or concentrated load, it is not possible to write one moment equation valid throughout the entire beam. In these cases, it is necessary to subdivide the beam into as many parts as there are separate moment equations. This will be illustrated in the following problem, Fig. 1.3.

Example: Determine the equation of the elastic curve for the beam and loading of Fig. 1.3.

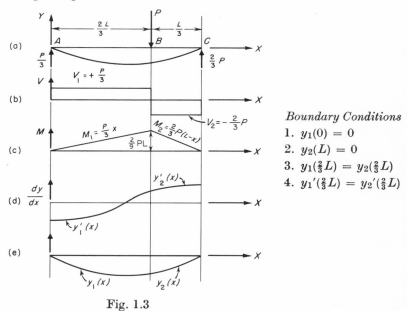

Boundary Conditions

1. $y_1(0) = 0$
2. $y_2(L) = 0$
3. $y_1(\tfrac{2}{3}L) = y_2(\tfrac{2}{3}L)$
4. $y_1{}'(\tfrac{2}{3}L) = y_2{}'(\tfrac{2}{3}L)$

Fig. 1.3

Solution: Equation (1-6) is applied separately to the two parts of the beam AB and BC as shown in Fig. 1.3. The integrations are obtained in the usual way.

$0 < x < \tfrac{2}{3}L$	$\tfrac{2}{3}L < x < L$
$EI\,y_1{}'' = \dfrac{P}{3}\,x$	$EI\,y_2{}'' = -\dfrac{2}{3}\,Px + \dfrac{2}{3}\,PL$
$EI\,y_1{}' = \dfrac{P}{6}\,x^2 + C_1$	$EI\,y_2{}' = -\dfrac{1}{3}\,Px^2 + \dfrac{2}{3}\,PLx + C_3$
$EI\,y_1 = \dfrac{Px^3}{18} + C_1 x + C_2$	$EI\,y_2 = -\dfrac{1}{9}\,Px^3 + \dfrac{1}{3}\,PLx^2 + C_3 x + C_4$

Substituting boundary condition 1 gives $C_2=0$. Condition 3 gives

$$\frac{P}{18}\frac{8}{27}L^3+\frac{2}{3}LC_1 = -\frac{1}{9}P\frac{8}{27}L^3+\frac{1}{3}PL\frac{4}{9}L^2+C_3\frac{2}{3}L+C_4$$

or

$$-\frac{4}{27}PL^2 = -C_1+C_3+\frac{3}{2L}C_4 \tag{1-12}$$

Using condition 4, one obtains

$$\frac{P}{6}\frac{4}{9}PL^2+C_1 = -\frac{1}{3}\frac{4}{9}PL^2+\frac{2}{3}\frac{2}{3}PL^2+C_3$$

or

$$-\frac{2}{9}PL^2 = -C_1+C_3 \tag{1-13}$$

Solving Equations (1-12) and (1-13) simultaneously gives the value of C_4.

$$+\frac{4}{81}PL^3 = C_4$$

Using boundary condition 2,

$$0 = -\frac{1}{9}PL^3+\frac{1}{3}PL^3+C_3L+C_4$$

or

$$C_3 = -\frac{22}{81}PL^2$$

From Equation (1-13), one obtains

$$C_1 = C_3+\frac{2}{9}PL^2 = -\frac{4}{81}PL^2 \text{ and}$$

$$EI\,y_1 = \frac{Px^3}{18}-\frac{4}{81}PL^2x \tag{1-14}$$

$$EI\,y_2 = -\frac{Px^3}{9}+\frac{1}{3}PLx^2-\frac{22}{81}PL^2x+\frac{4}{81}PL^3 \tag{1-15}$$

Equations (1-14) and (1-15) completely define the elastic curve for the beam of Fig. 1.3.

1-7 The relationship between load, shear, and moment

A free body diagram of a differential length of a beam is shown in Fig. 1.4. The shears and moments acting on faces AB and CD are shown positive by hypothesis in accordance with the arbitrary sign convention. This sign convention is repeated here for emphasis.

(a) The internal shear is positive if the moment of the shear force about any point within the free body is clockwise.

(b) The internal bending moment is positive if it produces compression in the upper fibers.

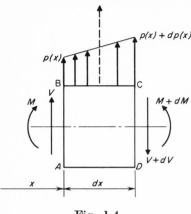

Fig. 1.4

It is assumed that the beam is loaded with some general static loading expressible as a function of x, $[p(x)]$.

If we now apply the conditions of static equilibrium to the free body, we obtain from $\sum F_V = 0$

$$V + [p(x) + \tfrac{1}{2}dp(x)]dx = V + dV$$

If we ignore differentials of higher order and simplify, this becomes

$$dV = p(x)dx \qquad (1\text{-}16)$$

or

$$\frac{dV}{dx} = p(x) \qquad (1\text{-}16a)$$

From $\sum M = 0$ (taking moments about point D),

$$V dx + M + \left[p(x) + \frac{dp(x)}{3} \right] dx \cdot \frac{dx}{2} = M + dM \qquad (1\text{-}17)$$

After simplifying and ignoring differentials of higher order, one obtains

$$dM = V dx \qquad (1\text{-}18)$$

or

$$\frac{dM}{dx} = V \qquad (1\text{-}18a)$$

Successive differentiations of Equation (1-6) give, for constant EI and from Equations (1-16a) and (1-18a),

$$\frac{d^2y}{dx^2} = \frac{M}{EI} \qquad (1\text{-}6)$$

$$EI \frac{d^3y}{dx^3} = \frac{dM}{dx} = V \qquad (1\text{-}19)$$

$$EI \frac{d^4y}{dx^4} = \frac{d^2M}{dx^2} = \frac{dV}{dx} = p(x) \qquad (1\text{-}20)$$

1-8   Deflections by solution of the fourth-order differential equation

Equation (1-20) is used effectively in the solution of deflection problems as follows:

Example: Determine the equations of the elastic curve for the beam and loading of Fig. 1.5.

Boundary Conditions

1. $y(0) = 0$
2. $y''(0) = 0$
3. $y(L) = 0$
4. $y''(L) = 0$

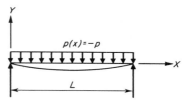

Fig. 1.5

Solution: For this beam and loading, Equation (1-20) gives

$$EI \frac{d^4y}{dx^4} = -p \tag{1-21}$$

Successive integrations give

$$EI \frac{d^3y}{dx^3} = -[px + C_1] \tag{1-22}$$

$$EI \frac{d^2y}{dx^2} = -\left[\frac{px^2}{2} + C_1 x + C_2\right] \tag{1-23}$$

$$EI \frac{dy}{dx} = -\left[\frac{px^3}{6} + C_1 \frac{x^2}{2} + C_2 x + C_3\right] \tag{1-24}$$

and

$$EI \, y = -\left[\frac{px^4}{24} + C_1 \frac{x^3}{6} + C_2 \frac{x^2}{2} + C_3 x + C_4\right] \tag{1-25}$$

The equation of the elastic curve has thus been obtained, by successive integration, in terms of four arbitrary constants.

To evaluate these constants of integration it is necessary to use the four boundary conditions.

From $y(0) = 0$, $C_4 = 0$.

From $y''(0) = 0$, $C_2 = 0$.

The use of condition 3 gives

$$\frac{pL^4}{24} + \frac{C_1 L^3}{6} + C_3 L = 0$$

or

$$\frac{1}{6} C_1 L^2 + C_3 + \frac{pL^3}{24} = 0 \tag{1-26}$$

The use of condition 4 yields

$$\frac{pL^2}{2} + C_1 L = 0, \quad \text{or} \quad C_1 = -\frac{pL}{2}$$

Substituting C_1 in Equation (1-26), we obtain

$$-\frac{1}{6}\frac{pL}{2}L^2+C_3+\frac{pL^3}{24} = 0$$

or

$$C_3 = \frac{1}{24}pL^3$$

and

$$EI\,y = -\frac{px^4}{24}+\frac{pL}{12}x^3-\frac{pL^3}{24}x \tag{1-27}$$

The solution checks the one previously obtained [see Equation (1-11)].

It can be shown in the later solution of Indeterminate Structures that the use of the fourth-order equation rather than the second-order equation of Art. 1-5 affords a more direct solution of many indeterminate problems. The techniques used therein are identical with those used in the preceding illustrative example.

1-9   Principles of moment area[3]

The moment area method is extensively used in the solution of beam deflection problems. It is expressed in the following two theorems.

THEOREM I: The difference in slope between any two points on the elastic curve is equal to the area of the M/EI diagram between those two points.

THEOREM II: The distance of any point B on the elastic curve, measured normal to the original position of the beam from a tangent drawn to the elastic curve at any other point A, is equal to the moment of the area of the M/EI diagram between the two points about point B.

Proofs of these two theorems can be demonstrated as follows (see Fig. 1.6).

Proof of Theorem I: The differential equation of bending expresses a relationship between the bending moments, EI and the elastic curve,

$$\frac{M}{EI} = \frac{d^2y}{dx^2} = \frac{d}{dx}\left(\frac{dy}{dx}\right) = \frac{d\theta}{dx}$$

from which

$$d\theta = \frac{M}{EI}dx \tag{1-28}$$

---

[3] This method (and also the conjugate beam method described in Art. 1-12) are essentially graphical successive integrations of the Bernoulli-Euler differential equation, in which the constants of integration are also determined graphically. The methods appear to have been developed in different countries at about the same time. In the United States, one of the early users was Professor Charles E. Greene of the University of Michigan in about 1873. Otto Mohr, the German engineer, outlined the Conjugate Beam Method in 1868.

and between any two points A and B on the elastic curve (see Fig. 1.6c)

$$\int_B^A d\theta = \theta_A - \theta_B = \int_B^A \frac{M}{EI} dx \qquad (1\text{-}29)$$

Equation (1-29) is the mathematical equivalent of Theorem I.

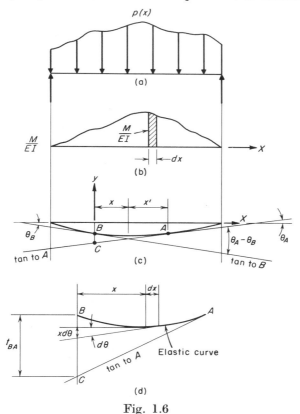

Fig. 1.6

Proof of Theorem II: Fig. 1.6c shows the elastic curve of a typical beam, and any two points on the elastic curve, A and B. For the sake of clarity, a portion of Fig. 1.6c is enlarged and shown in Fig. 1.6d. The distance BC is known as the tangential deviation of point B with respect to $A(=t_{BA})$. Points B and C are on a line through B and parallel to the y axis. From Fig. 1.6d, we have

$$t_{BA} = BC = \int_B^A x d\theta$$

But from Equation (1-28), $d\theta = \dfrac{M}{EI}\,dx$.   Hence,

$$t_{BA} = \int_B^A x\,\frac{M}{EI}\,dx \qquad (1\text{-}30)$$

Equation (1-30) is the mathematical equivalent of the statement of Theorem II.

1-10   Construction of the M/EI diagram

When EI is constant, the construction of the M/EI diagram involves only the reduction of the vertical scale of the moment diagram by EI. When EI is variable and expressible as a function of x, then M/EI can be found as a function of x and plotted.

1-11   Application of the moment area method

The principal advantage of the moment area method is that, in relating moment area to displacements and rotations, one may make

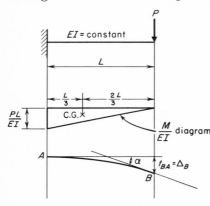

use of properties of known areas to find deflections. This will be illustrated in the following example.

Example: Given a cantilever beam with constant cross section loaded with a concentrated load P at its end, determine the deflection and the rotation of the end of the beam (Fig. 1.7).

Solution: The M/EI diagram is plotted as shown in Fig. 1.7. By Theorem I,

$$\alpha = \theta_B - \theta_A = \frac{1}{2}\frac{PL}{EI}\cdot L = \frac{PL^2}{2EI}$$

Fig. 1.7

By Theorem II

$$\Delta_B = t_{BA} = \frac{PL^2}{2EI}\cdot\frac{2}{3}\,L = \frac{PL^3}{3EI}$$

It will be noted that, in this example, use of the theorems of moment area give directly the required results.   This is not always the case as is shown in the next illustrative example.

Example: Given a simple beam with constant section loaded with a uniformily distributed load of p lb/ft, find the equation of the elastic curve, $y = f(x)$.   See Fig. 1.8.

Solution: By Theorem II, $CD = t_{CA} =$ moment of parabolic M/EI area about C,

$$t_{CA} = \frac{2}{3}\frac{pL^2}{8EI} \cdot L \cdot \frac{L}{2} = \frac{pL^4}{24EI}$$

By similar triangles,

$$EF = \frac{x}{L} \cdot CD = \frac{pxL^3}{24EI}$$

By Theorem II,
$BF = t_{BA} =$ moment of area of M/EI diagram between A and B about B

$$t_{BA} = \frac{1}{EI} \int_{z=0}^{z=x} (x-z)M\,dz$$

in which

$$M = \frac{pLz}{2} - \frac{pz^2}{2}$$

therefore,

$$t_{BA} = \frac{1}{EI} \int_0^x \left[\frac{pz^3}{2} - \frac{pz^2}{2}(L+x) + \frac{pLzx}{2} \right] dz$$

or

$$t_{BA} = \frac{1}{EI} \left[-\frac{px^4}{24} + \frac{pLx^3}{12} \right]$$

Now $EB = y = EF - BF = EF - t_{BA}$
or

$$y = \frac{pxL^3}{24EI} + \frac{px^4}{24EI} - \frac{pLx^3}{12EI}$$

which is the required answer.

It should be noted that in the above solutions the sign of the rotation and of the deflections were not specified; therefore the solutions may not agree in sign with those obtained by the method of double integration.

1-12 The conjugate beam method

The conjugate beam method of analysis is essentially equivalent to the moment area method. Indeed, the conjugate beam relations

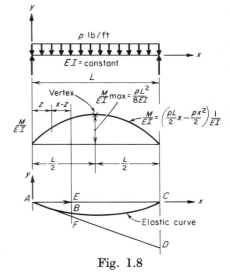

Fig. 1.8

can be most easily obtained by means of the moment area relations. This verification is left as an exercise for the student.

The advantage of the conjugate beam method over the moment area method lies in the very simple and straightforward sign convention which can be developed for the conjugate beam method. This sign convention is consistent with all previous conventions discussed in this chapter and hence does not require memorizing new conventions or rules.

The two conjugate beam relations will be stated first. Following this a simple example will be solved to fix ideas. Then the four special support conditions will be obtained. Finally, additional typical examples will be solved.

THE TWO CONJUGATE BEAM RELATIONS

Given any beam and loading, as shown in Fig. 1.9. This will hereafter be called the *actual beam*. Now consider a beam of the same length as the actual beam but loaded with the M/EI diagram of the

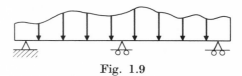

Fig. 1.9

actual beam. This M/EI loading is positive (i.e., up) for positive moment and negative (i.e., down) for negative moment. This beam and loading will henceforth be called the *conjugate beam*. The conjugate beam loading will be in static equilibrium with the support reactions. In addition, the following two conjugate beam relations hold:

    I. The shear, V_C (in value and sign), at any point on the conjugate beam is equal to the rotation θ at that point on the actual beam.

   II. The moment, M_C (in value and sign), at any point on the conjugate beam is equal to the deflection at that point on the actual beam.

A simple example will help to fix ideas. Consider the beam and loading shown in Fig. 1.10.

Example: Determine the deflection at point C on the beam due to the given loading.

Solution: Because of the simple end supports on the actual beam it is known that

    1. There is no deflection at A and B.
    2. There is a rotation at A and B.

Therefore, on the conjugate beam, there will be no end moments at A' and B'. There will, however, be concentrated reactions (shears) at these points. They are unknown initially and are assumed acting up, shown as R_{C_L} and R_{C_R}. Solving for R_{C_L} and R_{C_R} by statics, we find that

$$R_{C_L} = R_{C_R} = -\frac{PL^2}{16EI}$$

The negative sign indicates these reactions act in directions opposite to those shown. Hence V_{C_L} is negative and V_{C_R} is positive, so that θ_A is negative

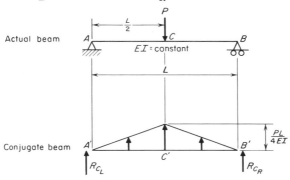

Fig. 1.10

and θ_B is positive. To determine the deflection at the point C, calculate the moment at point C' on the conjugate beam. This gives

$$M_{C_{C'}} = -\frac{PL^3}{48EI}$$

the negative sign indicating down deflection.

1-13   The four special support conditions for the conjugate beam method
Consider the cantilever beam and loading shown in Fig. 1.11.

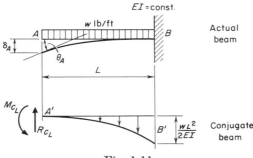

Fig. 1.11

Note, in the actual beam

at A $\begin{cases}\text{There is a change in slope, } \theta_A. \\ \text{There is a deflection, } \delta_A.\end{cases}$

and at B $\begin{cases}\text{There is zero change in slope.} \\ \text{There is zero deflection.}\end{cases}$

Therefore, in the conjugate beam

at A' $\begin{cases}\text{There is a concentrated reaction, shown as } R_{C_L}. \\ \text{There is a moment, shown as } M_{C_L}.\end{cases}$

and at B' $\begin{cases}\text{There is zero shear (i.e., reaction).} \\ \text{There is zero moment.}\end{cases}$

These conditions are typical of all built-in ended and free ended beams.

Now consider any continuous beam, a portion of which is shown in Fig. 1.12, with C an interior support.

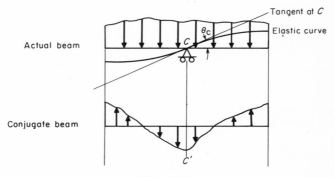

Fig. 1.12

Considering sections differential distances to the left and right of the support C of the actual beam, we see that the slope, θ_C is continuous at C. This means that the shear on the conjugate beam at C' must be continuous. That is, there cannot be a concentrated reaction at C' since this would imply an abrupt change in shear at this point and hence an abrupt change in slope (or discontinuity of slope) at C.

Finally, the moment at C' is zero if C is an unyielding support. If this support sags (i.e., deflects), the moment at C' is simply equal in value and sign to this sag.

The foregoing can be stated as the four special support conditions:

I. If the actual beam is built-in at its end, then the conjugate beam has zero reaction and zero moment at this end.

II. If the actual beam has a free end, then the conjugate beam has a reaction and moment at this end.

III. On the conjugate beam, there is zero reaction at all actual beam interior support points. An exception to this occurs only when the beam is hinged at an intermediate point. The hinge introduces an abrupt change in slope in the actual beam and, therefore, a concentrated force at that point of the conjugate beam.

IV. The moment, on the conjugate beam, at all actual beam interior support points, is equal to the sag or deflection of these actual supports. In the most commonly assumed case of unyielding supports the conjugate beam moment is zero.

1-14   Examples of conjugate beam method solutions[4]

Example 1: For the beam and loading shown in Fig. 1.13, determine θ_A and δ_B.

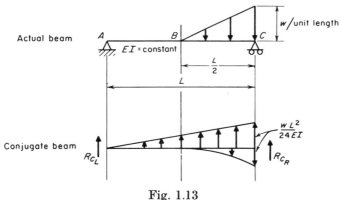

Fig. 1.13

Solution: From the conjugate beam figure, take moments about the right end,

$$R_{C_L}(L)+\frac{wL^2}{24EI}\cdot\frac{L}{2}\cdot\frac{L}{3}-\frac{wL^2}{24EI}\cdot\frac{L}{8}\cdot\frac{L}{10}=0$$

$$R_{C_L}=-\frac{37}{5760}\frac{wL^3}{EI}$$

---

[4] In the illustrative example in this article (and also in later articles), the moment diagrams are drawn by parts—i.e., a separate diagram is drawn for each load and the net moment at any point on the beam is given by the net ordinate due to the separate curves. In this way, the moment diagram, instead of being given by a single (and possibly complicated) curve, is given by a series of very simple curves whose area and moment properties are well known. This is advantageous in moment area and conjugate beam applications.

so that

$$\theta_A = -\frac{37}{5760}\frac{wL^3}{EI}, \text{ i.e., clockwise}$$

$$\delta_B = R_{C_L}\left(\frac{L}{2}\right) - \frac{wL^2}{24EI}\cdot\frac{L}{4}\cdot\frac{L}{6}$$

$$= -\frac{39wL^4}{11520EI}, \text{ i.e., down}$$

Example 2: For the beam and loading shown in Fig. 1.14, determine θ_A and δ_B.

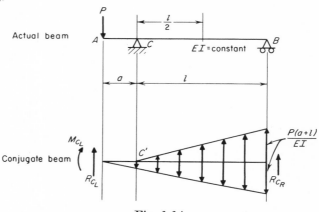

Fig. 1.14

Solution: Since support C is unyielding, it follows that $M_{C'}=0$, or

$$R_{C_R}(l)+\frac{P(a+l)}{EI}\left(\frac{l}{2}\right)\left(\frac{2l}{3}\right)-\frac{(Pa)}{EI}\,(l)\left(\frac{l}{2}\right)-\frac{Pl}{EI}\left(\frac{l}{2}\right)\left(\frac{2l}{3}\right) = 0$$

Hence,

$$R_{C_R} = \frac{Pal}{6EI}$$

Now, if we sum vertical forces on the conjugate beam,

$$R_{C_L}+R_{C_R}+\frac{P(a+l)}{EI}\left(\frac{l}{2}\right)-\frac{P(a+l)}{EI}\frac{(a+l)}{2} = 0$$

or

$$R_{C_L} = \frac{Pa^2}{2EI}+\frac{Pal}{3EI}$$

so that

$$\theta_A = \frac{Pa^2}{2EI}+\frac{Pal}{3EI}, \text{ i.e., counterclockwise}$$

Now noting that

$$M_{C'} = M_{C_L}+R_{C_L}a-\frac{Pa}{EI}\left(\frac{a}{2}\right)\left(\frac{a}{3}\right) = 0$$

we find that

$$M_{C_L} = -\frac{Pa^3}{3EI} - \frac{Pa^2l}{3EI}$$

and therefore

$$\delta_B = M_{C_L} + R_{C_L}\left(a+\frac{l}{2}\right) + \frac{P(a+l)}{2EI} \cdot \frac{l}{4} \cdot \frac{l}{6} - P\left(a+\frac{l}{2}\right)\left(\frac{a+\frac{l}{2}}{2}\right)\left(\frac{a+\frac{l}{2}}{3}\right) = +\frac{Pal^2}{16EI}$$

i.e., upward.

The beam with variable moment of inertia can be solved quite easily using conjugate beam methods. It is only necessary that the proper M/EI curve (and hence, loading) be used. To illustrate, consider the following example.

Example 3: Determine δ_C for the beam and loading shown in Fig. 1.15.

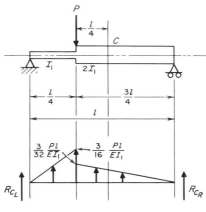

Fig. 1.15

Solution: Taking moments about R_{C_L}, we have

$$R_{C_R} \cdot l + \frac{3}{16} \frac{Pl}{EI_1} \cdot \frac{l}{8} \cdot \frac{l}{6} + \frac{3}{32} \frac{Pl}{EI_1} \cdot \frac{3}{8} l \cdot \frac{l}{2} = 0$$

or

$$R_{C_R} = -\frac{11}{512} \frac{Pl^2}{EI_1}$$

Then,

$$\delta_C = R_{C_R} \cdot \frac{l}{2} + \frac{Pl}{16EI_1} \cdot \frac{l}{4} \cdot \frac{l}{6} = -\frac{25}{3070} \frac{Pl^3}{EI_1}$$

1-15 Energy methods—introduction

The preceding methods for determining bending deflections are based essentially upon integrations of the differential equation of bending.

This equation is obtained from consideration of forces in equilibrium. Another group of methods can be developed from energy considerations. These energy methods are a powerful tool in obtaining the numerical solutions of deflection problems and also for solving statically indeterminate problems.

The fundamental quantity required for all energy analyses of structures is the so-called *strain energy*, or work stored in the structure due to deformations of the structure. We shall, therefore, begin our discussion of energy methods by discussing the physical as well as mathematical considerations involved in storing work in a body resulting from various types of structural action, such as direct load, bending, and shear. Following this, we will discuss the different forms of energy law relating to structures, and finally we will apply these forms to typical problems in order to illustrate their use in the solution of structural problems.

1-16   Strain energy due to normal stresses

Consider an elastic body acted upon by external forces causing deformations with consequent storing of energy within the body. This stored energy is called strain energy. Because the material is stressed within the proportional limit this energy is recoverable upon removal of the applied straining agent (if we neglect heat and similar internal frictional losses). For example, consider an axially loaded bar with constant section whose area and length are A and L, respectively, Fig. 1.16. This bar will have stretched under the applied

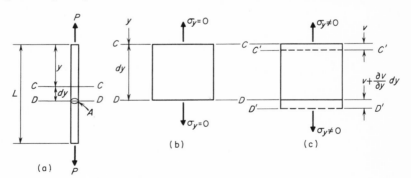

Fig. 1.16

normal load. The consequent tensile unit stress σ_y increases from zero to a value σ_y as the load is gradually applied. The original, unstrained position of any section such as C-C will be located by a coordinate y. As the load is applied, section C-C will become displaced by an amount v. A section D-D located a differential length below C-C will have been displaced an amount $v + \left(\dfrac{\partial v}{\partial y}\right)dy$, where the quantity $\left(\dfrac{\partial v}{\partial y}\right)dy$ represents the change in v with y through a distance dy. (Terms of higher order are neglected.) These relations are illustrated in Fig. 1.16.

From Fig. 1.16c, it can be seen that the element which originally had a length dy has a length after loading of

$$dy + v + \left(\frac{\partial v}{\partial y}\right)dy - v = dy\left(1 + \frac{\partial v}{\partial y}\right)$$

Since unit strain $= \dfrac{\text{change in length}}{\text{original length}} = \dfrac{\left(\dfrac{\partial v}{\partial y}\right)dy}{dy}$, the quantity $\dfrac{\partial v}{\partial y}$ then represents the tensile unit strain of the element

$$\frac{\partial v}{\partial y} = \epsilon_y \tag{1-31}$$

As the load is applied, the displacement of any section increases from zero to some amount corresponding to the unit strain. As the displacement v of section C-C changes by an amount dv, the displacement $\left(v + \dfrac{\partial v}{\partial y}\,dy\right)$ of section D-D changes by an amount $d\left(v + \dfrac{\partial v}{\partial y}\,dy\right)$, and σ_y changes by an amount $d\sigma_y$.

Consider the work done on the element by the external forces during a differential change in displacements of sections C-C and D-D. The work done (neglecting higher-order terms containing $d\sigma_y$) will be

$$A\sigma_y d\left(v + \frac{\partial v}{\partial y}\,dy\right) - A\sigma_y dv = A\sigma_y d\left(\frac{\partial v}{\partial y}\right)dy$$

As σ_y varies with the applied load, from zero to σ_y, the work done by the forces external to the element will be

$$dV = \int_{\sigma_y = 0}^{\sigma_y = \sigma_y} A\sigma_y d\left(\frac{\partial v}{\partial y}\right)dy$$

From Equation (1-31), this becomes

$$dV = \int_{\sigma_y = 0}^{\sigma_y = \sigma_y} A\sigma_y d\epsilon_y dy$$

But, from Hooke's Law, we have

$$\epsilon_y = \frac{\sigma_y}{E}$$

so that

$$dV = \int_{\sigma_y = 0}^{\sigma_y = \sigma_y} \frac{A}{E} \, dy\sigma_y d\sigma_y$$

or

$$dV = \frac{1}{2E} \sigma_y{}^2 A dy = \tfrac{1}{2}\sigma_y \epsilon_y A dy \qquad (1\text{-}32)$$

Equation (1-32) represents the work done by normal stresses in straining the element an amount ϵ_y. Since in the case of an elastic system this energy is recoverable, it is called the stored or strain energy of the element.

1-17   Strain energy of bending

In a manner similar to the derivation of Equation (1-32), it can be shown that the strain energy of a differential volume $dxdydz$ stressed in tension or compression in the x direction only by a normal stress x will be

$$dV = \frac{1}{2E} \sigma_x{}^2 dxdydz = \tfrac{1}{2}\sigma_x \epsilon_x dxdydz \qquad (1\text{-}33)$$

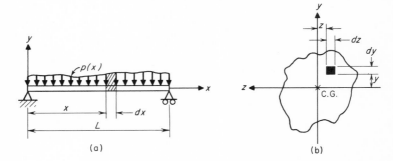

Fig. 1.17

When σ_x is the unit stress due to bending, $\sigma_x = \dfrac{My}{I}$ (see Fig. 1.17), then

$dV = \dfrac{1}{2E} \dfrac{M^2 y^2}{I^2} \, dxdydz$, where $I = \displaystyle\iint_A y^2 dzdy$ is the moment of inertia of the cross-sectional area about the neutral axis.

The total strain energy of bending of a beam is obtained by integrating the expression for the strain energy of a differential volume over the entire volume of the beam, or

$$V = \iiint_{\text{volume}} \frac{1}{2E} \frac{M^2}{I^2} \, y^2 dz dy dx$$

But

$$I = \iint_{\text{area}} y^2 dz dy$$

Hence,

$$V = \int_{\text{length}} \frac{M^2}{2EI} \, dx \qquad (1\text{-}34)$$

An alternative expression for the total strain energy of bending can be obtained from Equation (1-34), using Equation (1-6). This leads at once to

$$V = \int_L \frac{M^2}{2EI} \, dx = \int_L \frac{(EIy'')^2}{2EI} \, dx = \int_L \frac{EI}{2} \, y''^2 dx \qquad (1\text{-}35)$$

This form is frequently more useful than that given by Equation (1-34).

1-18 Strain energy of shear

An element of volume $dxdydz$ is subjected to shear stresses τ_{xy} and τ_{yx} (see Fig. 1.18). For static equilibrium, it can readily be shown that

$$\tau_{xy} = \tau_{yx} \qquad (1\text{-}36)$$

The shear deformation is as shown and the shear strain is defined as AB/AC. For small deformations, it follows that

$$\gamma_{xy} = \frac{AB}{AC}$$

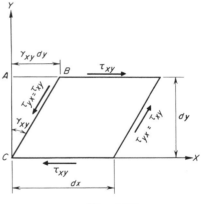

Fig. 1.18

Hence, the angle of deformation γ_{xy} is a measure of the shear strain. The strain energy for this differential volume is obtained by determining the work done by the shear forces acting on the differential volume. By reasoning similar to that used in deriving Equations (1-32) and (1-33), one can obtain

$$dV = \tfrac{1}{2}(\tau_{xy} \, dz \, dx)\gamma_{xy} \, dy = \tfrac{1}{2}\tau_{xy}\gamma_{xy} \, dx \, dy \, dz \qquad (1\text{-}37)$$

Hooke's Law for shear stresses and strains is

$$\gamma_{xy} = \frac{\tau_{xy}}{G} \qquad (1\text{-}38)$$

where G is the shearing modulus of elasticity of the material. Substituting Equation (1-38) into Equation (1-37) gives

$$dV = \frac{1}{2G}\, \tau_{xy}{}^2\, dx\, dy\, dz \qquad (1\text{-}39)$$

which is an expression for the strain energy in shear.

1-19 Plane-stress

In structural theory, when a body is subjected to a system of stresses such that

$$\sigma_x \neq 0,\ \sigma_y \neq 0,\ \tau_{xy} \neq 0, \qquad \sigma_z = \tau_{xz} = \tau_{yz} = 0$$

(for the xy plane, and similarly for the other two planes), the body is said to be in a state of plane stress.[5]

Many of the engineering type structures fall in this category. For the special plane stress case in which only

$$\sigma_x \neq 0,\ \tau_{xy} \neq 0$$

the total strain energy of the body is (see Equations 1-33 and 1-39)

$$V = \frac{1}{2} \iiint_{\text{volume}} \left(\frac{\sigma_x{}^2}{E} + \frac{\tau_{xy}{}^2}{G}\right) dx\, dy\, dz \qquad (1\text{-}39a)$$

1-20 The energy relations of structural theory

There are four energy relations or laws which are of fundamental importance in structural engineering. These are:

1. Law of Conservation of Energy
2. Theorem of Virtual Work
3. Theorem of Minimum Potential Energy
4. Theorem of Complementary Energy

---

[5] Another type of action is that of *plane strain* for which

$$\epsilon_x \neq 0,\ \epsilon_y \neq 0,\ \gamma_{xy} \neq 0,\ \epsilon_z = \gamma_{zz} = \gamma_{yz} = 0$$

A more complete discussion of these and other stress and strain systems will be found in textbooks dealing with the Mathematical Theory of Elasticity; for example,

A. E. H. Love, *A Treatise on the Mathematical Theory of Elasticity*, 3rd ed., Cambridge University Press, London, 1920.

S. Timoshenko and J. N. Goodier, *Theory of Elasticity*, 2nd Ed., McGraw-Hill Book Company, New York, 1951.

R. V. Southwell, *Theory of Elasticity for Engineers*, Oxford University Press, 1941.

I. S. Sokolnikoff, *Mathematical Theory of Elasticity*, McGraw-Hill Book Company, New York, 1946.

C. T. Wang, *Applied Elasticity*, McGraw-Hill Book Company, New York, 1953.

These energy relations are used in various ways in the theory of structures. Among these special uses we mention the following:

(a) Using energy methods it is possible to derive fundamental laws and relations of structural theory. For example, Kirchhoff, by minimizing the total energy in a plate was able to obtain the correct equations and boundary conditions for a particular plate problem. Previous to this, the boundary conditions, obtained on a purely physical basis, were incorrectly stated by Poisson.[6]

As another example, we shall use the Law of Conservation of Energy in order to derive the Theorem of Virtual Work and we shall use the Theorem of Virtual Work in order to derive the Theorem of Minimum Potential Energy.

(b) The energy laws, either applied directly in the form as herein stated (see Art. 1-21) or applied in a special form (as in Arts. 1-24 *et seq.*) enable one to solve for beam deflections and the beam redundants.

(c) The energy relations form the basis of several approximate methods for solving structures that frequently cannot be solved exactly. See Art. 6-5 for such an application to a simple beam. For a more complete discussion of this topic, see the references in footnote 5.

(d) The Theorem of Complementary Energy enables one to solve for the deflections of structures even for those cases in which the deflection does not vary linearly with the load. In this respect, the method has distinct advantages over some of the more commonly used energy methods which are restricted to structures with linear load-deflection properties (see Art. 1-34).

1-21 The law of conservation of energy

The Law of Conservation of Energy is a basic law of physics. There are many ways of stating this law in the different fields of physics where it applies. For our purposes it will be sufficient to state it in the following form:

If a structure and the external loads acting on it are isolated so that these neither receive nor give out energy, then the total energy of this system remains constant.

Its application to structures may be best explained by considering the simple helical spring and loading shown in Fig. 1.19a.

When a load is applied and equilibrium reached, it will be found that the spring has elongated an amount δ. For loads which are within

---

[6] See A. E. H. Love, *A Treatise on the Mathematical Theory of Elasticity*, 3rd Ed., Cambridge University Press, London, 1920.

the elastic limit of the spring, the relation between P and δ will be a linear one as shown in Fig. 1.19b.

In dealing with structures and loads in *static equilibrium*, it is important that the concept of *gradually applied loads* be understood. The physical meaning of this, and the significance of this insofar as energy is concerned, may be explained by referring to Fig. 1.19b.

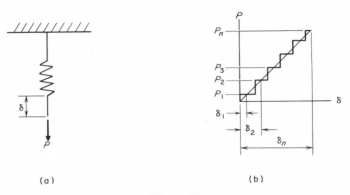

(a)　　　　　　　　　　　　　　(b)

Fig. 1.19

Assume a small load P_1 is applied to the spring. Immediately following application of this load, the spring oscillates slightly about an equilibrium point and finally comes to rest at this point, the deflection δ_1. In this operation the potential energy of the load has been decreased by the amount $P_1\delta_1$. According to the Law of Conservation of Energy this energy must appear within the system. It will appear in two forms—

1. Internal strain energy corresponding to internal stresses and deformations of the spring.
2. Heat energy caused by the oscillating spring and internal friction of sliding molecules.

Now increase the load slightly to P_2. The oscillation and equilibrium will be as before, the final deflection being δ_2. Do the same for small increments to P_3, etc., in every case allowing the structure to come to equilibrium before applying the next increment. The final load P_n and deflection δ_n, *in the limit as the increments approach zero*, are the "gradually applied load" and deflection and correspond to a change in potential energy given by the area under the curve, i.e.,

$$\Delta \text{P.E.} = \frac{P_n \delta_n}{2} \qquad (1\text{-}40)$$

By the Law of Conservation of Energy, this must also equal the internal strain energy stored in the spring. Because the load increments are assumed approaching zero, the frictional heat losses (caused by oscillations of the spring) are also assumed as negligible.

Although the derivation and discussion given above were made with reference to a spring, they hold equally for any elastic body—beam, truss, frame, plate, etc. Also, the argument may be extended without difficulty to the case in which the load-deformation relation is nonlinear. It is only necessary that the area under the load-deformation curve be taken as the change in potential energy. The Law of Conservation of Energy, which holds in any case, requires that the internal strain energy be equal to this change in potential energy.

A typical application of the Law of Conservation of Energy can be made by referring to Fig. 1.20, which shows a constant section cantilever beam subjected to a concentrated load at its end.

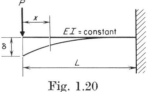

Fig. 1.20

If bending strain energy only is considered [see Equation (1-34)],

$$\text{External work} = \text{Internal work}$$

$$\frac{P\delta}{2} = \int_0^L \frac{M^2 dx}{2EI} \qquad (1\text{-}41)$$

Inasmuch as $M = -Px$, a simple integration and clearing of terms leads to

$$\delta = \frac{PL^3}{3EI} \qquad (1\text{-}42)$$

If the effect of shear on the deformation is desired, it is only necessary that the strain energy in shear term be included on the right-hand side of Equation (1-41). This strain energy, given by Equation (1-39), for the case of beams takes the form

$$V = C \int_0^L \frac{(\text{total shear})^2 dx}{2AG} \qquad (1\text{-}43)$$

in which C is a constant, the so-called "form factor" and has a numerical value equal to the ratio of the maximum shear stress (at the neutral axis) to the average shear stress over the cross section. In the present problem, since the total shear is constant at all stations and equal to P, the total deflection is given by

$$\delta_{\text{total}} = \frac{PL^3}{3EI} + \frac{CP^2L}{2AG} \qquad (1\text{-}44)$$

in which the last term is the shear contribution.

1-22 The theorem of virtual work

It is now possible to derive the Theorem of Virtual Work. This derivation will be largely nonmathematical and basically utilitarian in nature. More sophisticated derivations may be found in the literature of theory of elasticity.[7] The present derivation will, however, suffice for our purposes.

Consider the beam and loading of Fig. 1.21.

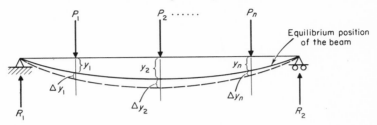

Fig. 1.21

The full curved line represents the equilibrium position of the beam under the given loads. Now assume the beam is given an additional small deformation consistent with the boundary conditions (i.e., one which is zero at R_1 and R_2). This is called a *virtual deformation* and corresponds to increments of deflection Δy_1, Δy_2, . . ., Δy_n at loads P_1, P_2, . . ., P_n as shown by the broken line.

The change in potential energy of the loads is given by

$$\Delta \text{P.E.} = \sum_{j=1}^{n} P_j \Delta y_j \tag{1-45}$$

and by the Law of Conservation of Energy this must be equal to the internal strain energy stored in the beam. Hence, we may state the Theorem of Virtual Work in the following form:

If a body which is in equilibrium under a system of external loads is given any small (virtual) deformation, then the work done by the external loads during this virtual deformation is equal to the increase in internal strain energy stored in the body.

This theorem will be used in deriving the Theorem of Minimum Potential Energy, which follows. It also has many applications in the solutions of deflections of structural components. Some of these will be illustrated in Chapter 6.

---

[7] See especially I. S. Sokolnikoff, *Mathematical Theory of Elasticity*, McGraw-Hill Book Company, 1946.

1-23   The theorem of minimum potential energy

A very useful and important theorem can be developed from considerations of bodies in equilibrium. For the derivation of this theorem a beam (see Fig. 1.22) will be used as an example.

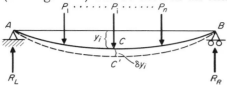

Fig. 1.22

Consider a beam in equilibrium under n loads, P_1, P_2, P_3, $\ldots$, P_i, $\ldots$, P_n. The curve ACB defines the equilibrium positions of the loads and reactions. It automatically follows that the boundary conditions are satisfied. For the beam shown, this means that $y = 0$ at A and B. Now apply by some means an additional small displacement to the curve so that it is defined by $AC'B$. Note that this new position of the curve also satisfies the boundary conditions that $y = 0$ at A and B, but it is not necessarily an equilibrium configuration. By small displacements we specifically mean displacements which are small in comparison with the original displacements. Accordingly they fall within our definition of virtual displacements. (See Art. 1-22.)

Let y_i be the original equilibrium displacement of the curve beneath a particular load P_i. The additional small displacement is called δy_i.

The potential energy of the system while it is in the equilibrium configuration is found by comparing the potential energy of the beam and loads in equilibrium and in the undeflected position.

The change in potential energy of the loads is

$$W = -[P_1 y_1 + P_2 y_2 + \ldots P_i y_i + \ldots P_n y_n] = -\sum_{i=1}^{i=n} P_i y_i \quad (1\text{-}46)$$

If the beam is elastic, the strain energy of the beam (shear strain energy neglected) from Equation (1-33) is

$$V = \int_{VOL.} \tfrac{1}{2} \sigma_x \epsilon_x \, dx \, dy \, dz$$

The total energy of the system is

$$U = W + V$$

$$U = -\sum_{i=1}^{i=n} P_i y_i + \int_V \tfrac{1}{2} \sigma_x \epsilon_x \, dx \, dy \, dz \quad (1\text{-}47a)$$

If we apply Hooke's Law, this becomes

$$U = - \sum_{i=1}^{i=n} P_i y_i + \int_V \frac{E}{2} \epsilon_x^2 \, dx \, dy \, dz \qquad (1\text{-}47\text{b})$$

The total energy of the system after the additional displacement to configuration $AC'B$ will be

$$U + \delta U = - \sum_{i=1}^{i=n} P_i(y_i + \delta y_i) + \int_V \frac{E}{2} (\epsilon_x + \delta \epsilon_x)^2 \, dx \, dy \, dz$$

$$= - \sum_{i=1}^{i=n} P_i y_i - \sum_{i=1}^{i=n} P_i \delta y_i + \int_V \frac{E}{2} [\epsilon_x^2 + 2 \epsilon_x \delta \epsilon_x + (\delta \epsilon_x)^2] \, dx \, dy \, dz$$

$$(1\text{-}48)$$

Subtracting Equation (1-47b) from Equation (1-48), we obtain the variation in the total potential energy of the system

$$\delta U = - \sum_{i=1}^{i=n} P_i \delta y_i + \int_V \frac{E}{2} [2 \epsilon_x \delta \epsilon_x + (\delta \epsilon_x)^2] \, dx \, dy \, dz \qquad (1\text{-}49)$$

The first part of δU is due to the loads and is called $\delta W \left(= - \sum_{i=1}^{i=n} P_i \delta y_i \right)$.

The second part of δU is the variation in strain energy$(= \delta V)$ which can be written as two integrals

$$\delta V = \int_V E \epsilon_x \delta \epsilon_x \, dx \, dy \, dz + \int_V \frac{E}{2} (\delta \epsilon_x)^2 \, dx \, dy \, dz \qquad (1\text{-}50)$$

$$\delta V = \int_V E \epsilon_x \delta \epsilon_x \, dx \, dy \, dz + V(\delta \epsilon_x) \qquad (1\text{-}51)$$

where $V(\delta \epsilon_x)$ is the second integral in Equation (1-50). Now

$$\int_V E \epsilon_x \delta \epsilon_x \, dx \, dy \, dz = \int_V \sigma_x \delta \epsilon_x \, dx \, dy \, dz$$

where σ_x was the stress in the elementary volume at equilibrium. By the Theorem of Virtual Work, $\int \sigma_x \delta \epsilon_x \, dx \, dy \, dz =$ the work done by the equilibrium stresses during the small additional deformations δy and is equal to the corresponding work of the P_i forces during these displacements, or

$$\int_V \sigma_x \delta \epsilon_x \, dx \, dy \, dz = \sum_{i=1}^{i=n} P_i \delta y_i$$

Therefore,

$$\delta V = \sum_{i=1}^{i=n} P_i \delta y_i + V(\delta \epsilon_x) \qquad (1\text{-}52)$$

Substituting Equation (1-52) in $\delta U = \delta W + \delta V$, we obtain

$$\delta U = -\sum_{i=1}^{i=n} P_i \delta y_i + \sum_{i=1}^{i=n} P_i \delta y_i + V(\delta \epsilon_x)$$

or

$$\delta U = V(\delta \epsilon_x) = \int_V \frac{E}{2} (\delta \epsilon_x)^2 \, dx \, dy \, dz \qquad (1\text{-}53)$$

The unit strain ϵ_x can be written in terms of the displacements u in the x direction

$$\epsilon_x = \frac{\partial u}{\partial x}$$

Then the variation in ϵ_x due to the small displacements δy is $\delta \epsilon_x = \delta \left(\dfrac{\partial u}{\partial x} \right) = \dfrac{\partial(\delta u)}{\partial x}$ which is a second-order term and $(\delta \epsilon_x)^2 = \left[\dfrac{\partial(\delta u)}{\partial x} \right]^2 =$ a positive second-order term squared. Hence from Equation (1-53), $\delta U = 0 +$ positive second-order terms in u. If we neglect the second-order terms,

$$\delta U = \delta(W + V) = 0 \qquad (1\text{-}54)$$

Since the variation in U is zero as shown above, it follows that the value of U at equilibrium is stationary or, in other words, a maximum or a minimum. Furthermore, since the second-order terms neglected were positive, the total potential energy must be a minimum.

The above is expressed as the well known Principle or Theorem of Minimum Potential Energy:

Of all displacements satisfying given boundary conditions, those that satisfy the equilibrium conditions make the potential energy a minimum.[8]

A nonmathematical development of the above principle will now be given to enable the student to see the physical significance of it and also of the Principle of Virtual Work. Assume a beam loaded with a single load P. The relation between the load and the value of the equilibrium deflection under the load can be plotted for different values of P. The result will generally be a curve (Fig. 1.23). For an elastic beam, the curve will be a straight line. For a given value of $P = P_1$, the corresponding deflection is Δ_1 and the beam is in equilibrium. Now by some means, let the beam be given additional small displacements resulting in a change in Δ_1 by some small amount $\delta\Delta$. The new configuration need not be one of equilibrium. The resulting decrease in the potential energy of the load is $\delta W = -P_1(\delta\Delta) = -$ (area $AECD$)

[8] For a more rigorous proof see Sokolnikoff, *ibid.*

of Fig. 1.23. The resulting increase in strain energy of the beam is
the area $ABCD = \delta V$. The change in total energy

$$\delta U = \delta W + \delta V = \text{area } ABE \text{ (a positive quantity)} \qquad (1\text{-}55a)$$

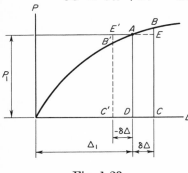

If $\delta\Delta$ is very small, in the limit,
area ABE becomes a negligible
quantity, a differential of higher
order. Hence, $-\delta V = \delta W +$ negligible terms or change in strain energy
equals change in potential energy of
loads, which is a physical demonstration of the Principle of Virtual
Work.

Note also that the variation of
total energy $\delta U = 0 +$ positive negligible terms.

Fig. 1.23

If, starting once again at the position of equilibrium, the beam is
given an upward small displacement such that Δ decreases by $\delta\Delta$, then

$$\delta W = +P_1\delta\Delta = \text{area } AE'C'D$$

$$-\delta V = \text{area } AB'C'D = \delta W - \text{area } AE'B'$$

$$\delta U = \delta W + \delta V = \text{area } AE'B' \text{ (a higher-order positive quantity)}$$

$$= 0 + \text{positive negligible terms} \qquad (1\text{-}55b)$$

Since a small variation in Δ either up or down produces a variation
in the total energy consisting of positive higher-order differentials, the
total energy U at equilibrium must be a minimum.

Thus, by this simplified analysis the physical meaning of the Principle
of Minimum Potential Energy and also the Principle of Virtual Work
has been demonstrated.

1-24 Castigliano's theorem

A classical application of work methods to the field of structural
engineering is the Castigliano Theorem. Alberto Castigliano, an
Italian engineer, published a dissertation in 1873 for his engineering
diploma, in which he described his method. His theorem applies only
to structures stressed within the elastic limit and, in addition, contains
the important restriction that all deformations must be linear homogeneous functions of the loads.[9] The student should note particularly
where these two requirements enter in the derivation of the theorem.

[9] The two requirements given in this sentence are not equivalent, since it is possible
for a structure to be stressed within the elastic limit and still have deformations which
are not linear functions of the loads. Many examples of this type of structure may be
cited. A typical one is the elastica (very thin column for the solution of which the
exact curvature relation must be used). The deflection for this structure is not pro-

We shall derive the Castigliano Theorem using the expression for total potential energy as follows: For a beam in equilibrium loaded as in Fig. 1.21, the total energy was

$$U = -[P_1y_1 + P_2y_2 + \cdots P_jy_j + \cdots P_ny_n] + V \qquad (1\text{-}56)$$

For an elastic system, the strain energy, V, turns out to be one half the change in the potential energy of the loads (see Art. 1-21).

$$V = \tfrac{1}{2} \sum_{i=1}^{i=n} P_iy_i$$

Castigliano's Theorem results from studying the variation in the strain energy, V, produced by a differential change in one of the loads, say P_j.

If the load P_j is changed by a differential amount δP_j and if the deflections y are linear functions of the loads, then

$$\frac{\partial V}{\partial P_j} = \frac{1}{2} \sum_{i=1}^{i=n} P_i \frac{\partial y_i}{\partial P_j} + \frac{1}{2}y_j = y_j \qquad (1\text{-}57)$$

To show that the above expression is equivalent to y_j, which is the deflection at the point of application of the load, P_j, we proceed as follows:

It was stated that the deflections are assumed to be linear functions of the loads. This is possible only in an elastic system. Then

$$\left. \begin{aligned} y_1 &= a_{11}P_1 + a_{12}P_2 + \cdots a_{1j}P_j + \cdots a_{1n}P_n \\ y_2 &= a_{21}P_1 + a_{22}P_2 + \cdots a_{2j}P_j + \cdots a_{2n}P_n \\ y_j &= a_{j1}P_1 + a_{j2}P_2 + \cdots a_{jj}P_j + \cdots a_{jn}P_n \end{aligned} \right\} \qquad (1\text{-}57a)$$

where the coefficients a_{1j}, etc., are constants of linearity. Then

$$\frac{\partial y_1}{\partial P_j} = a_{1j}, \quad \frac{\partial y_2}{\partial P_j} = a_{2j} \text{ etc.}$$

and

$$\sum_{i=1}^{i=n} P_i \frac{\partial y_i}{\partial P_j} = P_1a_{1j} + P_2a_{2j} + \cdots P_ja_{jj} + \cdots P_na_{nj}$$

It will now be shown that, in general,

$$a_{kj} = a_{jk}$$

so that

$$\sum_{i=1}^{i=n} P_i \frac{\partial y_i}{\partial P_j} = P_1a_{j1} + P_2a_{j2} + \cdots P_ja_{jj} + \cdots P_na_{jn} = y_j \qquad (1\text{-}57b)$$

which proves Castigliano's Theorem, Equation (1-57b).

---

portional to the load although the stresses may be within the proportional limit. See S. Timoshenko, *Theory of Elastic Stability*, McGraw-Hill Book Company, New York, 1936, p. 69.

The proof that $a_{kj} = a_{jk}$ depends upon the fact that the strain energy stored in a beam under gradually applied loads is independent of the order in which the loads are applied, but depends only upon the final configuration of the beam.

For example, consider the beam of Fig. 1.22 under the loads P_1 and P_2 only. Assume the following two sequences of events,

CASE 1   First the load P_1 is gradually applied, and then the load P_2 is gradually applied.

CASE 2   First the load P_2 is gradually applied, and then the load P_1 is gradually applied.

In view of the above, the strain energy must be the same in both cases. That is,

CASE 1

Strain energy due to $P_1 = W_{11} = \frac{1}{2} P_1 y_1 = \frac{1}{2} a_{11} P_1{}^2$

When P_2 is applied, P_1 does work $W_{12} = (a_{12}P_2)P_1$

and P_2 does work $W_{22} = \frac{1}{2} a_{22} P_2{}^2$

so that the total strain energy is given by

$$W_1 = W_{11} + W_{12} + W_{22}$$
$$= \tfrac{1}{2} a_{11} P_1{}^2 + a_{12} P_1 P_2 + \tfrac{1}{2} a_{22} P_2{}^2$$

Similarly, we have

CASE 2

Strain energy due to $P_2 = W_{22} = \frac{1}{2} P_2 y_2 = \frac{1}{2} a_{22} P_2{}^2$

When P_1 is applied, P_2 does work $W_{21} = (a_{21}P_1)P_2$

and P_1 does work $W_{11} = \frac{1}{2} a_{11} P_1{}^2$

so that the total strain energy is given by

$$W_2 = W_{22} + W_{21} + W_{11}$$
$$= \tfrac{1}{2} a_{22} P_2{}^2 + a_{21} P_1 P_2 + \tfrac{1}{2} a_{11} P_1{}^2$$

Now equating $W_1 = W_2$ we obtain $a_{21} = a_{12}$, which proves Equation (1-57b) and hence Equation (1-57). [See also Art. 2-10.]

Castigliano's Theorem, Equation (1-57), is stated as follows:

The partial derivatives of the total strain energy of any structure with respect to any one of the applied forces is equal to the displacement of the point of application of the force in the direction of the force.

A complementary theorem to Castigliano's Theorem can be developed as follows:

For a beam in equilibrium, assume a small additional displacement

δy_j of one of the loads (say P_j) to take place, at the same time maintaining all loads constant. The variation in total energy due to the variation in y_j will be

$$\delta U = \frac{\partial U}{\partial y_j}\, \delta y_j$$

Applying the Law of Minimum Potential Energy, this variation must be zero, or, since δy_j is not zero, $\partial U/\partial y_j = 0$

Operating on Equation (1-56), one obtains

$$\frac{\partial U}{\partial y_j} = -P_j + \frac{\partial V}{\partial y_j} = 0$$

or

$$P_j = \frac{\partial V}{\partial y_j} \qquad (1\text{-}58)$$

It is seen, therefore, that the partial derivative of the strain energy with respect to any one of the displacements of the applied loads in the direction of the applied load is equal to the load. It should be noted that the complementary theorem is not dependent upon the assumption of an elastic system and of a linear relation between the loads and displacements.

Although a beam was used as an example in the above derivations, it may be shown that the results apply to any structure in equilibrium.

In applying the above principles, it will be convenient to take advantage of differentiating under the integral sign; for example, for the beam subject to bending moments, M, with constant EI

$$\frac{\partial V}{\partial P_j} = \frac{\partial}{\partial P_j} \int_L \frac{M^2}{2EI}\, dx = \int_L \frac{\partial}{\partial P_j} \frac{M^2}{2EI}\, dx = \int_L \frac{M}{EI} \frac{\partial M}{\partial P_j}\, dx$$

1-25 Applications of Castigliano's theorem

The following example will illustrate how Castigliano's Theorem may be used to find the deflection of the end of a cantilever beam.

Example: Given the cantilever beam loaded as shown in Fig. 1.24 find the deflection of the free end due to bending only.

Solution:

$$V = \int_0^L \frac{M^2}{2EI}\, dx$$

$$\Delta = \frac{\partial V}{\partial P} = \frac{\partial}{\partial P} \int_0^L \frac{M^2}{2EI}\, dx = \int_0^L \frac{M}{EI} \frac{\partial M}{\partial P}\, dx$$

$$\Delta = \frac{1}{EI} \int_0^L -\left[Px + \frac{px^2}{2} \right](-x)dx = +\frac{1}{EI} \int_0^L \left(Px^2 + \frac{px^3}{2} \right)dx$$

$$\Delta = +\frac{1}{EI} \left(\frac{PL^3}{3} + \frac{pL^4}{8} \right)$$

Note that the answer carries a positive sign which denotes that the deflection is in the same direction as P. If it was required to solve for the maximum deflection of a cantilever beam loaded with only the uniformly distributed load p lb/ft, it would only be necessary to set $P=0$ in the preceding problem and $\Delta = +\dfrac{pL^4}{8EI}$ would be the answer.

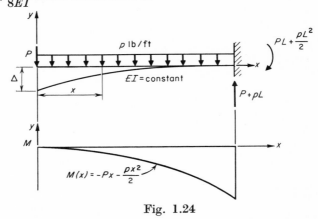

Fig. 1.24

In general, to find the deflection of a point of a beam that is not the point of application of a concentrated load, apply a load $P=0$ at that point, carry the term P into the strain energy equation, and introduce the true value of $P=0$ into the final expression for the answer.

Example: Given the simple beam with uniform load as shown in Fig. 1.25, find the deflection y_a of a point located a distance a from the left support.

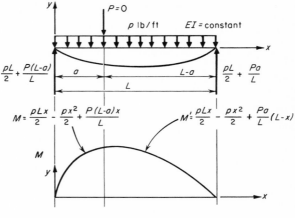

Fig. 1.25

Solution: Apply a load $P=0$ at the point whose deflection is desired. The moment equations will be discontinuous at the load and are shown on the moment diagram.

From Castigliano's Theorem:

$$y_a = \frac{\partial V}{\partial P} = \int_0^a \frac{M}{EI} \frac{\partial M}{\partial P} \, dx + \int_a^L \frac{M'}{EI} \frac{\partial M'}{\partial P} \, dx$$

$$y_a = \frac{1}{EI} \int_0^a \left[\frac{pLx}{2} - \frac{px^2}{2} + P\left(\frac{L-a}{L}\right)x \right] \left(\frac{L-a}{L}\right) x \, dx$$

$$+ \frac{1}{EI} \int_a^L \left[\frac{pLx}{2} - \frac{px^2}{2} + \frac{Pa}{L}(L-x) \right] \frac{a}{L}(L-x) dx$$

At this point, make use of the condition $P=0$ to eliminate the terms containing P from the integrals

$$y_a = \frac{1}{EI} \int_0^a \left[\frac{pLx}{2} - \frac{px^2}{2} \right] \left(\frac{L-a}{L}\right) x \, dx + \frac{1}{EI} \int_a^L \left[\frac{pLx}{2} - \frac{px^2}{2} \right] \frac{a}{L}(L-x) dx$$

Solving the integrals, we obtain

$$y_a = \frac{1}{EI} \left[\frac{1}{24} pa^4 - \frac{1}{12} pLa^3 + \frac{paL^3}{24} \right]$$

The equation of the elastic curve of the beam may be obtained by substituting x for a in the above.

1-26 Deflections of trusses by Castigliano's theorem

To apply Castigliano's Theorem to trusses, it is necessary to know the strain energy of an axially loaded bar. From Equation (1-32), the increment of strain energy for an axially loaded bar is

$$dV = \frac{1}{2E} \sigma_y^2 A dy$$

For an axially loaded bar of constant area A and length L, $\sigma_y = S/A$, where S is the total axial load on the bar. Then the total strain energy of the bar is

$$V = \int_0^L \frac{1}{2E} \left(\frac{S}{A}\right)^2 A dy = \frac{S^2 L}{2AE}$$

For a truss of n bars, the total strain energy is

$$V = \sum_n \frac{S^2 L}{2AE} \tag{1-59}$$

By Castigliano's Theorem the component deflection Δ_i of the point of application of a load P_i in the direction of P_i is equal to $\partial V/\partial P_i$. That is,

$$\Delta_i = \frac{\partial V}{\partial P_i} = \frac{\partial}{\partial P_i}\sum\frac{S^2 L}{2AE} = \sum\frac{S\dfrac{\partial S}{\partial P_i}L}{AE} \qquad (1\text{-}60)$$

Example: For the given truss, find the horizontal deflection of point C using Castigliano's Theorem.

$$AE = \text{constant for all members}$$
$$= 10{,}000 \text{ kip}$$

Solution: The solution is completely given in the following table.

Member	Length (ft)	$S = S_1 + S_2$	$\dfrac{\partial S}{\partial P}$	$S\dfrac{\partial S}{\partial P}L$
AB	20	$-15 + \frac{5}{12}P$	$+\frac{5}{12}$	-125
BE	20	$0 - \frac{5}{12}P$	$-\frac{5}{12}$	0
CD	20	$-15 - \frac{5}{12}P$	$-\frac{5}{12}$	$+125$
BF	12	$+ 9 + 0$	0	0
CE	12	$+ 9 + P/4$	$+\frac{1}{4}$	$+ 27$
BC	16	$-12 + \frac{2}{3}P$	$+\frac{2}{3}$	-128
AF	16	$+12 + \frac{2}{3}P$	$+\frac{2}{3}$	$+128$
FE	16	$+12 + \frac{2}{3}P$	$+\frac{2}{3}$	$+128$
ED	16	$+12 + P/3$	$+\frac{1}{3}$	$+ 64$

$$+219 = \sum S\frac{\partial S}{\partial P}L$$

$$\Delta = +\frac{219}{AE} = +0.0219 \text{ ft}$$

Note, in the last column of the table, the P terms were omitted since $P = 0$. Also, the plus sign indicates a deflection in the direction of P, that is, to the right.

1-27 Dummy load method

The dummy load or unit load method is a very important and versatile tool in the solution of deflections of both trusses and beams. The underlying principles can be developed directly from Castigliano's Theorem as follows:

Let an elastic body be in equilibrium under loads P_1, P_2, P_3, P_4, ... P_n and a load f applied at point k, Fig. 1.27.

By Castigliano's Theorem, the component of the deflection of point k in the direction of the applied force f is

$$\delta_{k_f} = \frac{\partial V}{\partial f} \qquad (1\text{-}61)$$

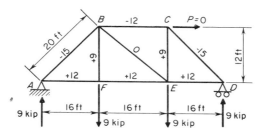

(a) Stresses S_1 due to given loads

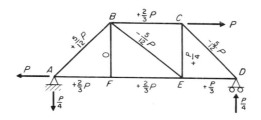

(b) Stresses S_2 due to load P

Fig. 1.26.

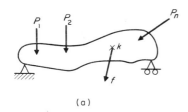

(a)   (b)

Fig. 1.27

It has been shown in Equation (1-39a), that the strain energy of a body for normal stress σ_x and shear stress τ_{xy} is given by

$$V = \frac{1}{2}\int_V \left(\frac{\sigma_x{}^2}{E} + \frac{\tau_{xy}{}^2}{G}\right) dx\, dy\, dz$$

and that if the elastic body is a beam and shear effects are ignored,

$$V = \int_L \frac{M^2}{2EI}\, dx$$

Also it was shown that if the elastic body is a truss, from Equation (1-59),

$$V = \sum \frac{S^2 L}{2AE}$$

For a beam, therefore, from Equation (1-61),

$$\delta_{k_f} = \int_L \frac{M \frac{\partial M}{\partial f} dx}{EI} \tag{1-62}$$

and for a truss,

$$\delta_{k_f} = \sum \frac{S \frac{\partial S}{\partial f} L}{AE} \tag{1-63}$$

Now consider the bending moments M and the stresses S. They are necessarily functions of the load f as well as of the loads $P_1, P_2, \ldots P_n$.

Suppose that a unit load is applied at k in place of the load f. Let the unit load be the only load on the elastic body. Then let the moments produced by the unit load be m if the body is a beam, and let the stresses in the members of the body be u if the body is a truss. The moments and stresses produced by a force f applied in place of the unit load will then be m_f and u_f, respectively, where

$$m_f = f \cdot m \tag{1-64}$$

$$u_f = f \cdot u \tag{1-65}$$

Now, in the body loaded as shown in Fig. 1.27, the moments M and the stresses S will equal by superposition the moments M_P or stresses S_P produced by the P force system plus the moments m_f or stresses u_f produced by the f force

$$M = M_P + m_f = M_P + f \cdot m \tag{1-66}$$

$$S = S_P + u_f = S_P + f \cdot u \tag{1-67}$$

Then

$$\frac{\partial M}{\partial f} = m = \text{moments produced by a unit load at } k \tag{1-68}$$

$$\frac{\partial S}{\partial f} = u = \text{stresses produced by a unit load at } k \tag{1-69}$$

Using Equation (1-68) in Equation (1-62) gives for beams

$$\delta_{k_f} = \int_L \frac{Mm\,dx}{EI} \tag{1-70}$$

Using Equation (1-69) in Equation (1-63) gives for trusses

$$\delta_{k_f} = \sum \frac{Su L}{AE} \tag{1-71}$$

In like manner it can be shown that if v represents the internal shear produced by the unit load, the deflection of the point of application of the unit load in the direction of the unit load, due to shear, is

$$\delta_{k_v} = C \int_L \frac{Vvdx}{AG} \tag{1-72}$$

where A, G, V, and C are as previously defined in Art. 1-21.

It may now be pointed out and emphasized that in the above derivation the deflection of point k due to the P force system alone can be found by setting $f = 0$. Then the stresses S and the moments M will equal S_p and M_p, respectively. Therefore, it is not necessary actually to apply the load f to a body in order to find the deflection of a point. The dummy load method is by this derivation shown to be a numerical method of finding the partial derivatives of the stresses and moments with respect to f. The derivatives will be found by computing the stresses and moments produced by a unit load applied, at the point whose deflection is desired, in the direction of the desired deflection.

1-28 Deflections of beams by the dummy load method

The application of the dummy load method to beam problems will be shown in the following illustrative examples.

Example: Find the maximum deflection of a cantilever beam with constant section loaded with a uniform load. The quantities needed for the solution are shown in Fig. 1.28.

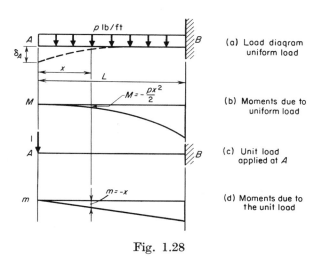

(a) Load diagram uniform load

(b) Moments due to uniform load

(c) Unit load applied at A

(d) Moments due to the unit load

Fig. 1.28

Solution: Applying Equation (1-70) gives

$$\delta_A = \int_0^L \frac{Mm}{EI}\,dx = \frac{1}{EI}\int_0^L \left(-\frac{px^2}{2}\right)(-x)dx = +\frac{pL^4}{8EI}$$

The plus sign means that the deflection is in the direction of the unit load.

The following example shows the application of the method to a problem involving discontinuous moment functions.

Example: Find the deflection of the third point of a simple beam with constant section loaded as shown. Fig. 1.29 shows the quantities needed for the solution.

Solution: Equation (1-70) gives at once

$$\delta_B = \int_0^L \frac{Mm\,dx}{EI} = \frac{1}{EI}\int_0^{\frac{L}{3}} (+Px)(+\tfrac{2}{3}x)dx + \frac{1}{EI}\int_{\frac{L}{3}}^{\frac{2}{3}L} \left(+\frac{PL}{3}\right)\tfrac{1}{3}(L-x)dx +$$

$$\frac{1}{EI}\int_{\frac{2}{3}L}^{L} P(L-x)\tfrac{1}{3}(L-x)dx$$

or

$$\delta_B = \frac{PL^3}{EI}\left[+\frac{2}{9\times 27}+\frac{1}{9\times 6}+\frac{1}{9\times 27}\right] = +\frac{5}{162}\frac{PL^3}{EI}$$

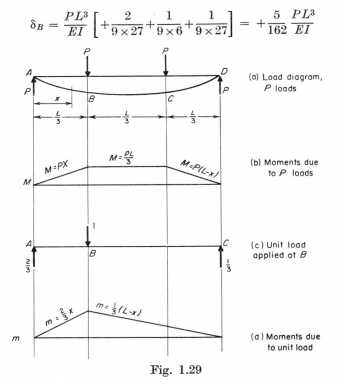

(a) Load diagram, P loads

(b) Moments due to P loads

(c) Unit load applied at B

(d) Moments due to unit load

Fig. 1.29

The plus sign means that the deflection is in the direction of the unit load or downward.

1-29 Deflection of a truss by the dummy load method

Example: For the truss and loading shown, find the vertical deflection of L_2.

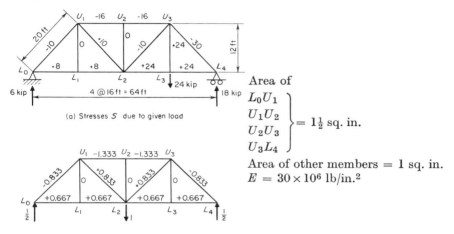

(a) Stresses S due to given load

(b) Stresses U due to unit load at L_2

Area of
$$\left.\begin{array}{c} L_0U_1 \\ U_1U_2 \\ U_2U_3 \\ U_3L_4 \end{array}\right\} = 1\tfrac{1}{2} \text{ sq. in.}$$

Area of other members $= 1$ sq. in.
$E = 30 \times 10^6$ lb/in.^{2}

Fig. 1.30

Solution: The solution is completely shown in the table and Fig. 1.30.

Member	S	u	L/A in./in.^{2}	SuL/A +	SuL/A −
L_0L_1	+ 8	+0.677	192	1024	
L_1L_2	+ 8	+0.677	192	1024	
L_2L_3	+24	+0.677	192	3072	
L_3L_4	+24	+0.677	192	3072	
L_0U_1	−10	−0.833	160	1333	
U_3L_4	−30	−0.833	160	4000	
U_1U_2	−16	−1.333	128	2730	
U_2U_3	−16	−1.333	128	2730	
U_1L_2	+10	+0.833	240	2000	
L_2U_3	−10	+0.833	240	—	2000
U_1L_1	0	0	144	—	—
U_2L_2	0	0	144	—	—
U_3L_3	+24	0	144	—	—

$$\sum \frac{Sul}{A} = +20{,}975 - 2000 = +18{,}985$$

$$\sum \frac{Sul}{AE} = +\frac{18{,}985}{30{,}000} = +0.063 \text{ in.} \downarrow = \text{vertical deflection of } L_3$$

The plus sign indicates that the deflection is in the direction of the unit load or downward.

1-30   Rotation of beams by the dummy load method

Consider the beam of Fig. 1.31 loaded with a force system P_1, P_2, P_3, ... P_k and a moment at section C equal to f. The strain energy of the system V with reference to the undeflected position is

$$V = \int_L \frac{M^2 dx}{2EI} \tag{1-73}$$

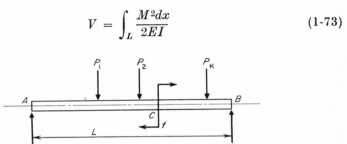

Fig. 1.31

If θ_C is the rotation of the section of the beam where the external moment f is applied and if we proceed as in Art. 1-24,

$$\theta_C = \frac{\partial V}{\partial f} = \int_L \frac{M \frac{\partial M}{\partial f} dx}{EI} \tag{1-74}$$

Let m be the moment at any section due to a value $f = 1$. Then the moment at any section due to f will be $f \cdot m$.

Let M_p be the moment at any section due to the loads P_1, P_2, ... P_k, f being excluded.

The moment at any section of the beam due to both the P force system and f will be

$$M = M_p + m \cdot f$$

and $\partial M / \partial f = m =$ moment at any section due to $f = 1$. Then from Equation (1-74) substituting m for $\partial M / \partial f$, it follows that

$$\theta_C = \int_L \frac{M m dx}{EI} \tag{1-75}$$

To illustrate the solution for the rotation of a beam, consider the following example.

Example: Find the rotation of the end of a simple beam loaded with a uniform load. The quantities required for the solution are shown in Fig. 1.32

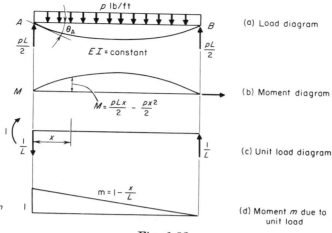

Fig. 1.32

Solution: Applying Equation (1-75) to this beam, we obtain at once

$$\theta_A = \int_L \frac{Mm\,dx}{EI} = \frac{1}{EI} \int_0^L \left(\frac{pL}{2}x - \frac{px^2}{2}\right)\left(1 - \frac{x}{L}\right)dx = \frac{pL^3}{24EI}$$

1-31 Graphical integration or visual integration [10]

In the solution of deflection problems by the dummy load method, the solution of the integrals $\int \frac{Mm\,dx}{EI}$ often involves much labor. The visual or graphical integration method now presented often permits a saving of time and labor in the solution of the integrals.

Consider the function M/EI. It can be plotted as a curve. In general, for constant EI, this curve will be either a combination of straight lines or parabolas. The function m will *always* be a combination of straight lines. The integral $\int \frac{Mm\,dx}{EI}$ thus can be seen to represent a volume whose base will be the area bounded by the M/EI curve and whose altitude will be bounded by a plane whose equation is m. Fig. 1.33 shows such a volume for the simple beam of Fig. 1.32. The element of area of the base $\frac{M\,dx}{EI}$ is shown as the shaded area $AA'B'B$ and the element of volume $\frac{Mm}{EI}dx$ is shown as the volume bounded by $ABCD$ and $A'B'C'D'$.

---

[10] The origin of this method is obscure but it was used and taught to students in Civil Engineering by Prof. J. Charles Rathbun of City College, New York, during the years 1930–1949.

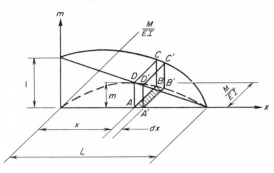

Fig. 1.33

The integral $\int \frac{M m dx}{EI}$ over the length L is thus the volume of the figure shown. It will now be proved that the volume of the figure is

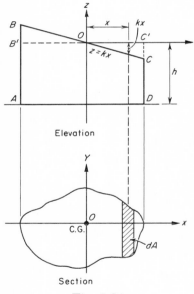

Elevation

Section

Fig. 1.34

the area of the base $\left(=\frac{2}{3} \cdot \frac{pL^2}{8EI} \cdot L\right)$ multiplied by the height of the figure measured through the center of gravity of the area of the base $(= +\frac{1}{2})$. That is, the following theorem will now be proved:

Given a right prism with constant cross section cut by a single inclined plane, the volume of the portion of the prism bounded by the cutting plane is equal to its cross-sectional area multiplied by its height measured through the center of gravity of the cross section.

Proof: It is established and proved in courses in elementary mathematics that the volume of a right prism $AB'C'D$ is the cross-sectional area A times the height of the prism, h

$$\text{vol } AB'C'D = A \cdot h$$

We want the volume $ABCD = \text{vol } AB'C'D + \text{vol } OBB' - \text{vol } OC'C$

$\text{vol } OBB' - \text{vol } OC'C = \int_A kxdA = 0$ since x is measured from an axis through the center of gravity of the cross section.

Hence vol $ABCD = \text{vol } AB'C'D = A \cdot h$.

1-32 Application of the visual integration method

Example: Given a cantilever beam loaded with a uniformly distributed load of p lb/ft, find the deflection and the rotation of the free end, Fig. 1.35.

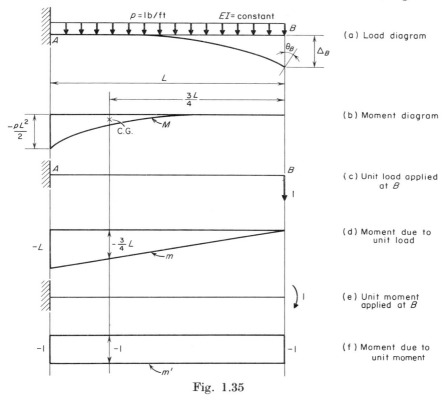

Fig. 1.35

Solution:

$$\Delta_B = \int_L \frac{Mm\,dx}{EI} = \frac{1}{3}\left(-\frac{pL^2}{2EI}\right)L\left(-\frac{3}{4}L\right) = +\frac{pL^4}{8EI}\Big\downarrow$$

$$\theta_B = \int_L \frac{Mm'\,dx}{EI} = \frac{1}{3}\left(-\frac{pL^2}{2EI}\right)L(-1) = +\frac{pL^3}{6EI} \text{ clockwise}$$

In the event that the moments due to the dummy load are discontinuous, it will be necessary to divide the integration into two or more parts depending upon the number of discontinuities.

Example: A simple beam of constant cross section is loaded with a concentrated load at the center. Find the deflection of the third point of the beam.

Solution: The visual integration is carried out by dividing the M diagram into two parts, ABC and $CBDE$. To avoid having to calculate the center of gravity of $CBDE$, this area is further divided into two triangles, BCE and BDE. The locations of the centers of gravity of the triangle are shown in

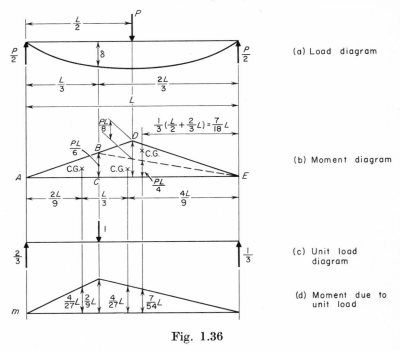

Fig. 1.36

Fig. 1.36a and the corresponding ordinates on the m diagram are shown in Fig. 1.36b. Then,

$$\int_{ABC}\frac{Mm\,dx}{EI} = \left(+\frac{1}{2}\cdot\frac{PL}{6EI}\cdot\frac{L}{3}\right)\left(+\frac{4}{27}\,L\right) = \frac{1}{243}\frac{PL^3}{EI} = 0.00411\,\frac{PL^3}{EI}$$

$$\int_{BCE}\frac{Mm\,dx}{EI} = \left(+\frac{1}{2}\cdot\frac{PL}{6EI}\cdot\frac{2}{3}L\right)\left(+\frac{4}{27}\,L\right) = \frac{2}{243}\frac{PL^3}{EI} = 0.00822\,\frac{PL^3}{EI}$$

$$\int_{BDE}\frac{Mm\,dx}{EI} = \left(+\frac{1}{2}\cdot\frac{PL}{8EI}\cdot\frac{2L}{3}\right)\left(+\frac{7}{54}L\right) = \frac{7}{1296}\frac{PL^3}{EI} = 0.00542\,\frac{PL^3}{EI}$$

$$\delta = (0.00411+0.00822+0.00542)\frac{PL^3}{EI} = 0.0178\,\frac{PL^3}{EI}\;\downarrow$$

1-33   Numerical methods for evaluating $\int\dfrac{Mm\,dx}{EI}$

Although visual integration is extremely useful in solving a great variety of problems, it can become involved numerically for areas bounded by segments of parabolas, especially if there are a number of discontinuities in the m diagram. It is more practical in these cases to set up approximate numerical methods for evaluating the integral. One such method will be discussed in Chapter 5.

1-34   The theorem of complementary energy

The Theorem of Complementary Energy was first stated by Engesser in 1889. More recently it was revived by Westergaard[11] who also gave various applications of the theorem. The importance of the theorem lies in the fact that it enables one to solve for structural deflections even if the load-deflection relation is nonlinear. In this respect it has a considerable advantage over the Castigliano method which is restricted to linear load-deflection structures only.

The Theorem of Complementary Energy will be given herein without proof. Following this, a simple application of the deflection relation which follows therefrom will be given.[12]

Of all stress states satisfying the conditions of equilibrium in the interior of a body and on that portion of the surface where the surface forces are prescribed, the actual state of stress is such as to minimize the complementary energy U^*,

$$U^* = \int \Delta d\sigma - \sum rR \qquad (1\text{-}76)$$

in which R = reaction, i.e., a force exerted by a support; r = path of R, the displacement of a support in the direction of R; σ = internal stress; Δ = the deformation in the direction of σ. It can be shown that for a structure subjected to any loading

$$\delta = \frac{\partial U^*}{\partial P} \qquad (1\text{-}77)$$

in which δ is the deflection and P is the load in the direction of the deflection.

A typical application of the Theorem of Complementary Energy follows.

Example: For an ordinary structure, of which Fig. 1.37 is a representative load-deflection curve, U^* is given by the shaded area which is also given by

$$U^* = \int_0^P \delta dP = \frac{\delta_1}{P_1{}^2} \frac{P^3}{3} \qquad (1\text{-}78)$$

[11] H. M. Westergaard, "On the Method of Complementary Energy," *Transactions,* A.S.C.E., Vol. 107, 1942.

[12] For a complete proof see I. S. Sokolnikoff, *Mathematical Theory of Elasticity,* McGraw-Hill Book Company, 1946.

Then, from Equation (1-77)

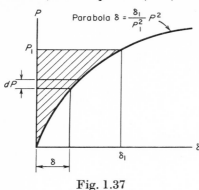

Fig. 1.37

$$\delta = \frac{dU^*}{dP} = \frac{\delta_1}{P_1{}^2} P^2 \qquad (1\text{-}79)$$

as required.

If, on the other hand, we had applied the Castigliano Theorem

$$\delta = \frac{\partial V}{\partial P}$$

where V is the area *under* the curve, we would obtain

$$\delta = \frac{2\delta_1}{P_1{}^2} P^2 \qquad (1\text{-}80)$$

which is obviously incorrect.

1-35   The Williot-Mohr diagram [13]

The Williot-Mohr diagram is a graphical method for determining directly the deflections of the panel points of a truss. It consists of two separate graphical constructions. The first is the Williot diagram and the second is the Mohr correction diagram which may be needed to correct the Williot diagram.

In applying the Williot method to the determination of truss panel point deflections, it is first necessary to compute

1. The stresses in all members of the truss due to the given loading.
2. The elongation or shortening of each member of the truss $\Delta = PL/EA$.

An explanation of the construction of the Williot diagram (and of the Mohr correction diagram) is given in Fig. 1.38. It should be noted that all of the diagrams described must be drawn to scale.

Referring to Fig. 1.38 it is seen that in order graphically to locate the deflected position of point C, one must begin the construction from two fixed points A and B. It is always necessary to select the panel points of the truss that may be considered fixed in space before attempting to draw a Williot diagram.

Referring to Fig. 1.38 again, it is clear that the new location C' of panel point C is located by swinging two arcs of radius $(AC + \Delta_{AC})$ and $(BC + \Delta_{BC})$ where Δ_{AC} and Δ_{BC} are the changes in length of AC and BC due to elastic action. The point of intersection of the two arcs will be C'.

---

[13] Named after the French engineer, M. Williot, and the German engineer, Otto Mohr, who first presented the methods described in this article.

Bearing in mind that all the elongations considered are small when compared with the lengths of the members, then a perpendicular offset from the member may be substituted for the arc.   The accuracy of the final result will not be affected by this substitution.

Fig. 1.38b is an enlarged portion of Fig. 1.38a.   It shows that the deflection of point C may be determined graphically by enlarging the "deflection part" of the truss diagram (Fig. 1.38a).   Note, in particular, how Δ_{AC} and Δ_{BC} are laid off to scale from the point C, in the actual directions that the point C of the members BC and AC moves in the deformed truss of Fig. 1.38a.

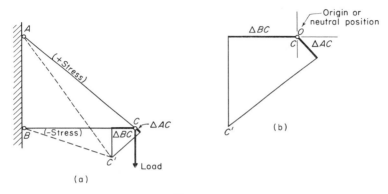

Fig. 1.38

A more complex truss is illustrated in Fig. 1.39a.   The Williot diagram for this truss is drawn as follows.

Starting with the fixed points A and B, locate C' as in Fig. 1.38, using the deformations of members AC and BC which are the only members that fix the location of C'.

Next, obtain the deflection of point D using A and C' as the known fixed points. D must move along with C' when it is deflected and also have movement relative to A and C' caused by the deformations of members AD and CD.   Therefore from position C', lay off the shortening in member CD and swing an arc.   Likewise, from D, lay off the lengthening of member AD and swing an arc.   The intersection point of the two arcs locates the deflected position of D, or D'. E' is located in a similar manner.   Note that here, as in Fig. 1.38, perpendicular offsets are substituted for arcs.

Fig. 1.39b, upon inspection, will be found to be identical with the "deflection part" of diagram (a) for panel point E.

Therefore, distance OC' on Fig. 1.39b is the deflection of $C(=CC')$; OD' is the deflection of $D(=DD')$; OE' is the deflection of $E(=EE')$.

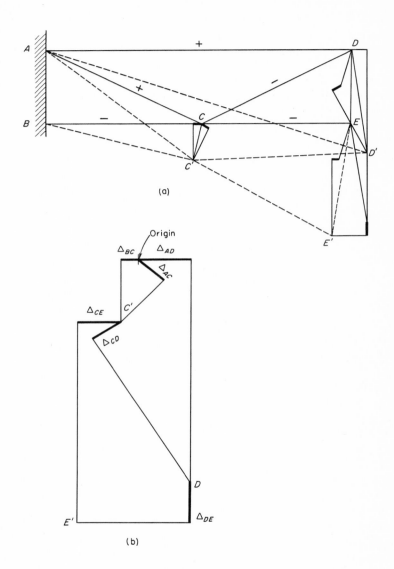

(a)

(b)

Fig. 1.39

Fig. 1.39b gives one a graphical solution for the deflections of all the points of the truss. This diagram is known as the Williot diagram.

Fig. 1.40a shows a truss which falls into a different category from those of Figs. 1.38 and 1.39. In Fig. 1.40 there is but one point that

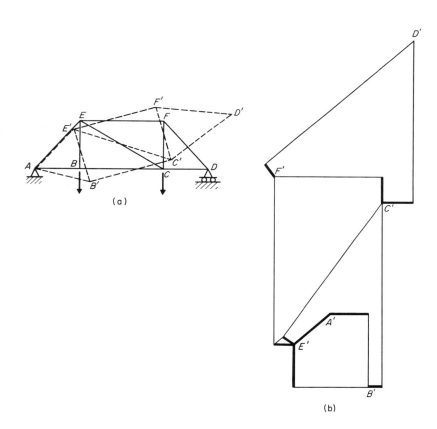

Fig. 1.40

can be called fixed and that is A. In order to draw a Williot diagram, we need either another fixed point or a fixed direction.

Suppose direction AE is assumed to be fixed. Upon drawing the Williot diagram, as shown in Fig. 1.40b, it is found that the truss deflects as shown by the dotted lines in Fig. 1.40a. This result is impossible; therefore it is necessary to apply corrections to bring panel point D back to its proper position. The diagram which performs this function is called the Mohr correction diagram and its construction is based on the fact that D' should be on the same level as A (since it is on level rollers). To bring D' on a level with A, it will be necessary to rotate the entire truss clockwise (through a small angle) about A as a center. The radius of rotation for D is AD. The other panel points will also rotate about A but with different radii. For instance, the radius for point F is AF. The displacements caused by the rotations may be shown as perpendicular offsets to the radii since the angle of rotation is small and since the entire truss is rotated as a rigid body.

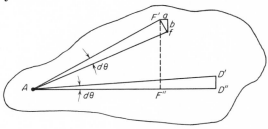

Fig. 1.41

Fig. 1.41 serves to illustrate the explanation which follows:

(a) $D'D''$ is the displacement of point D due to the rotation of the rigid body shown. It is a vertical line since AD' is practically a horizontal line.

(b) $F'f = \dfrac{AF'}{AD'} \times D'D'' = $ displacement of F due to rotation $d\theta$

(c) $a = $ horizontal component of $F'f$

$$a = \frac{F'F''}{AD'} \times D'D''$$

(d) $b = $ vertical component of $F'f$

$$b = \frac{AF''}{AD'} \times D'D''$$

These principles will now be used to develop the Mohr correction diagram which will graphically correct the Williot deflections to give the true deflections of the truss. Part of Fig. 1.40a and 1.40b are reproduced in Fig. 1.42 for this purpose.

Fig. 1.42a shows the deflected position of the truss based on the assumptions that point A and direction AE are fixed. Fig. 1.42b is the corresponding Williot diagram.

The truss will now be rotated through an angle $D'Ad$. Each part of the deflected truss must rotate through the same angle.

This rotation will cause D' to move to d. Any other point such as E' will rotate through the same angular change to e. The distance

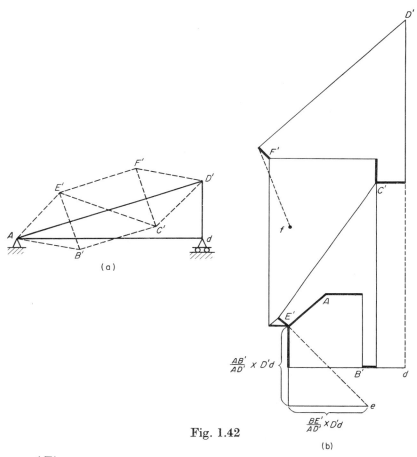

(a)

Fig. 1.42

(b)

$E'e = \dfrac{AE'}{AD'} \times D'd$. The direction of $E'e$ must be perpendicular to AE'.

The horizontal component of movement $E'e = \dfrac{B'E'}{AD'} \times D'd$. The vertical

component of movement $E'e = \dfrac{AB'}{AD'} \times D'd$. These rotative movements

are indicated on Fig. 1.42b. The rotative displacements for the other panel points are determined in the same manner.

The true deflections of the various panel points of the truss are therefore given by the vector addition of the deflections given by the Williot diagram and the deflections due to the rotations described above.

Thus, from Fig. 1.42b, it can be seen that:

Deflection of point A = zero

Deflection of point B = $AB' + B'b$ = Ab in the direction from A to b

Deflection of point C = $AC' + C'c$ = Ac in the direction from A to c

Deflection of point D = $AD' + D'd$ = Ad in the direction from A to d

Deflection of point E = $AE' + E'e$ = Ae in the direction from A to e

Deflection of point F = $AF' + F'f$ = Af in the direction from A to f

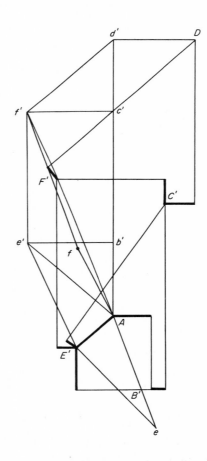

Fig. 1.43

DEFLECTIONS

It will be noted that the deflection of $D=Ad$ is also equal to distance $d'D'$ in Fig. 1.43. Likewise, the deflection of $C=Ac$ may be laid up from $C'=c'C'$, the deflection of $B=Ab$ may be laid up from $B'=B'b'$, the deflection of $E=Ae$ is laid up from $E'=E'e'$, and the deflection of $F=Af$ is laid up from $F'=F'f'$.

It will also be noted that all points thus laid out, ($Ab'c'd'e'f'$), if connected together, will yield a miniature truss exactly similar to the given truss except that the sides will be mutually perpendicular. This must be so, because each side of the miniature truss as laid out is perpendicular to the rotative correction and must come out perpendicular to the same side on the original truss.

It should be evident from the above that the simple procedure of laying out a truss, starting at point A, similar in every respect to the original truss and whose sides will be mutually perpendicular to those of the given truss and whose base length will be equal to $D'd$, will yield an automatic correction diagram for the Williot diagram. This diagram is known as the Mohr diagram, and the combined construction is called the Williot-Mohr diagram.

To get the absolute deflection of any point on the truss, we need but scale the distance between the point on the correction truss and the corresponding point on the Williot diagram. Therefore, $\delta E=e'E'$ in the direction from e' to E' and similarly for all other panel points.

Problems

1. Find the deflection under the 10,000-lb load using the following methods:

(a) Double integration
(b) Moment area
(c) Conjugate beam
(d) Castigliano's Theorem
(e) Dummy load
(f) Visual integration

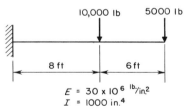

2. Find the vertical deflection and the rotation of the free end C of the beam shown using the methods of problem 1. Determine the equation of the elastic curve.

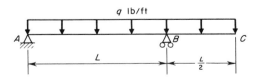

3. Find the deflections under the loads and also the maximum upward deflection for the beam shown using the methods of problem 1.

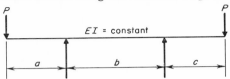

4. Find Δ_A by dummy load and visual integration.

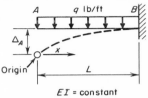

5. Find the deflection at $x = L/3$ using dummy load and visual integration.

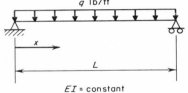

6. Find Δ_C by dummy load.

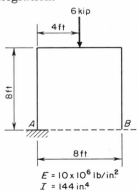

$$E = 30 \times 10^6 \text{ lb/in.}^2$$
$$I = 144 \text{ in.}^4$$

7. Compute the horizontal deflection and the rotation of point B using dummy load and visual integration.

$$E = 10 \times 10^6 \text{ lb/in.}^2$$
$$I = 144 \text{ in.}^4$$

8. Find the vertical deflection and the rotation of the free end B of the rigid frame shown using dummy load and visual integration.

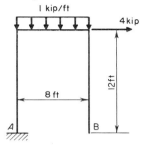

$$E = 10 \times 10^6 \text{ lb/in.}^2$$
$$I = 144 \text{ in.}^4$$

9. (a) Find the vertical component of deflection of panel point L_2. (b) Find the horizontal component of deflection of panel point U_3. (c) Find the relative deflection (along direction U_1L_3) between panel points U_1 and L_3.

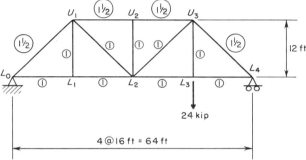

(Areas in in.^{2} shown circled on diagram)

10. For the truss of problem 9, find the deflections of all panel points using the Williot-Mohr diagram. Check the results of problem 9.

References

Following are some references (in addition to those given in footnotes) containing discussions of various portions of the material contained in this chapter:

Cassie, W. Fisher, *Structural Analysis*, 2nd Ed., Longmans, Green and Company, London, 1954.

Girvin, H. F., *A Historical Appraisal of Mechanics*, International Textbook Company, Scranton, Pa., 1948.

Gray, C. S., Kent, L. E., Mitchell, W. A. and Godfrey, G. B., *Steel Designers' Manual*, Frederick Ungar Publishing Company, New York, 1955.

Grinter, L. E., *Theory of Modern Steel Structures*, Vol. 2, 2nd Ed., The Macmillan Company, New York, 1949.

Johnson, J. B., Bryan, C. W. and Turneaure, F. E., *The Theory and Practise of Modern Framed Structures*, Part 2, 10th Ed., John Wiley and Sons, Inc., New York, 1932.

Parcel, J. I. and Moorman, R. B., *Analysis of Statically Indeterminate Structures*, John Wiley and Sons, Inc., New York, 1955.

Shedd, T. C. and Vawter, J., *Theory of Simple Structures*, 2nd Ed., John Wiley and Sons, Inc., New York, 1941.

Timoshenko, S. and Young, D. H., *Theory of Structures*, McGraw-Hill Book Company, New York, 1945.

Timoshenko, S., *Strength of Materials*, Part 1, D. Van Nostrand Company, Inc., Princeton, N.J., 1955.

Wilbur, J. B. and Norris, C. H., *Elementary Structural Analysis*, McGraw-Hill Book Company, New York, 1948.

Williams, C. D., *An Analysis of Statically Indeterminate Structures*, International Textbook Company, Scranton, Pa., 1951.

Chapter 2

STATICALLY INDETERMINATE STRUCTURES

2-1 Introduction

In this chapter, some of the methods developed in the first chapter will be applied to the solution of indeterminate beam, truss, and frame structures. Therefore, the discussion will begin with a consideration of the general problem of redundance and the connected problem of stability. Having established the criteria and meaning of redundance, we will develop various methods for solving the indeterminate structure. Following is a list of the methods which will be discussed in this chapter:

a. The method of superposition.
b. The three-moment equation
c. The method of least work or Castigliano's Theorem
d. The elastic center method

Some discussion will be given to different methods for solving simultaneous equations, since this is an important part of the solutions of some of the redundant structures considered herein. Also, a brief discussion will be given of the Mohr circle construction which is particularly useful in the elastic center method of solution.

2-2 Stability of structures

A stable beam will in general have enough, or more than enough, reaction components to satisfy the equations of equilibrium, $\sum H = 0$, $\sum V = 0$, $\sum M = 0$, plus any conditional equations that may be obtained by considering some special conditions regarding moments and shears which may exist in the beam. Several examples of stable and unstable beams are shown in Fig. 2.1.

For trusses it is necessary to consider the internal stability of the structure as well as the number of reactions present. Several examples of stable and unstable trusses are shown in Fig. 2.2. In general, a stable truss will have enough or more than enough reaction components and members to satisfy the equations of equilibrium plus the equations of condition.

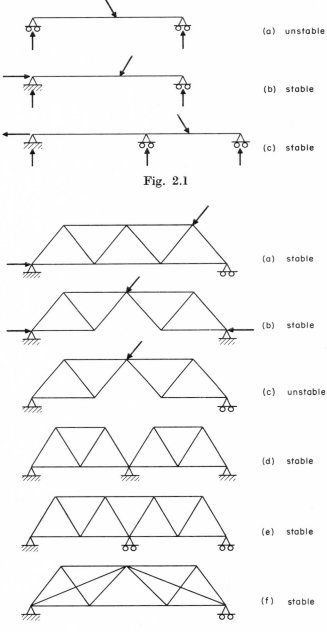

Fig. 2.1

Fig. 2.2

The conditional equations are that the moment at each joint is zero.

Although various tests for stability of structures have been prescribed, for the general structure these tests become complicated so that it is probably best to rely primarily upon visual inspection to determine whether or not a structure is stable. In general, this requires a study of the structure with a view toward determining whether or not the structure will collapse under any possible condition of loading.

2-3 Statically indeterminate structures

Any structure whose reactions or internal stresses cannot be found by using the conditions of equilibrium plus the conditional equations (if any) is a statically indeterminate structure. For instance, the beam of Fig. 2.1c has four reaction components. We cannot solve for all four components using the three available equations of equilibrium $\sum H = 0$, $\sum V = 0$, $\sum M = 0$. Hence, it is statically indeterminate to the first degree. We would need one additional equation to find all four reactions. If this beam had an additional roller support, we would have five unknown reactions, but still only three equations of equilibrium. We would then need two additional equations in order to be able to solve for all reactions and the beam would then be indeterminate to the second degree.

The additional equations necessary to solve statically indeterminate structures come from prescribed conditions of deflection or rotation, sometimes called the requirements of "consistent deformations."

2-4 Definition of redundancy

A redundant may be defined as any reaction component or member not necessary for stability. A statically determinate structure possesses no redundants. All parts and all reaction components of a statically determinate structure are necessary for stability. A statically indeterminate structure to the first degree can possess more than one reaction or member which may be considered as the redundant, but only one redunant can be removed at a time or the structure will become unstable. For instance, in Fig. 2.1c, either (redundant) roller support can be removed without the structure becoming unstable, but if they are both removed at one time the structure collapses about the hinge. It follows similarly that in a structure statically indeterminate to the second degree, if two redundants are removed simultaneously, the remaining structure will be statically determinate and stable. If more than two redundants are removed, the remaining structure is unstable.

For a structure statically indeterminate to the nth degree, n

redundants may be simultaneously removed and the remaining structure will be statically determinate and stable.

2-5   Solution of indeterminate structures by superposition

The solution of an indeterminate structure by superposition is obtained in the following manner:

(a) Remove a number of redundants equal to the degree of redundancy of the problem, thus reducing the structure to a statically determinate one.

(b) Calculate the deflections and/or rotations of a number of points equal to the degree of redundancy, the points being points of application of the redundants and the deflections being in the directions of the redundants.

(c) Apply each redundant as a load and find the deflections of the points of application of the redundants due to each redundant. These deflections will be given in terms of the unknown redundants.

(d) Add the deflection at each point due to the loads on the statically determinate structure to the deflection produced by the redundants. The total deflection of the point must conform with the prescribed boundary conditions.

(e) The equations resulting from step (d) are solved simultaneously to find the numerical values of the redundants.

(f) Knowing the value of the redundants, we can draw the shear and moment diagrams for the statically indeterminate structure.

In the above steps, any method of finding deflections can be used in obtaining the solution. In some problems however, one particular method may offer time-saving advantages over another method.

2-6   Indeterminate beams solved by superposition

Some examples of the solution of indeterminate beams using the superposition method will now be given.

Example: Given the beam of Fig. 2.3a, find the reactions.

Solution: We have a choice in this problem of removing either redundant, M_A or R_B. We have chosen R_B as the redundant to be removed. The conditional equation is that the deflection of point B is zero,

$$\delta_p + \delta_{R_B} = 0 \tag{2-1}$$

By moment area, we can find δ_p and δ_{R_B}. Thus

$$\delta_p = -\frac{1}{2}\frac{PL}{2EI}\cdot\frac{L}{2}\cdot\frac{5}{6}\,L = -\frac{5PL^3}{48EI} \tag{2-2}$$

and

$$\delta_{R_B} = +\frac{1}{2}\frac{R_B L}{EI}\cdot L\cdot\frac{2}{3}\,L = +\frac{R_B L^3}{3EI} \tag{2-3}$$

Substituting in Equation (2-1), we obtain

$$-\frac{5}{48}\frac{PL^3}{EI}+\frac{R_BL^3}{3EI}=0$$

or

$$R_B = +\frac{5}{16}P\uparrow$$

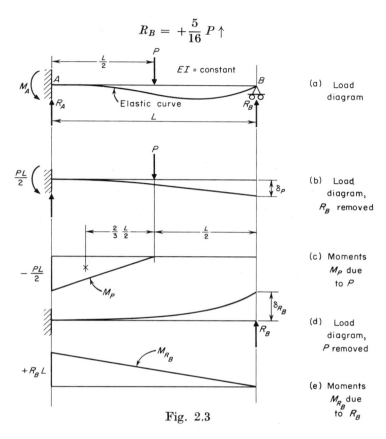

(a) Load diagram

(b) Load diagram, R_B removed

(c) Moments M_P due to P

(d) Load diagram, P removed

(e) Moments M_{R_B} due to R_B

Fig. 2.3

Knowing R_B, we can draw the shear and moment diagrams by the super-position of Fig. 2.3c and Fig. 2.3e.

By superposition,

$$M_A = -\frac{PL}{2}+\frac{5}{16}PL = -\frac{3}{16}PL\,\rangle$$

and

$$R_A = P-\frac{5}{16}P = \frac{11}{16}P\uparrow$$

The same beam can be solved by removing redundant M_A and using as a conditional equation $\theta_A = 0$ (see Fig. 2.4).

Then,

$$\theta_A = \theta_{AP} + \theta_{AM} = 0 = -\frac{1}{2}\frac{PL}{4EI}\cdot\frac{L}{2}+\frac{t_{BA}}{L} = 0 \qquad (2\text{-}4)$$

$$-\frac{PL^2}{16EI}+\frac{1}{2}\cdot\frac{M_AL}{EI}\cdot\frac{2}{3}\frac{L}{L} = 0$$

$$-\frac{PL^2}{16}+\frac{M_AL}{3} = 0$$

or

$$M_A = +\frac{3}{16}\,PL\,\rangle$$

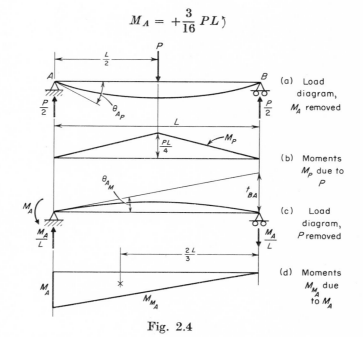

Fig. 2.4

R_A and R_B are obtained by superposition as follows,

$$R_A = \frac{P}{2}+\frac{M_A}{L} = +\frac{11}{16}\,P\uparrow$$

$$R_B = \frac{P}{2}-\frac{M_A}{L} = +\frac{5}{16}\,P\uparrow$$

The superposition method will now be used to solve a problem indeterminate to the second degree.

Example: Given the beam shown in Fig. 2.5a, find the reactions.

Solution: The conditional equations to be used if the redundants M_A and M_B are removed are

$$\theta_A = 0 = [\theta_P+\theta_{M_A}+\theta_{M_B}]_A \qquad (2\text{-}5)$$

$$\theta_B = 0 = [\theta_P+\theta_{M_A}+\theta_{M_B}]_B \qquad (2\text{-}6)$$

Let θ_{1P} = rotation of A due to load P

$\quad\ \theta_{11}$ = rotation of A due to load M_A

$\quad\ \theta_{12}$ = rotation of A due to load M_B

$\quad\ \theta_{21}$ = rotation of B due to load M_A

$\quad\ \theta_{22}$ = rotation of B due to load M_B

$\quad\ \theta_{2P}$ = rotation of B due to load P

Equations (2-5) and (2-6) now become

$$\theta_{11}+\theta_{12}+\theta_{1P} = 0 \tag{2-7}$$

$$\theta_{21}+\theta_{22}+\theta_{2P} = 0 \tag{2-8}$$

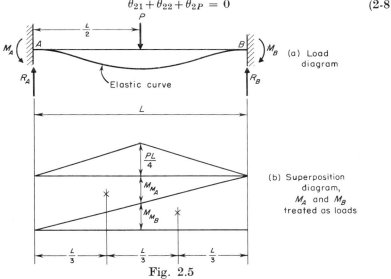

Fig. 2.5

By moment area, $L\cdot\theta_{11}=\dfrac{1}{EI}$ (t_{BA} due to moment triangle due to M_A)

$$= \frac{1}{2}\frac{M_A\cdot L}{EI}\cdot\frac{2}{3}L = \frac{M_A L^2}{3EI}$$

or

$$\theta_{11} = \frac{M_A L}{3EI}$$

Also

$$L\cdot\theta_{12} = \frac{1}{EI}\ (t_{BA}\ \text{due to moment triangle due to}\ M_B)$$

$$= \frac{1}{2}\frac{M_B\cdot L}{EI}\cdot\frac{L}{3} = \frac{M_B L^2}{6EI}$$

or

$$\theta_{12} = \frac{M_B L}{6EI}$$

Likewise,

$$\theta_{21} = -\frac{M_A L}{6EI}$$

$$\theta_{22} = -\frac{M_B L}{3EI}$$

$$\theta_{1P} = -\frac{1}{2}\frac{PL}{4EI}\cdot\frac{L}{2} = -\frac{PL^2}{16EI}$$

$$\theta_{2P} = +\frac{PL^2}{16EI} \text{ (from symmetry)}$$

Substituting these values in Equation (2-7) and Equation (2-8), we obtain

$$\frac{M_A L}{3EI} + \frac{M_B L}{6EI} - \frac{PL^2}{16EI} = 0 \tag{2-9}$$

$$-\frac{M_A L}{6EI} - \frac{M_B L}{3EI} + \frac{PL^2}{16EI} = 0 \tag{2-9a}$$

Solving for M_A and M_B gives

$$M_A = M_B = +\frac{PL}{8}$$

The plus sign indicates that M_A and M_B are in the assumed directions shown in Fig. 2.5a.

2-7 Relative motion between two panel points of a truss

In the solution of statically indeterminate trusses it is sometimes necessary to obtain the relative movement between panel points such as U_1 and L_2 in the truss of Fig. 2.6a. The dummy load principle can be used to advantage in this case.

The component displacement of panel point U_1 in the direction of $U_1 L_2$ can be found by computing $\delta_{U_1} = \sum \frac{Su'L}{AE}$, where u' is the stress in any member due to a unit load applied at U_1 in the direction $U_1 L_2$. The component displacement of panel point L_2 in the direction of $U_1 L_2$ could be found by computing $\delta_{L_2} = \sum \frac{Su''L}{AE}$, where u'' is the stress in any member due to a unit load applied at L_2 in the direction $L_2 U_1$.

It is desired to find the relative movement $\delta_{U_1 L_2}$, where $\delta_{U_1 L_2} = \delta_{U_1} + \delta_{L_2}$. Then

$$\delta_{U_1 L_2} = \sum \frac{Su'L}{AE} + \sum \frac{Su''L}{AE}$$

or

$$\delta_{U_1 L_2} = \sum \frac{S(u' + u'')L}{AE} = \sum \frac{SuL}{AE} \tag{2-10}$$

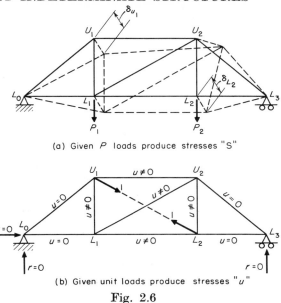

(a) Given P loads produce stresses "S"

(b) Given unit loads produce stresses "u"

Fig. 2.6

Note, $u = u' + u'' =$ the stress in any member due to a pair of unit loads applied simultaneously at U_1 and L_2 as shown in Fig. 2.6b.

2-8   The solution of indeterminate trusses by superposition

Stresses in statically determinate trusses may, of course, be determined by using the three equations of equilibrium.   If a truss contains more members or reactions than are necessary for stability, the stresses in the truss cannot be computed solely from the equations of statics. Such a truss would be a statically indeterminate truss.   A truss may be statically indeterminate internally or externally; i.e., it may have more members than are necessary for stability or it may have more reactions than are necessary for stability.   Some trusses may be statically indeterminate both internally and externally.

Fig. 2.7a illustrates a truss which is statically indeterminate internally.   Fig. 2.7b illustrates a truss which may be considered as statically indeterminate externally.

As previously stated, a redundant is any member or reaction which is not necessary for stability, such as AC or BD or AB or DC in Fig. 2.7a and R_A or R_B or R_C in Fig. 2.7b.   Note that in Figs. 2.7a and 2.7b only one of the possible redundants may be removed at one time or the truss will collapse.   Consequently there is only one more member or reaction than is needed for stability.   If a truss is constructed so that only one redundant may be removed without destroying the

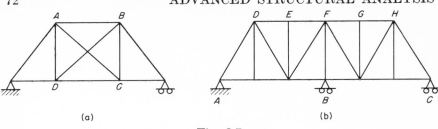

Fig. 2.7

stability of the truss, then the truss is statically indeterminate to the first degree. If two redundants may be removed without destroying stability, then the truss is statically indeterminate to the second degree. If n redundants may be removed without destroying stability, then it is statically indeterminate to the nth degree.

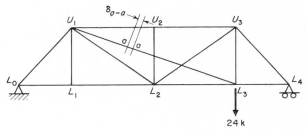

Fig. 2.8

Fig. 2.8 illustrates a truss statically indeterminate to the first degree. Let U_1L_3 be the redundant member. If we were to cut U_1L_3 at a-a, points a-a would move apart a distance $\delta_{a\text{-}a} = \sum \dfrac{SuL}{AE}$, where S are the stresses in the members with U_1L_3 cut, and u are the stresses in the truss produced by unit loads applied as shown in Fig. 2.9.

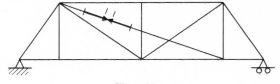

Fig. 2.9

Let X be the true stress in the redundant member. The stresses produced by X on the members of the truss are Xu. The resultant true stress in each member is $S + Xu$, and X must be of such a magnitude as to bring the cut ends of U_1L_3 a distance $\delta_{a\text{-}a}$ toward each other, i.e., it must be large enough to restore the member U_1L_3 to its original length before cutting. Then,

$$-\delta_{a \cdot a} \text{ (produced by cutting)} = \delta_{a \cdot a} \text{ (produced by } X\text{)}$$

$$-\sum \frac{SuL}{AE} = \sum \frac{Xu \cdot uL}{AE} = X \sum \frac{u^2L}{AE}$$

from which

$$X = -\frac{\sum \dfrac{SuL}{AE}}{\sum \dfrac{u^2L}{AE}} = -\frac{\sum \dfrac{SuL}{A}}{\sum \dfrac{u^2L}{A}}$$

Note, in the denominator, the summation extends over all members, including U_1L_3. This member is, however, omitted in the numerator

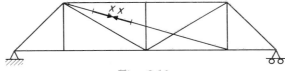

Fig. 2.10

since $S = 0$. The value of X having been determined, the stress in any member can be computed by superposition as

$$S' = S + Xu \qquad\qquad (2\text{-}11a)$$

In these problems it is well to adopt the sign convention that $(+)$ stresses are tensile, $(-)$ stresses are compressive. The use of this sign convention will result in numerical answers bearing the true tensile $(+)$ or compressive $(-)$ sign.

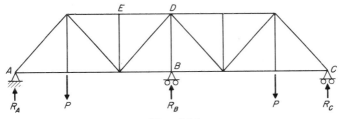

Fig. 2.11

A truss, such as that of Fig. 2.11, may be solved by treating R_B as the redundant and proceeding as follows:

1. Remove R_B and solve for the stresses in the members produced by the given loading. These are the stresses S.

2. Apply a unit vertical load at R_B and solve for the stresses.   These are the stresses u.

3. Compute the vertical deflection of $B = \sum \dfrac{SuL}{AE}$.

4. Apply R_B at B, removing the given loads on the truss.

5. The stresses produced in the members by R_B will be $R_B \cdot u$.

6. Compute the deflection at B produced by R_B

$$= \sum R_B u \cdot \frac{uL}{AE} = R_B \sum \frac{u^2 L}{AE}$$

7. By superposition of deflections,

$$\sum \frac{SuL}{AE} + R_B \sum \frac{u^2 L}{AE} = 0, \text{ and solve for } R_B.$$

8. The final stress in any member is $S' = S + R_B \cdot u$.

This same problem could be solved by removing any internal member not necessary for stability.   For example, by considering ED as the redundant, we proceed as follows:

1. Cut member ED.

2. Solve for the reactions and the stresses S.

3. Solve for deflection of the cut ends of ED, which is given by $\sum \dfrac{SvL}{AE}$ where v is the stress in any member produced by a pair of unit loads applied at the cut ends of ED.

4. Let X be the stress in member ED.   Then Xv is the stress in any member produced by X.

5. Equate $-\sum \dfrac{SvL}{AE} = X \sum \dfrac{v^2 L}{AE}$ and solve for X.

6. The final stress in any member is $S' = S + Xv$.

This method can be extended to provide solutions for the stresses in trusses statically indeterminate to any degree.   To illustrate this, the solution for the truss of Fig. 2.12 will be indicated.

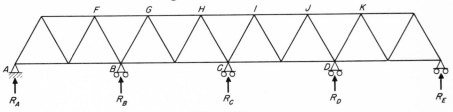

Fig. 2.12

METHOD I

1. There are three redundants.
2. Remove the redundants R_B, R_C, R_D.
3. Let u be stresses produced in the truss by a unit vertical load at B with the redundants removed.
4. Let v be stresses under same condition due to a unit load at C.
5. Let w be stresses under same condition due to a unit load at D.
6. Let S be stresses under same condition due to the given loads.
7. Then $R_B u$ will be the stresses in members due to R_B.
8. $R_C v$ will be the stresses in members due to R_C.
9. $R_D w$ will be stresses in members due to R_D.
10. The deflection at B produced by S equals $\sum \dfrac{SuL}{AE}$.

11. The deflection at B produced by R_B equals $\sum \dfrac{R_B u^2 L}{AE}$.

12. The deflection at B produced by R_C equals $\sum R_C v \dfrac{uL}{AE}$.

13. The deflection at B produced by R_D equals $\sum R_D w \dfrac{uL}{AE}$.

14. The resultant deflection at B must be zero or

$$R_B \sum \frac{u^2 L}{AE} + R_C \sum \frac{vuL}{AE} + R_D \sum \frac{wuL}{AE} + \sum \frac{SuL}{AE} = 0 \qquad (2\text{-}12)$$

15. Likewise for point C,

$$R_B \sum \frac{uvL}{AE} + R_C \sum \frac{v^2 L}{AE} + R_D \sum \frac{wvL}{AE} + \sum \frac{SvL}{AE} = 0 \qquad (2\text{-}13)$$

16. For point D,

$$R_B \sum \frac{uwL}{AE} + R_C \sum \frac{vwL}{AE} + R_D \sum \frac{w^2 L}{AE} + \sum \frac{SwL}{AE} = 0 \qquad (2\text{-}14)$$

We now have three equations in three unknowns R_B, R_C, and R_D which may be solved simultaneously. The stress in any member will then be equal to

$$S' = S + R_B u + R_C v + R_D w \qquad (2\text{-}15)$$

METHOD II

The same problem may also be solved by using any other three redundants, such as members FG, HI, and JK. The procedure will be similar to that used in Method I.

2-9   Example of the solution of an indeterminate truss by superposition

Given the truss of Fig. 2.13, find the stresses in the members.

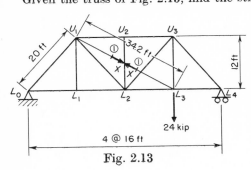

Area of L_0U_1
U_1U_2
U_2U_3
U_3L_4 $\Big\} = 1\frac{1}{2}$ in.^{2}

Area of other members = 1 in.^{2}

There is one redundant member.

Let U_1L_3 be the redundant.

Fig. 2.13

Solution: Cut U_1L_3; then $S =$ stress in members, and

$$\sum \frac{SuL}{AE} + X \sum \frac{u^2L}{AE} = 0,$$

where $u =$ stresses due to unit loads. Total stress $S' = S + Xu$. The complete solution is shown in Table 2.1. The total stress in each member is listed in the last column under S'.

TABLE 2.1

Member	S	u	L/A	$\dfrac{SuL}{A}$	u^2	$\dfrac{u^2L}{A}$	Xu	S'
L_0L_1	$+\ 8$	0	192	0	0	0	0	$+8$
L_1L_2	$+\ 8$	0	192	0	0	0	0	$+8$
L_2L_3	$+24$	-0.936	192	-4320	$+0.876$	$+168.5$	-7.36	$+16.64$
L_3L_4	$+24$	0	192	0	0	0	0	$+24$
L_0U_1	-10	0	160	0	0	0	0	-10
U_3L_4	-30	0	160	0	0	0	0	-30
U_1U_2	-16	-0.468	128	$+959$	$+0.218$	$+27.9$	-3.67	-19.67
U_2U_3	-16	-0.468	128	$+959$	$+0.218$	$+27.9$	-3.67	-19.67
U_1L_2	$+10$	-0.587	240	-1407	$+0.345$	$+82.8$	-4.60	$+5.40$
L_2U_3	-10	-0.587	240	-1407	$+0.345$	$+82.8$	$+4.60$	-5.40
U_2L_2	0	0	144	0	0	0	0	0
U_3L_3	$+24$	-0.352	144	-1216	$+0.124$	$+17.9$	-2.67	$+21.33$
U_1L_3	0	$+1$	411	0	$+1$	$+411$	$+7.87$	$+7.87$
UL_1	0	0	144	0	0	0	0	0

$$\sum = -6432 \qquad \sum = 818.8$$

$$X = \frac{+6432}{818.8} = +7.86 \text{ kip (tension)}$$

2-10   Solution of a structure indeterminate to the nth degree

It was shown in the previous articles that the superposition solution of first- and higher-degree indeterminate structures involves setting up a number of deflection equations equal to the degree of indeterminacy and then solving these equations simultaneously to determine the numerical values of the redundants. For a structure indeterminate to the nth degree, there will be n deflection equations, each written for the component of deflection in the direction of and at the point of application of each redundant. These equations are

$$\delta_{11} + \delta_{12} + \delta_{13} + \cdots \delta_{1n} + \delta_{1P} = 0$$
$$\delta_{21} + \delta_{22} + \delta_{23} + \cdots \delta_{2n} + \delta_{2P} = 0 \qquad (2\text{-}16)$$
$$\vdots$$
$$\delta_{n1} + \delta_{n2} + \delta_{n3} + \cdots \delta_{nn} + \delta_{nP} = 0$$

where δ_{11} = the displacement of point 1 in the determinate structure due to redundant X_1 applied at point 1, in the determinate structure.

δ_{12} = the displacement of point 1 due to redundant X_2 applied at point 2, in the determinate structure.

δ_{1n} = the displacement of point 1 due to redundant X_n applied at point n, in the determinate structure.

δ_{1P} = the displacement of point 1 due to given P loads with the redundants removed.

Each δ must be evaluated before the n equations can be solved simultaneously. Each equation contains $(n+1)$ terms and there are n equations; hence $n(n+1)$ terms are to be evaluated.

A single experience of solving a third-degree indeterminate structure will prove that there is a great deal of work involved in setting up and evaluating the n equations. Therefore, any knowledge that can be applied in reducing this amount of labor will obviously be advantageous. It will now be shown that certain relations exist between the displacements δ_{12}, δ_{21}, etc. In order to do this, we will express these quantities in terms of the dummy load expressions. Let us consider a structure composed of parts which resist axial loads and bending.

Let u_1, m_1 be the axial stress and moment respectively anywhere in the structure due to a unit load applied at 1.

u_2, m_2 be the axial stress and moment respectively anywhere in the structure due to a unit load applied at 2.

u_n, m_n be the axial stress and moment respectively anywhere in the structure due to a unit load applied at n.

Let X_1 be the redundant reaction or internal unknown acting at 1.

X_2 be the redundant reaction or internal unknown acting at 2.

X_n be the redundant reaction or internal unknown acting at n.

Then X_1u_1, X_1m_1 are the axial stresses and moments anywhere in the structure due to X_1.

X_2u_2, X_2m_2 are the axial stresses and moments anywhere in the structure due to X_2.

X_nu_n, X_nm_n are the axial stresses and moments anywhere in the structure due to X_n.

Let M, S be the axial stress and moment in any part of the structure due to given P loads with the redundants removed.

Then

$$\delta_{11} = X_1\left[\int \frac{m_1{}^2 ds}{EI} + \sum \frac{u_1{}^2 L}{AE}\right] = X_1\delta'_{11} \tag{2-17}$$

where

$$\delta'_{11} = \left[\int \frac{m_1{}^2 ds}{EI} + \sum \frac{u_1{}^2 L}{AE}\right] \tag{2-17a}$$

Similarly,

$$\delta_{12} = X_2\left[\int \frac{m_1 m_2 ds}{EI} + \sum \frac{u_1 u_2 L}{AE}\right] = X_2\delta'_{12}$$

and the general term

$$\delta_{pk} = X_k\left[\int \frac{m_p m_k ds}{EI} + \sum \frac{u_p u_k L}{AE}\right] = X_k\delta'_{pk} \tag{2-18}$$

It will now be observed that

$$\delta'_{pk} = \left[\int \frac{m_p m_k ds}{EI} + \sum \frac{u_p u_k L}{AE}\right] \text{ and } \delta'_{kp} = \left[\int \frac{m_k m_p ds}{EI} + \sum \frac{u_k u_p L}{AE}\right]$$

Therefore

$$\delta'_{pk} = \delta'_{kp} \tag{2-18a}$$

Thus, we see that $\delta'_{12} = \delta'_{21}$, $\delta'_{13} = \delta'_{31} \cdots$ etc.

Equations (2-16) can now be rewritten as follows:

$$X_1\delta'_{11} + X_2\delta'_{12} + X_3\delta'_{13} + \cdots X_n\delta'_{1n} + \delta_{1P} = 0$$
$$X_1\delta'_{12} + X_2\delta'_{22} + X_3\delta'_{23} + \cdots X_n\delta'_{2n} + \delta_{2P} = 0$$
$$X_1\delta'_{13} + X_2\delta'_{23} + X_3\delta'_{33} + \cdots X_n\delta'_{3n} + \delta_{3P} = 0 \tag{2-19}$$
$$\cdot \quad \cdot \quad \cdot \quad \cdot \quad \cdot \quad \cdot \quad \cdot \quad \cdot \quad \cdot \quad \cdot$$
$$X_1\delta'_{1n} + X_2\delta'_{2n} + X_3\delta'_{3n} + \cdots X_n\delta'_{nn} + \delta_{nP} = 0$$

where

$$\delta_{iP} = \int \frac{M m_i ds}{EI} + \sum \frac{S u_i L}{AE} \qquad (i = 1, 2, 3, \cdots n) \tag{2-20}$$

If we examine Equations (2-19), it is seen that the coefficients of the unknown redundant forces are symmetric about a diagonal connecting the δ'_{11}, δ'_{22}, $\cdots \delta'_{nn}$ terms. Therefore, the number of δ' coefficients to be evaluated is $n(\delta'_{pp})$ terms, $[n^2 - (1 + 2 + \cdots n)]\delta'_{pk}$ terms, and $(n)\delta_{iP}$ terms or a total of $[n + n^2 - (1 + 2 + \cdots n) + n]$ terms. This compares with $n(n + 1)$ terms to be evaluated for Equation (2-16).

Thus, if we have a third-degree indeterminate structure, we have $[n^2 + 2n - (1 + 2 + \cdots n)] = 9 + 6 - 1 - 2 - 3 = 9$ terms and $n(n + 1) = 12$ terms, which is a saving of 3 terms in the computation due to the symmetry of the coefficients.

2-11 Reciprocal deflections

The result, Equation (2-18a), obtained in the previous article is one statement of the Law of Reciprocal Deflections. A simple form of the law was first given by James Clerk Maxwell in about 1864. His statement of the law is essentially the following:

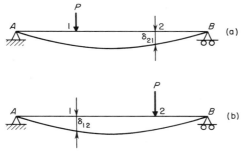

Fig. 2.14

Given an elastic body in equilibrium under a force P acting at point 1, the deflection at point 2 produced by this load is equal to the deflection of point 1 if the load is moved to point 2, the deflections being measured in the directions of the applied loads.

The student should note that this statement is included in the more general statement of Equation (2-18a).

A more general statement of reciprocal effects was given by E. Betti in about 1872. Betti's Law is stated here without proof for the sake of completeness.

In an elastic structure with unyielding supports and at constant temperature the external work done by a system of forces P during a distortion caused by a system of forces Q is equal to the external work done by the Q system during a distortion caused by the P system.

As indicated in Equation (2-18a), the reciprocal relation holds for generalized forces and deflections—i.e., for moments and angular deflections (in the direction of the moments) as well as for forces and

linear deflections. It also holds for vibratory elastic systems as was
shown by Lord Rayleigh in 1873.

2-12   The theorem of three moments

In the solution of indeterminate beam problems, the work involved
in setting up the simultaneous equations is greatly reduced by using the
Theorem of Three Moments developed by B. P. E. Clapeyron in 1857.
A general form of the Theorem of Three Moments will now be developed
using the dummy load method simplified by the use of visual integration.

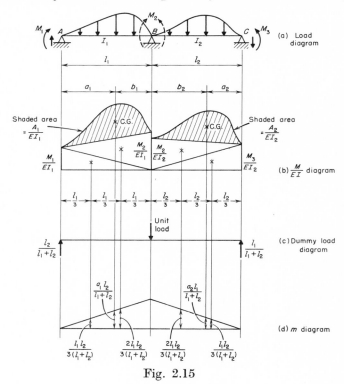

Fig. 2.15

Two spans of a continuous beam of lengths l_1 and l_2, and of sectional
inertia I_1 and I_2, respectively, are isolated and a free body diagram
drawn showing the applied loads on the spans and the reactions, shears,
and internal bending moments acting exterior to the free body (see
Fig. 2.15a). The moments are assumed positive and are so indicated.
The loads are shown as downward or negative loads. The moment
diagrams divided by EI are indicated in Fig. 2.15b together with the
locations of the centers of gravities of the component M/EI areas.

(Note that A_1 = area of the moment diagram produced by the vertical loads on the simple span l_1 and that A_2 is the similar area for span l_2.)

The deflection of point B is zero and expressing this as the superposition of the deflections produced by M_1, M_2, M_3 and the given loads we obtain, by using visual integration (Figs. 2.15c and 2.15d)

$$\frac{1}{2}\frac{M_1l_1}{EI_1}\cdot\frac{l_1l_2}{3(l_1+l_2)}+\frac{1}{2}\frac{M_2l_1}{EI_1}\cdot\frac{2l_1l_2}{3(l_1+l_2)}+\frac{A_1}{EI_1}\cdot\frac{a_1l_2}{l_1+l_2}$$

$$+\frac{1}{2}\frac{M_2l_2}{EI_2}\cdot\frac{2l_1l_2}{3(l_1+l_2)}+\frac{1}{2}\frac{M_3l_2}{EI_2}\cdot\frac{l_1l_2}{3(l_1+l_2)}+\frac{A_2}{EI_2}\cdot\frac{a_2l_1}{l_1+l_2}=0 \qquad (2\text{-}21)$$

Multiplying each term of Equation (2-21) by $6E\dfrac{(l_1+l_2)}{l_1l_2}$, we obtain

$$\frac{M_1l_1}{I_1}+2M_2\left(\frac{l_1}{I_1}+\frac{l_2}{I_2}\right)+M_3\frac{l_2}{I_2}=-\left(\frac{6A_1a_1}{I_1l_1}+\frac{6A_2a_2}{I_2l_2}\right) \qquad (2\text{-}22)$$

Equation (2-22) represents one form of the theorem of three moments.

2-13 Applications of the theorem of three moments

The use of Equation (2-22) will now be demonstrated by solving several typical continuous beam problems.

Example: Given the three span continuous beam of Fig. 2.16a, find the moments at the supports and the reactions. Draw the moment diagram.

Solution: The problem is indeterminate to the second degree and requires the use of two conditional equations. The three-moment equation if used twice, once for the two left-hand spans (Fig. 2.16b) and once for the two right-hand spans (Fig. 2.16d), supplies the two required conditional equations.

Applying Equation (2-22) to the left-hand spans and letting $M_A = M_1$, $M_B = M_2$, $M_C = M_3$, we obtain

$$M_A\frac{l}{I}+2M_B\left(\frac{l}{I}+\frac{1.5l}{2I}\right)+M_C\frac{1.5l}{2I}=-\frac{6\times\frac{2}{3}\times\frac{p(1.5l)^2}{8}+1.5l\times0.75l}{2I\times1.5l}$$

Since $M_A = 0$, this simplifies to

$$M_B(3.5l)+M_C(0.75l)=-\tfrac{1}{4}p(2.25l^2)(0.75l)$$

or

$$3.5M_B+0.75M_C=-0.5625pl(0.75l) \qquad (2\text{-}23a)$$

Operating likewise on the two right-hand spans, we obtain

$$0.75M_B+3.5M_C=-0.5625pl(0.75l) \qquad (2\text{-}23b)$$

If we solve Equations (2-23a) and (2-23b) simultaneously or note $M_B = M_C$ from symmetry, we obtain

$$M_B = M_C = -0.0993pl^2$$

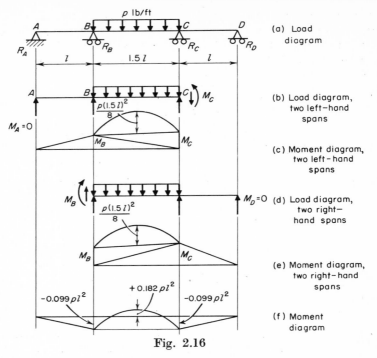

Fig. 2.16

The reactions are determined by applying the equations of equilibrium as follows:

$$R_A = +\frac{M_B}{l} = -0.0993pl \text{ (the minus sign indicates uplift at } A \text{ or a downward reaction)}$$

and

$$R_B = \frac{M_C}{1.5l} - \frac{R_A(2.5l)}{1.5l} + \frac{p(1.5l)^2 \times \frac{1}{2}}{1.5l} = +0.839pl \uparrow$$

The moment diagram is shown in Fig. 2.16f.

An example of the application to built-in indeterminate beams follows.

Example: Beam built-in at both ends, find M_A and M_B.

Solution: Writing the three-moment equation for spans 1 and 2 $(M_2 = M_A, M_3 = M_B)$ gives

$$M_1 \frac{L_1}{\infty} + 2M_A\left(\frac{L_1}{\infty} + \frac{L}{I}\right) + M_B \frac{L}{I} = \frac{-6 \times \frac{1}{2} \times \frac{2}{9}PL^2 \times \frac{5}{9}L}{IL}$$

or

$$2M_A + M_B = -\frac{10}{27}PL \qquad (2\text{-}24a)$$

If we write the three-moment equation for spans 2 and 3 ($M_1 = M_A$, $M_2 = M_B$),

$$M_A \frac{L}{I} + 2M_B\left(\frac{L}{I} + \frac{L_3}{\infty}\right) + M_3 \frac{L_3}{\infty} = \frac{-6 \times \frac{1}{2} \times \frac{2}{9}PL^2 \times \frac{4}{9}L}{IL}$$

or

$$M_A + 2M_B = -\frac{8}{27}PL \qquad (2\text{-}24\text{b})$$

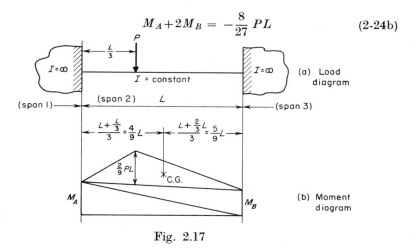

(a) Load diagram

(b) Moment diagram

Fig. 2.17

Solving Equations (2-24a) and (2-24b) simultaneously, we obtain

$$M_A = -\frac{4}{27}PL$$

$$M_B = -\frac{2}{27}PL$$

The reactions can be obtained from the equilibrium conditions if required. The shear and moment diagrams can then be constructed.

2-14 Settlement of supports

The superposition Equations (2-19) can be easily adapted to take care of sagging or settling supports by equating the right-hand side of the equation to the known settlement instead of to zero. For example, if point 2 sags an amount δ_2 the second equation of the set of Equations (2-19) would become

$$X_1\delta'_{12} + X_2\delta'_{22} + X_3\delta'_{23} + \cdots X_n\delta'_{2n} + \delta_{2P} = \delta_2$$

The remaining equations are the same.

To illustrate, consider the following problem.

Example: A cantilever beam loaded with a uniform load rests on a support B which sags an amount $= k \times R_B$ where k is a known constant. Find the reactions.

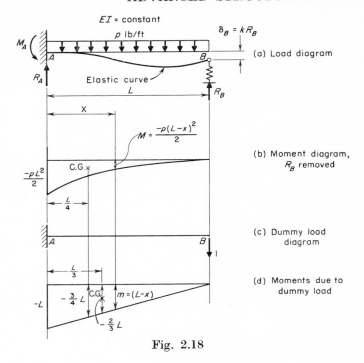

$$\text{Fig. 2.18}$$

Solution: The conditional equation for the deflection of B is

$$\delta_{Bp} + \delta_{B_R} = \delta_B \tag{2-25}$$

where $\delta_{Bp} =$ deflection of B due to the uniform load

$\delta_{B_R} =$ deflection of B due to the redundant reaction R_B

By visual integration,

$$\delta_{Bp} = \frac{1}{3}\left(-\frac{pL^3}{2EI}\right)\left(-\frac{3}{4}L\right) = +\frac{pL^4}{8EI}$$

$$\delta_{B_R} = \frac{1}{2}\frac{R_B L^2}{EI}\left(-\frac{2}{3}L\right) = -\frac{1}{3}\frac{R_B L^3}{EI}$$

where the moments due to R_B are $-R_B m$.   Substituting in Equation (2-25), we obtain,

$$\frac{pL^4}{8EI} - \frac{1}{3}\frac{R_B L^3}{EI} = kR_B$$

from which

$$R_B = +\frac{pL^4}{8kEI + \frac{8}{3}L^3} \quad \begin{array}{l} \uparrow \text{ upward} \\ \ \ \text{as assumed} \end{array}$$

Then

$$R_A = pL - R_B = pL\left[1 - \frac{L^3}{8kEI + \frac{8}{3}L^3}\right] \uparrow$$

and

$$M_A = -\frac{pL^2}{2} + R_B L = -\frac{pL^2}{2}\left[1 - \frac{2L^3}{8kEI + \frac{8}{3}L^3}\right]$$

$$= -\frac{pL^2}{2}\left[1 - \frac{L^3}{4kEI + \frac{4}{3}L^3}\right]$$

2-15 The theorem of three moments modified for settlement of supports

If supports A, B, and C of Fig. 2.15a settle downward an amount δ_A, δ_B, and δ_C, respectively, then, altering the derivation of Art. 2-12 accordingly, Equation (2-22) becomes

$$M_1\frac{L_1}{I_1} + 2M_2\left[\frac{L_1}{I_1} + \frac{L_2}{I_2}\right] + M_3\frac{L_2}{I_2}$$

$$= -\left[\frac{6A_1a_1}{I_1L_1} + \frac{6A_2a_2}{I_2L_2}\right] + \frac{6E}{L_1}(\delta_B - \delta_A) + \frac{6E}{L_2}(\delta_B - \delta_C) \quad (2\text{-}26)$$

We note that in using Equation (2-26), δ is taken as positive if it is a downward settlement (i.e., in the direction of the unit load).

Example: As an illustration of a typical application of this formula, the problem of Art. 2-14 will now be solved. For this problem we have, using the method of Art. 2-13, the following solution.

Solution:

$$2M_A\frac{L}{I} = -\frac{pL^3}{4I} - \frac{6E}{L}kR_B$$

or since

$$M_A = -\frac{pL^2}{2} + R_B L$$

we have

$$R_B L + \frac{3EI}{L^2}kR_B = \frac{3}{8}pL^2$$

from which

$$R_B = +\frac{pL^4}{8kEI + \frac{8}{3}L^3} \quad \begin{array}{l} \uparrow \text{ upward} \\ | \text{ as assumed} \end{array}$$

2-16 The method of least work

Castigliano's Theorem, which was described in Art. 1-24, enables one to solve a large variety of statically indeterminate structures. For the structure with unyielding supports, the solution is equivalent to a mathematical minimizing of the energy function. That is, as will be shown in the following, the redundants must have such values that the strain energy of the structure is a minimum. For this reason, the method is frequently called the Method of Least Work.

A simple statement of the theory is as follows:

For a structure indeterminate to the nth degree, i.e., with n redundant reactions, all immovable,

$$\frac{\partial V}{\partial X_1} = \frac{\partial V}{\partial X_2} = \cdots = \frac{\partial V}{\partial X_n} = 0 \qquad (2\text{-}27)$$

where X_1, X_2, $\cdots$ X_n are the redundants and V is the strain energy of the system.

Proof: By Castigliano's Theorem, $\partial V/\partial X_1 =$ deflection of point 1, which is zero by hypothesis. The other terms follow in a similar manner.

The method of least work is frequently called the *classical method* of indeterminate structural analysis. It can be used to solve beams, trusses, and frames as well as combinations of these and other structural components. Although newer methods of analysis frequently will enable one to solve particular problems more directly than can be done using least work, the method is still in common use and preferred by many engineers. A typical application of the method to an indeterminate beam is given in the next article.

2-17 Example of use of the method of least work

Example: Find the reactions for the beam.

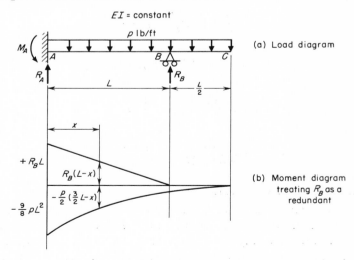

(a) Load diagram

(b) Moment diagram treating R_B as a redundant

Fig. 2.19

Solution: If we consider bending effects only, the strain energy, V, in the entire beam is given by

$$V = \int \frac{M^2 dx}{2EI} = \frac{1}{2EI} \int_0^L \left[R_B(L-x) - \frac{p}{2}\left(\frac{3}{2} L - x\right)^2 \right]^2 dx$$

$$+ \frac{1}{2EI} \int_L^{\frac{3}{2}L} \left[-\frac{p}{2}\left(\frac{3}{2} L - x\right)^2 \right]^2 dx \quad (2\text{-}28a)$$

Differentiating under the integral sign and utilizing Castigliano's Theorem (or the Method of Least Work) give

$$\frac{\partial V}{\partial R_B} = \frac{1}{EI} \int_0^L \left[R_B(L-x) - \frac{p}{2}\left(\frac{3}{2} L - x\right)^2 \right](L-x)dx = 0 \quad (2\text{-}28b)$$

It should be noted that the second integral of Equation (2-28a) does not appear in Equation (2-28b) since it was not a function of R_B. Solving Equation (2-28b), we obtain

$$R_B = +\tfrac{51}{48} pL \uparrow$$

Then, using the equations of statics,

$$M_A = -\tfrac{1}{16} pL^2, \quad R_A = \tfrac{7}{16} pL \uparrow$$

This problem could be solved much more directly and with considerably less effort, using the three-moment equation of Art. 2-12.

2-18 Indeterminate rigid frames—solution by superposition

The rigid frame is a fundamental structural unit, just as are the beam, column, or truss. It is usually made up of a series of straight members rigidly joined together. A typical rigid frame is shown in Fig. 2.20.

Because of the rigid connections at the corners, it follows that

(a) All members meeting at a joint rotate through the same angle at the joint.

(b) At any joint—say, B of Fig. 2.20, the moment M_{BC} (i.e., the moment at B of member BC) is equal to the moment M_{BA} (i.e., the moment at B of member BA).

Rigid frames are generally supported in either of three ways,

1. On rollers, corresponding to one reaction.
2. Hinged, corresponding to two reaction components.
3. Built-in, corresponding to three reaction components.

Example: Given a rigid frame with fixed supports as illustrated. Determine the reactions.

Solution: The general method of solution for frames will be illustrated by solving the frame of Fig. 2.20a. Since there are six unknown reaction

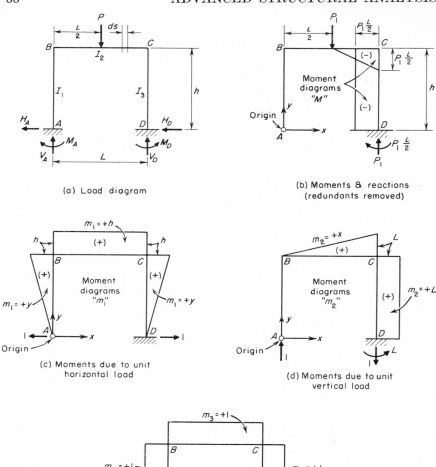

(a) Load diagram

(b) Moments & reactions
(redundants removed)

(c) Moments due to unit
horizontal load

(d) Moments due to unit
vertical load

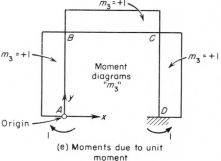

(e) Moments due to unit
moment

Fig. 2.20

components, and only three independent equations of statics, the frame is indeterminate to the third degree. The reaction components H_A, M_A and V_A will be treated as redundants. Remove the redundants.

For the horizontal deflection of point A, we can write

$$H_A\delta'_{11} + V_A\delta'_{12} + M_A\delta'_{13} + \delta_{1P} = 0 \qquad (2\text{-}29a)$$

where δ'_{11} = horizontal component of deflection of point A due to a horizontal unit load at A. Then $H_A\delta'_{11}$ = horizontal component of deflection of point A due to H_A. Likewise,

δ'_{12} = horizontal component of deflection of A due to unit vertical load at A.

$V_A\delta'_{12}$ = horizontal component of deflection of A due to V_A.

δ'_{13} = horizontal component of deflection of A due to unit moment at A.

$M_A\delta'_{13}$ = horizontal component of deflection of A due to M_A.

δ_{1P} = horizontal component of deflection of A due to P_1.

In a similar way, for the vertical deflection of point A,

$$H_A\delta'_{21} + V_A\delta'_{22} + M_A\delta'_{23} + \delta_{2P} = 0 \qquad (2\text{-}29b)$$

and for the rotation of point A,

$$H_A\delta'_{31} + V_A\delta'_{32} + M_A\delta'_{33} + \delta_{3P} = 0 \qquad (2\text{-}29c)$$

where, for example, the term $V_A\delta'_{32}$ = the rotation of a tangent to the elastic curve at A due to V_A.

The δ' terms can be obtained by using the dummy load method,

$$\delta'_{11} = \int m^2_1 \frac{ds}{EI} = \int_0^h y^2 \frac{dy}{EI_1} + \int_0^L h^2 \frac{dx}{EI_2} + \int_0^h y^2 \frac{dy}{EI_3} = \int y^2 \frac{ds}{EI} \text{ (generally)}$$

$$\delta'_{12} = \delta'_{21} = \int xy \frac{ds}{EI} \text{ (generally)}$$

$$\delta'_{13} = \delta'_{31} = \int y \frac{ds}{EI} \text{ (generally)}$$

$$\delta'_{22} = \int x^2 \frac{ds}{EI} \text{ (generally)}$$

$$\delta'_{23} = \delta'_{32} = \int x \frac{ds}{EI} \text{ (generally)}$$

$$\delta'_{33} = \int \frac{ds}{EI} \text{ (generally)}$$

$$\delta_{1P} = \int My \frac{ds}{EI}, \quad \delta_{2P} = \int Mx \frac{ds}{EI}, \quad \delta_{3P} = \int M \frac{ds}{EI} \text{ (generally)}$$

In the foregoing expressions bending effects only have been considered and axial deformations have been ignored. Neglecting axial effects does not normally lend to serious errors in rigid frame design.

If we use the above values, Equations (2-29) become

$$H_A\int y^2 \frac{ds}{EI} + V_A\int xy \frac{ds}{EI} + M_A\int y \frac{ds}{EI} + \int My \frac{ds}{EI} = 0$$

$$H_A\int xy \frac{ds}{EI} + V_A\int x^2 \frac{ds}{EI} + M_A\int x \frac{ds}{EI} + \int Mx \frac{ds}{EI} = 0 \qquad (2\text{-}30)$$

$$H_A\int y \frac{ds}{EI} + V_A\int x \frac{ds}{EI} + M_A\int \frac{ds}{EI} + \int M \frac{ds}{EI} = 0$$

These are three equations in three unknowns for which nine separate coefficients have to be evaluated, each coefficient containing three separate integrations (one for each column and one for the beam). Direct integration or visual integration can be used to solve for these coefficients.

For the example set up in Fig. 2.20a, let $I_1 = I_2 = I_3 = I$, and $h = L = 10$ ft. Since EI is constant, it can be canceled from all terms. Then,

$$\int y^2 ds = 2\int_0^h y^2 dy + \int_0^L h^2 dx = \tfrac{2}{3}h^3 + h^2 L = 1667$$

If visual integration is used, then

$$\int y^2 ds = (\tfrac{1}{2}h^2 \cdot \tfrac{2}{3}h)2 + hL \cdot h$$
$$= \tfrac{2}{3}h^3 + h^2 L \text{ as before}$$

Similarly, we obtain for all the other terms,

$$\int x^2 ds = \int_0^L x^2 dx + \int_0^h L^2 dy = \frac{L^3}{3} + L^2 h = 1333$$

$$\int ds = 2\int_0^h dy + \int_0^L dx = 2h + L = 30$$

$$\int xy ds = \int_0^L xh dx + \int_0^h Ly dy = \frac{hL^2}{2} + \frac{Lh^2}{2} = 1000$$

$$\int y ds = 2\int_0^h y dy + \int_0^L h dx = h^2 + hL = 200$$

$$\int x ds = \int_0^L x dx + \int_0^h L dx = \frac{L^2}{2} + Lh = 150$$

$$\int M y ds = \int_{L/2}^L -P_1\left(x - \frac{L}{2}\right)h dx + \int_0^h -\frac{P_1 L}{2} y dy = -P_1\left[\frac{L^2 h}{8} + \frac{Lh^2}{4}\right]$$
$$= -375 P_1$$

$$\int M x ds = \int_{L/2}^L -P_1\left(x - \frac{L}{2}\right)x dx + \int_0^h -\frac{P_1 L}{2} x dy = -P_1\left[\frac{5}{48} L^3 + \frac{L^2 h}{2}\right]$$
$$= -604.2 P_1$$

$$\int M ds = \int_{L/2}^L -P_1\left(x - \frac{L}{2}\right)dx + \int_0^h -\frac{P_1 L}{2} dy = -P_1\left[\frac{L^2}{8} + \frac{Lh}{2}\right]$$
$$= -62.5 P_1$$

Equations (2-30) become

$$1667 H_A + 1000 V_A + 200 M_A - 375 P_1 = 0 \qquad (2\text{-}31a)$$
$$1000 H_A + 1333 V_A + 150 M_A - 604.2 P_1 = 0 \qquad (2\text{-}31b)$$
$$200 H_A + 150 V_A + 30 M_A - 62.5 P_1 = 0 \qquad (2\text{-}31c)$$

The three simultaneous equations in three unknowns (the redundants) can be solved for H_A, V_A, and M_A. Having these values, the remaining reactions can be obtained by using the equilibrium equations or by superposition of reactions produced by each redundant and the given loads. For example, M_D (referring to Figs. 2.20a through 2.20c) could be obtained as follows:

$$M_D = -P_1 \frac{L}{2} + V_A \cdot L + M_A$$

The shears and moments at any section can be obtained in a similar way.

2-19   Exact solutions of simultaneous equations

It can be seen from the foregoing that in the solution of indeterminate problems it frequently becomes necessary to solve simultaneous equations. The solution of these equations can be an exact solution, as will be presented in this article, or an approximate numerical solution, of which an example is given in Art. 2-20.

Exact solutions may be obtained by successive elimination of unknowns. For example, the simple equations,

$$2x + y = 30 \qquad (2\text{-}32a)$$

$$x + 2y = 20 \qquad (2\text{-}32b)$$

give

$$2x + y = 30$$

$$\underline{2x + 4y = 40} \qquad 2 \times (2\text{-}32b)$$

Subtracting,

$$-3y = -10$$

or

$$y = +\tfrac{10}{3}$$

Using this value of y in Equation (2-32a), we obtain

$$2x + \tfrac{10}{3} = 30$$

$$2x = \tfrac{80}{3}$$

$$x = \tfrac{40}{3}$$

To check, substitute x and y in Equation (2-32b), which gives

$$\tfrac{40}{3} + \tfrac{20}{3} = 20, \text{ as required}$$

For a set of 3 or more equations in 3 or more unknowns, the above procedure can still be used effectively but it will be most convenient to adopt some systematic procedure for recording the operations. One such system is the Gauss Scheme in which a tabular form is used and only the coefficients of the unknowns are listed. For an example of a solution of simultaneous equations using this scheme, see Salvadori and Baron.[1]

Exact solutions may also be obtained using determinants. A powerful tool in reducing these determinants is the method of pivotal condensation.[1] These methods will not be presented here, but the reader who has occasion to solve many simultaneous equations will find them discussed in the reference cited.

2-20 Approximate solutions of simultaneous equations

In the usual set of simultaneous equations that one encounters in structural problems, the system is frequently diagonal, in the sense that in each equation the coefficient of a different unknown is greater in absolute value than the sum of the absolute values of the other coefficients. The dominant coefficients in structural equations will usually be the δ'_{kk} terms. The Gauss–Seidel iterative process can then be used effectively to obtain approximate solutions of these equations.[2]

For example, the following equations are obtained in the solution of a continuous truss problem:

$$1149.6X + 130.0Y + 10.0Z = 16,380 \qquad (2\text{-}33a)$$

$$130.0X + 1149.6Y + 130.0Z = 16,380 \qquad (2\text{-}33b)$$

$$10.0X + 130.0Y + 1149.6Z = 16,380 \qquad (2\text{-}33c)$$

From Equation (2-33a),

$$X = 14.24 - 0.113Y - 0.0087Z \qquad (2\text{-}33d)$$

From Equation (2-33b),

$$Y = 14.24 - 0.113X - 0.113Z \qquad (2\text{-}33e)$$

From Equation (2-33c),

$$Z = 14.24 - 0.0087X - 0.113Y \qquad (2\text{-}33f)$$

From Equation (2-33d), letting $Y = Z = 0$ calculate $X = 14.24$

From Equation (2-33e), letting $Z = 0$, $X = 14.24$ calculate Y:

$$Y = 14.24 - 1.61 = 12.63$$

[1] M. G. Salvadori and M. L. Baron, *Numerical Methods in Engineering*, Prentice-Hall, Inc., New York, 1952.
[2] See Salvadori and Baron, *Ibid.*

From Equation (2-33f), letting $X = 14.24$, $Y = 12.63$ calculate Z:

$$Z = 14.24 - 0.0087 \times 14.24 - 0.113 \times 12.63$$
$$= 14.24 - 0.12 - 1.43 = 12.69$$

From Equation (2-33d), letting $Y = 12.63$, $Z = 12.69$, find

$$X = 14.24 - 0.113 \times 12.63 - 0.0087 \times 12.69$$
$$= 14.24 - 1.43 - 0.11 = 12.70$$

From Equation (2-33e), letting $X = 12.70$, $Z = 12.69$, find

$$Y = 14.24 - 0.113 \times 12.70 - 0.113 \times 12.69$$
$$= 14.24 - 1.44 - 1.43 = 11.37$$

From Equation (2-33f), letting $X = 12.70$, $Y = 11.37$, find

$$Z = 14.24 - 0.0087 \times 12.70 - 0.113 \times 11.37$$
$$= 14.24 - 0.11 - 1.28 = 12.85$$

From Equation (2-33d), letting $Y = 11.37$, $Z = 12.85$, find

$$X = 14.24 - 0.113 \times 11.37 - 0.0087 \times 12.85$$
$$= 14.24 - 1.28 - 0.11 = 12.85$$

This procedure can be continued indefinitely, or until the required degree of precision is reached. The results of the above computations can be arranged in tabular form as indicated in Table 2.2.

TABLE 2.2

Trial No.	1	2	3	4
X	14.24	12.70	12.85	12.85
Y	12.63	11.20	11.37	11.37
Z	12.69	12.87	12.85	12.85

In four trials, it is seen that the results have converged to values accurate within the limits of slide-rule work.

It must be emphasized that only one approximate method of solving simultaneous equations has been presented here. Among other important methods is the relaxation procedure of Southwell.[3] For others the reader is referred to Salvadori and Baron.[4]

[3] R. V. Southwell, *Relaxation Methods in Theoretical Physics*, Oxford University Press, London, 1946. Also, *Relaxation Methods in Engineering Science*, 1940.

[4] M. G. Salvadori and M. L. Baron, *Numerical Methods in Engineering*, Prentice-Hall, Inc., New York, 1952.

2.21 The elastic center method—theory

It was shown that the superposition equations for the solution of a rigid frame take the following form,

$$H_A \int y^2 \frac{ds}{EI} + V_A \int xy \frac{ds}{EI} + M_A \int y \frac{ds}{EI} + \int My \frac{ds}{EI} = 0$$

$$H_A \int yx \frac{ds}{EI} + V_A \int x^2 \frac{ds}{EI} + M_A \int x \frac{ds}{EI} + \int Mx \frac{ds}{EI} = 0$$

$$H_A \int y \frac{ds}{EI} + V_A \int x \frac{ds}{EI} + M_A \int \frac{ds}{EI} + \int M \frac{ds}{EI} = 0$$

In the above set of equations H_A, V_A, and M_A are the unknown redundant reactions and x and y are the coordinates of any point on the elastic axes of the rigid frame measured from an origin of coordinates which is also the point of application of the redundants.

To obtain H_A, V_A, and M_A, one must solve three simultaneous equations. If some way could be found to put these equations in a form such that each contains only one unknown, then the redundants could be found very simply from these equations and the amount of labor required for the solution of these equations would be very greatly reduced. This is accomplished in the *elastic center* method for solving redundant frames.[5]

The integrals terms in the above set of equations resemble the integrals one may set up to define the properties of an area. For example,

$$\text{moment of inertia of an area about } x \text{ axis} = \int y^2 dA$$
$$\text{moment of inertia of an area about } y \text{ axis} = \int x^2 dA$$
$$\text{product of inertia of an area} = \int xy dA$$
$$\text{statical moment of an area about } x \text{ axis} = \int y dA$$
$$\text{statical moment of an area about } y \text{ axis} = \int x dA$$
$$\text{total area} = \int dA$$

The analogy between the frame coefficients and the above terms can be seen by noting that the two sets of terms are identical if the increment of area dA is replaced by an increment of length ds multiplied by a width $1/EI$.

---

[5] It can be shown that the integral multipliers of H_A, V_A, and M_A in the above equations are the elements of a symmetric tensor. In matrix-tensor theory it is proved that a symmetric tensor can be put in diagonal form and it is this diagonalization which is accomplished by the elastic center method. For a more detailed discussion of this and related points, see S. F. Borg, *An Introduction to Matrix Tensor Methods in Theoretical and Applied Mechanics*, Edwards Bros., Ann Arbor, Mich., 1956.

For a given area it is known that under certain conditions the integrals $\int xy\,dA = \int x\,dA = \int y\,dA = 0$.

If these conditions apply to the problem involving a rigid frame, then the simultaneous equations will be simplified to the following (diagonal) form:

$$H_A \int y^2 \frac{ds}{EI} + \int My \frac{ds}{EI} = 0 \qquad (2\text{-}34a)$$

$$V_A \int x^2 \frac{ds}{EI} + \int Mx \frac{ds}{EI} = 0 \qquad (2\text{-}34b)$$

$$M_A \int \frac{ds}{EI} + \int M \frac{ds}{EI} = 0 \qquad (2\text{-}34c)$$

Let us examine the conditions necessary for $\int xy\,dA = \int x\,dA = \int y\,dA = 0$. For a given area, in order that the statical moments of that area $\int x\,dA = \int y\,dA = 0$, it is only necessary that the origin of coordinates be at the center of gravity of the cross section. Hence, these integrals can be made zero by selecting the center of gravity as the origin of co-ordinates (see Fig. 2.21). We shall now establish those conditions for which $\int xy\,dA = 0$.

For the developments which follow, it is necessary to obtain the two-dimensional form of the rotation of axes relations—i.e., the relations

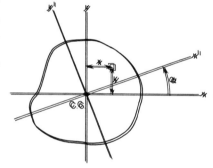

Fig. 2.21

between the coordinates of a point in an x, y system of coordinates and the coordinates of the same point in an x', y' system which has the same origin but is rotated through an angle α with respect to the x, y set of axes.

Fig. 2.22 shows the differential increment of area located from two sets of coordinate axes X, Y and X', Y'.

Since $AB = CD = y \sin \alpha$ and $OA = OD \cos \alpha = x \cos \alpha$, then,

$$x' = OA + AB = x \cos \alpha + y \sin \alpha \qquad (2\text{-}35a)$$

and

$$y' = EC - BC = y \cos \alpha - x \sin \alpha \qquad (2\text{-}35b)$$

from which

$$x = x' \cos \alpha - y' \sin \alpha \qquad (2\text{-}35c)$$

$$y = x' \sin \alpha + y' \cos \alpha \qquad (2\text{-}35d)$$

Equations (2-35a) and (2-35b) are the transformation equations relating the coordinates of a point x', y', to the coordinates of the same point x, y. Equations (2-35c) and (2-35d) relate the coordinates of the point x, y, to the coordinates x', y'.

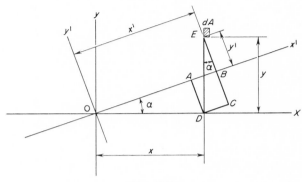

Fig. 2.22

For a given area the product of inertia with respect to the X', Y' axis is

$$\int_A x'y'dA = I_{x'y'} \tag{2-36}$$

Substituting Equations (2-35a) and (2-35b) in Equation (2-36) gives

$$I_{x'y'} = \int_A x'y'dA = \int_A (x \cos \alpha + y \sin \alpha)(-x \sin \alpha + y \cos \alpha)dA$$

$$= \int_A (-x^2 \sin \alpha \cos \alpha - xy \sin^2 \alpha + xy \cos^2 \alpha + y^2 \sin \alpha \cos \alpha)dA$$

$$= \int_A -x^2 \sin \alpha \cos \alpha \, dA + \int_A xy(\cos^2 \alpha - \sin^2 \alpha)dA + \int_A y^2 \sin \alpha \cos \alpha \, dA$$

$$= -\sin \alpha \cos \alpha \int_A x^2 dA + (\cos^2 \alpha - \sin^2 \alpha) \int_A xy dA$$

$$+ \sin \alpha \cos \alpha \int_A y^2 dA$$

The integral terms are by definition

$$\int_A x^2 dA = I_{yy} = \text{moment of inertia of area about the } Y \text{ axis}$$

$$\int_A xy dA = I_{xy} = \text{product of inertia of area about the } XY \text{ axes}$$

$$\int_A y^2 dA = I_{xx} = \text{moment of inertia of area about the } X \text{ axis}$$

It is required that $I_{x'y'} = $ zero, or

$$I_{x'y'} = -\sin \alpha \cos \alpha\, I_{yy} + (\cos^2 \alpha - \sin^2 \alpha)I_{xy} + \sin \alpha \cos \alpha\, I_{xx} = 0$$

Using the trigonometric relations,

$$\sin \alpha \cos \alpha = \tfrac{1}{2} \sin 2\alpha$$

$$\cos^2 \alpha - \sin^2 \alpha = \cos 2\alpha$$

we obtain,

$$(I_{xx} - I_{yy})\tfrac{1}{2} \sin 2\alpha + I_{xy}(\cos 2\alpha) = 0$$

$$\tan 2\alpha = \frac{-2I_{xy}}{I_{xx} - I_{yy}} \tag{2-37}$$

In other words, if α has such a value as to satisfy Equation (2-37), then the product of inertia with respect to the X', Y' coordinate axes will be zero.

An alternate procedure can be developed so that the product of inertia with respect to the skew X', Y coordinate axis will be zero.

$$\int_A xy'dA = I_{x'y} = 0$$

Using Equation (2-35b), we obtain

$$I_{x'y} = \int_A x(y \cos \alpha - x \sin \alpha)dA = 0$$

$$= \int_A xy \cos \alpha\, dA - \int_A x^2 \sin \alpha\, dA = 0$$

$$= \cos \alpha \int_A xy dA - \sin \alpha \int x^2 dA = 0$$

$$= \cos \alpha\, I_{xy} - \sin \alpha\, I_{yy} = 0$$

from which

$$\tan \alpha = \frac{I_{xy}}{I_{yy}} \tag{2-38}$$

Either condition on α as expressed by Equation (2-37) and Equation (2-38) will enable us to establish a coordinate system for which $\int_A xy dA = \int_A y dA = \int_A x dA = 0$.

The variation in moment of inertia of a section with changing angle α can best be shown by using Mohr's circle (Fig. 2.23), presented here without proof.[6]

[6] Mohr's circle is a graphical representation of the general two-dimensional tensor and can, therefore, be applied to any tensor—stress, strain, inertia, etc. Culmann, in 1866, obtained this circle for the stress tensor. Mohr, in 1882, extended Culmann's work, and the construction has, since that time, carried Mohr's name.

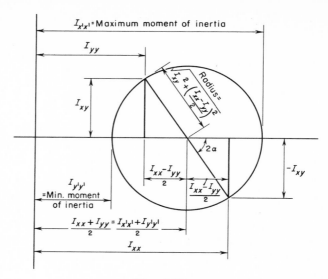

Fig. 2.23

The circle of inertia can be constructed if its center and radius are known, or if two points on the circumference and the diameter are known. Therefore, given I_{xx}, I_{yy}, and I_{xy}, the circle can be constructed, or given $I_{x'x'}$, $I_{y'y'}$, the circle can be constructed.

The mathematical relations between the different inertias can be picked off the diagram. For instance, from the figure,

$$\tan 2\alpha = \frac{-2I_{xy}}{I_{xx} - I_{yy}}$$

and this will be recognized as Equation (2-37), previously derived.

$I_{y'y'}$ and $I_{x'x'}$, the minimum and maximum moments of inertia, are called the principal moments of inertia and the $X'Y'$ axes are called the principal axes. Since the product of inertia is zero when the corresponding moments of inertia are principal moments of inertia, it follows that axes of symmetry are principal axes.

2-22 The elastic center method—application

Given a symmetric rigid frame (Fig. 2.24a), it is desired to solve for the reactions using the method presented in the previous article to reduce the amount of labor required to set up and solve the necessary simultaneous equations. We will conceive of a transformation of our frame into areas of width $1/EI$. Let us locate the center of gravity of these areas and call this point the elastic center.

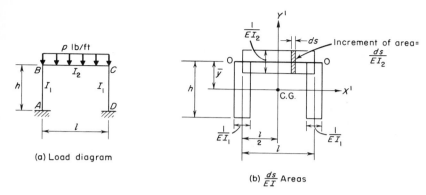

(a) Load diagram

(b) $\frac{ds}{EI}$ Areas

Fig. 2.24

Since the areas (see Fig. 2.24b) are symmetric, the center of gravity and also the Y' axis (a principal axis since it is an axis of symmetry) are located halfway between the columns. To find $\bar{y}$ which locates the X' axis (also a principal axis since it is at right angles to Y'), we may take moments of the areas about line 0–0. This gives,

$$\bar{y} = \frac{\dfrac{2h}{EI_1} \times \dfrac{h}{2}}{\dfrac{2h}{EI_1} + \dfrac{l}{EI_2}} = \frac{\dfrac{2h^2}{I_1}}{\dfrac{2h}{I_1} + \dfrac{l}{I_2}} = \frac{2I_2h^2}{2I_2h + I_1l}$$

or

$$\bar{y} = \frac{h}{1 + \dfrac{I_1l}{2I_2h}} = Kh \text{ where } K = \frac{1}{1 + \dfrac{I_1l}{2I_2h}}$$

$I_{x'x'}$ and $I_{y'y'}$ which are principal moments of inertia, may now be found using properties of rectangular areas and the parallel axis theorem. Thus

$$I_{x'x'} = 2\left[\frac{h^3}{12EI_1} + \frac{h}{EI_1}\left(\frac{h}{2} - Kh\right)^2\right] + \left[\frac{l}{EI_2}(Kh)^2\right]$$

and

$$I_{y'y'} = 2\left[\frac{h}{EI_1}\left(\frac{l}{2}\right)^2\right] + \frac{l^3}{12EI_2}$$

The total area $A = \dfrac{2h}{EI_1} + \dfrac{l}{EI_2}$.

Note that in computing the moments of inertia, the terms for the moment of inertia of an area about its own axis are omitted. For the beam, for instance, it would be wrong to include a term $\dfrac{l}{12}\left(\dfrac{1}{EI_2}\right)^3$ in $I_{x'x'}$. There is no physical significance to this term as y for the beam does not vary between the limits $\bar{y} \pm \dfrac{1}{2EI_2}$. Likewise, the terms $\dfrac{h}{12}\left(\dfrac{1}{EI_1}\right)^3$ are omitted from $I_{y'y'}$.

At this point it is necessary to solve for the integrals $\displaystyle\int My\,\dfrac{ds}{EI}$, $\displaystyle\int Mx\,\dfrac{ds}{EI}$, $\displaystyle\int M\,\dfrac{ds}{EI}$. Knowing these, we can solve Equations (2-34) for H_A, V_A, and M_A, since

$$H_A = \frac{-\displaystyle\int My'\,\dfrac{ds}{EI}}{\displaystyle\int y^2\,\dfrac{ds}{EI}} = \frac{-\displaystyle\int My'\,\dfrac{ds}{EI}}{I_{x'x'}} \tag{2-39a}$$

$$V_A = \frac{-\displaystyle\int Mx'\,\dfrac{ds}{EI}}{\displaystyle\int x'^2\,\dfrac{ds}{EI}} = \frac{-\displaystyle\int Mx'\,\dfrac{ds}{EI}}{I_{y'y'}} \tag{2-39b}$$

$$M_A = \frac{-\displaystyle\int M\,\dfrac{ds}{EI}}{\displaystyle\int \dfrac{ds}{EI}} = \frac{-\displaystyle\int M\,\dfrac{ds}{EI}}{A} \tag{2-39c}$$

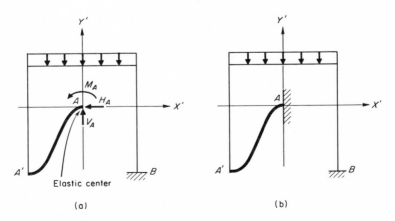

Fig. 2.25

It is seen that, by following the above procedure, the labor necessary to set up and solve the usual set of simultaneous equations encountered in problems of this kind is reduced. However, it must be remembered that the superposition equations were originally written for the left-hand support of the rigid frame and that, in transforming the axis, we have moved from this point to the center of gravity (elastic center) of the ds/EI areas. Hence, the reactions which are obtained act through the elastic center and not at the support as originally intended. Obviously, this is not possible in practice; but, to make the solution mathematically compatible with the true conditions, we need only assume the elastic center to be attached to the support point by a rigid piece, usually called a rigid arm (Fig. 2.25a). The solution obtained is for the problem of a rigid frame supported as shown in Fig. 2.25b. The addition of a rigid arm does not change any of the coefficients of the superposition equations, since they originate from elastic deformations. Hence, Equations (2-39) still hold. To transform back to the original problem, it is only necessary to apply the equations of statics to the rigid arm. Then

$$V_{A'} = V_A \tag{2-40a}$$

$$H_{A'} = H_A \tag{2-40b}$$

$$M_{A'} = M_A + H_A \cdot b + V_A \cdot a \tag{2-40c}$$

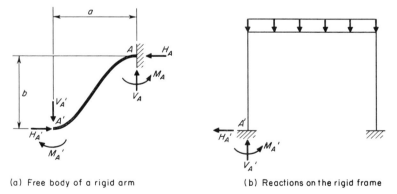

(a) Free body of a rigid arm   (b) Reactions on the rigid frame

Fig. 2.26

2-23 The elastic center method—Example

To illustrate a complete application of the method, we shall solve the frame of Fig. 2.27a.

Example:

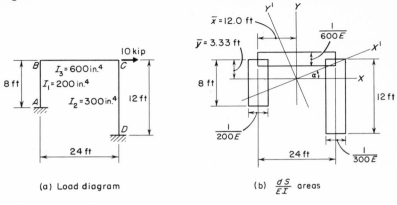

(a) Load diagram   (b) $\frac{dS}{EI}$ areas

Fig. 2.27

Solution: To locate the elastic center (see Fig. 2.27b),

$$\int \frac{ds}{EI} = \frac{8}{200E} + \frac{24}{600E} + \frac{12}{300E} = \frac{3}{25E}$$

$$\bar{y} = \frac{\dfrac{8}{200E} \times 4 + \dfrac{12}{300E} \times 6}{\dfrac{8}{200E} + \dfrac{24}{600E} + \dfrac{12}{300E}} = 3.33 \text{ ft}$$

$$\bar{x} = \frac{\dfrac{24}{600E} \times 12 + \dfrac{12}{300E} \times 24}{\dfrac{8}{200E} + \dfrac{24}{600E} + \dfrac{12}{300E}} = 12.0 \text{ ft}$$

Calculate I_{xx}, I_{yy}, I_{xy} (omit E, since it appears in all terms)

$$I_{xx} = \left[\frac{1}{200} \frac{(8)^3}{12} + \frac{8}{200}(0.67)^2 \right] + \left[\frac{1}{300} \frac{(12)^3}{12} + \frac{12}{300}(2.67)^2 \right] + \left[\frac{24}{600}(3.33)^2 \right] = 1.44$$

$$I_{yy} = \left[\frac{8}{200}(12)^2 \right] + \left[\frac{12}{300}(12)^2 \right] + \left[\frac{1}{600} \frac{(24)^3}{12} \right] = 13.45$$

$$I_{xy} = \left[\frac{8}{200}(-12)(-0.67) \right] + \left[\frac{12}{300}(+12)(-2.67) \right] - \left[\frac{24}{600}(0)(+3.33) \right] = -0.95$$

Find $I_{x'x'}$, $I_{y'y'}$ by Mohr's circle. This construction is shown in Fig. 2.28. Analytical determination of $I_{x'x'}$, $I_{y'y'}$

$$\tan 2\alpha = \frac{-2I_{xy}}{I_{xx} - I_{yy}} = \frac{-2(-0.95)}{1.44 - 13.45} = -0.1586$$

$$2\alpha = -9° \, 0', \quad \alpha = -4° \, 30'$$

$$R = \frac{(I_{yy} - I_{xx})}{2 \cos 2\alpha} = \frac{13.45 - 1.44}{2 \times 0.99692} = 6.08$$

$$I_{y'y'} = \frac{I_{xx} + I_{yy}}{2} + R = \frac{1.44 + 13.45}{2} + 6.08 = 13.53$$

$$I_{x'x'} = \frac{I_{xx} + I_{yy}}{2} - R = 1.37$$

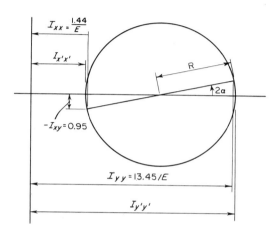

Fig. 2.28. Mohr's Circle

We now wish to find $\int Mx' \frac{ds}{EI}, \int My' \frac{ds}{EI}, \int M \frac{ds}{EI}$, see Figs. 2.29a and 2.29b.

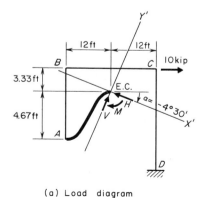

(a) Load diagram   (b) Moments due to 10 kip load

Fig. 2.29

From Equations (2.35a) and (2.35b),

$$\left.\begin{aligned} \int Mx' \frac{ds}{I} &= \int M(x \cos \alpha + y \sin \alpha) \frac{ds}{I} \\ \int My' \frac{ds}{I} &= \int M(y \cos \alpha - x \sin \alpha) \frac{ds}{I} \end{aligned}\right\}$$

or

$$\left.\begin{aligned} \int Mx' \frac{ds}{I} &= \int_{-8.67}^{+3.33} 10(3.33-y)[12 \times 0.997 + 0.0785y] \frac{dy}{300} = 29.5 \\ \int My' \frac{ds}{I} &= \int_{-8.67}^{+3.33} 10(3.33-y)[0.997y + 12 \times 0.0785] \frac{dy}{300} = -8.96 \end{aligned}\right\}$$

and

$$\int M \frac{ds}{I} = \int_{-8.67}^{+3.33} 10(3.33-y) \frac{dy}{300} = +2.40$$

Having evaluated the integrals, we can find H, V, and M at the elastic center from

$$H = \frac{-\int My' \frac{ds}{I}}{I_{x'x'}} = \frac{+8.96}{1.37} = +6.53 \text{ kip}$$

$$V = \frac{-\int Mx' \frac{ds}{I}}{I_{y'y'}} = \frac{-29.5}{13.53} = -2.16 \text{ kip}$$

$$M = \frac{-\int M \frac{ds}{I}}{\int \frac{ds}{I}} = \frac{-2.40}{\frac{3}{25}} = -20.0 \text{ kip-ft}$$

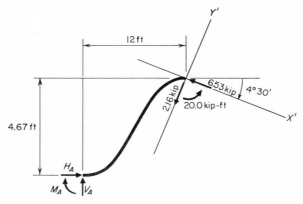

Fig. 2.30—Free Body of Rigid Arm

Applying the equilibrium equations to the free body of the rigid arm (Fig. 2.30), we obtain

$H_A = 6.53 \cos 4°30' + 2.16 \sin 4°30'$

$\quad = 6.53 \times 0.997 + 2.16 \times 0.0785$

$\quad = 6.51 + 0.16 = 6.67$ kip

$V_A = 2.16 \times 0.997 - 6.53 \times 0.0785$

$\quad = 2.15 - 0.51 = 1.64$ kip

$M_A = 20.0 - 2.16 \times 0.997 \times 12 + 2.16$
$\quad \times 0.0785 \times 4.67 + 6.53 \times 0.0785$
$\quad \times 12 + 6.53 \times 0.997 \times 4.67$

$M_A = 31.0$ kip-ft

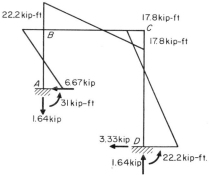

Fig. 2.31—Reactions and Moments Diagram

Now, by statics, the reactions can be found at the other support, and the complete moment diagram can be drawn. This is shown in Fig. 2.31.

2-24   Other methods in structural analysis

There are other excellent techniques for solving indeterminate structures such as the Column Analogy, Flotation Analogy, Traversing the Elastic Curve, and Method of Elastic Weights. The reader will find that the necessary foundation material for understanding these methods has been presented in this chapter.

Problems

1. Find the reactions using (a) method of superposition, (b) Theorem of Three Moments. In method (a) use dummy load and visual integration.

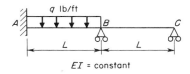

2. Show that the equation of the elastic curve is

$$EI\,y = \frac{Mx^2}{4}\left(1 - \frac{x}{L}\right)$$

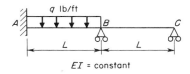

3. By means of the reciprocal theorem (using the results of problem 2) show that $M_{F_{BA}} = \dfrac{Wx^2}{L}\left(1 - \dfrac{x}{L}\right).$

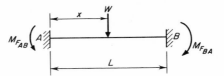

4. Find the stresses in the members.

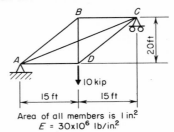

Area of all members is 1 in.²
$E = 30 \times 10^6$ lb/in²

5. Find the stresses in all members.

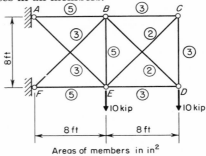

Areas of members in in²
shown circled on diagram
$E = 30 \times 10^6$ lb/in²

6. One span of a four-span continuous truss bridge is fully dimensioned in the figure. Areas of the members in square inches are shown. All other spans have the same dimensions and cross sections as the one span that is dimensioned except as shown. Find the stresses in the members. (Hint: treat members ab, cd, and ef as redundants.)

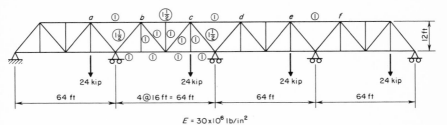

$E = 30 \times 10^6$ lb/in²

7. Find the reactions and draw the final moment diagram for the rigid frame shown. Use dummy load and visual integration.

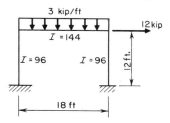

8. Solve problem 7 by the elastic center method.

9. Solve problem 1 by Least Work.

10. Solve problem 4 by Least Work.

11. Find the reactions and draw the final moment diagrams for the gabled bent shown. Separate the solutions for the vertical uniformly distributed load q_1, and the horizontal uniformly distributed load q_2. Use dummy load and visual integration.

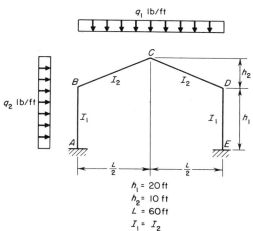

$h_1 = 20$ ft
$h_2 = 10$ ft
$L = 60$ ft
$I_1 = I_2$

12. If support B of problem 1 settles an amount "δ", calculate the change in reactions.

13. Find the reactions of the two span continuous beam shown if the center support is a spring with spring constant $= k$ ft/lb.

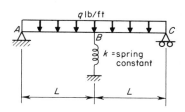

References

In addition to the references mentioned in the footnotes of this chapter, all references listed in the previous chapter apply to this chapter.

Chapter 3

THE SLOPE-DEFLECTION METHOD

3-1   Introduction

The slope-deflection method was developed by Axel Bendixen in Germany in 1914 and is particularly useful for solving rigid-joint structures such as continuous beams or rigid frames. The unknowns in the slope-deflection solutions are joint rotations, θ, and relative joint deflections, ψ. In this chapter, the general slope-deflection equations will be obtained. These will then be applied to the solution of typical beam and rigid-frame structures, of constant and variable moment of inertia. Also, the solution of problems by means of tabulated coefficients will be discussed and the results so obtained (for a particular problem) will be compared with those obtained using the slope-deflection method.

3-2   Derivation of the slope-deflection equation

The general loading and deformation of a beam with variable section is shown in Fig. 3.1. The original beam is shown dotted. The final, deformed beam is shown in full lines.

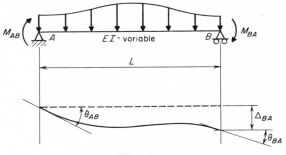

Fig. 3.1

The sign convention will be as follows: Positive moments are moments which are clockwise acting on the end of the beam. Positive rotations are clockwise. Thus, in Fig. 3.1, the moments, angles, and also Δ_{BA} are all shown positive.

To derive the slope-deflection equation we shall consider each effect

108

separately and then add them to obtain the complete equation. The conjugate beam method will be used to develop these equations. For example, due to M_{AB} (Fig. 3.2) the conjugate beam diagram is as shown and the slopes are

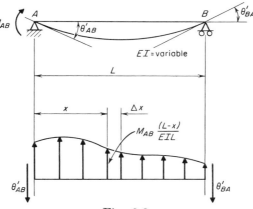

Fig. 3.2

$$\theta'_{AB} = M_{AB} \sum \left(\frac{L-x}{L}\right)\left(\frac{L-x}{L}\right)\frac{\Delta x}{EI} \tag{3-1a}$$

$$\theta'_{BA} = -M_{AB} \sum \left(\frac{L-x}{L}\right)\left(\frac{x}{L}\right)\frac{\Delta x}{EI} \tag{3-1b}$$

For M_{BA}, in exactly the same way we obtain

$$\theta''_{AB} = -M_{BA} \sum \left(\frac{L-x}{L}\right)\left(\frac{x}{L}\right)\frac{\Delta x}{EI} \tag{3-2a}$$

$$\theta''_{BA} = M_{BA} \sum \left(\frac{x}{L}\right)\left(\frac{x}{L}\right)\frac{\Delta x}{EI} \tag{3-2b}$$

Corresponding to Δ_{BA}, we have

$$\theta'''_{AB} = \theta'''_{BA} = +\frac{\Delta_{BA}}{L} \tag{3-3}$$

Finally, for the general lateral load, with M_0 equal to the moment at any point x (see Fig. 3.3), we have

$$\theta^{\text{iv}}_{AB} = \sum \frac{M_0}{EI}\left(\frac{L-x}{L}\right)\Delta x \tag{3-4a}$$

$$\theta^{\text{iv}}_{BA} = -\sum \frac{M_0}{EI}\left(\frac{x}{L}\right)\Delta x \tag{3-4b}$$

Now if we add the separate effects in Equations (3-1), (3-2), (3-3), and (3-4),

$$\theta_{AB} = M_{AB}\sum\left(\frac{L-x}{L}\right)^2\frac{\Delta x}{EI} - M_{BA}\sum\left(\frac{L-x}{L}\right)\left(\frac{x}{L}\right)\frac{\Delta x}{EI} + \frac{\Delta_{BA}}{L}$$

$$+ \sum M_0\left(\frac{L-x}{L}\right)\frac{\Delta x}{EI} \quad \text{(3-5a)}$$

$$\theta_{BA} = -M_{AB}\sum\left(\frac{L-x}{L}\right)\left(\frac{x}{L}\right)\frac{\Delta x}{EI} + M_{BA}\sum\left(\frac{x}{L}\right)^2\frac{\Delta x}{EI} + \frac{\Delta_{BA}}{L}$$

$$- \sum M_0\left(\frac{x}{L}\right)\frac{\Delta x}{EI} \quad \text{(3-5b)}$$

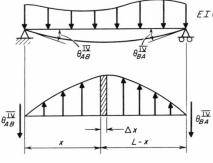

Fig. 3.3

To simplify the above expressions and those which will be obtained later, let us introduce the following notation:

$$I = I_C \cdot i \quad \text{(3-6a)}$$

with i representing some functional variation, and

$$p_{11} = \frac{1}{L}\sum\frac{\Delta x}{i}\left(\frac{L-x}{L}\right)^2 \quad \text{(3-6b)}$$

$$p_{12} = \frac{1}{L}\sum\frac{\Delta x}{i}\left(\frac{L-x}{L}\right)\left(\frac{x}{L}\right) \quad \text{(3-6c)}$$

$$p_{22} = \frac{1}{L}\sum\frac{\Delta x}{i}\left(\frac{x}{L}\right)^2 \quad \text{(3-6d)}$$

$$\psi_{AB} = \psi_{BA} = \frac{\Delta_{BA}}{L} \quad \text{(3-6e)}$$

Then Equations (3-5) become

$$\theta_{AB} = \frac{M_{AB}L}{EI_C}p_{11} - \frac{M_{BA}L}{EI_C}p_{12} + \psi_{AB} + \sum M_0\left(\frac{L-x}{L}\right)\frac{\Delta x}{EI} \quad \text{(3-7a)}$$

$$\theta_{BA} = -\frac{M_{AB}L}{EI_C}p_{12} + \frac{M_{BA}L}{EI_C}p_{22} + \psi_{AB} - \sum M_0\left(\frac{x}{L}\right)\frac{\Delta x}{EI} \quad \text{(3-7b)}$$

Solve Equations (3-7a) and (3-7b) simultaneously for M_{AB} and M_{BA} to obtain

$$M_{AB} = \frac{EI_C}{L}\left[\frac{p_{22}}{p_{11}p_{22}-p_{12}{}^2}\theta_{AB}+\frac{p_{12}}{p_{11}p_{22}-p_{12}{}^2}\theta_{BA}-\left(\frac{p_{12}+p_{22}}{p_{11}p_{22}-p_{12}{}^2}\right)\psi_{AB}\right]$$
$$-\frac{EI_C}{L}\frac{p_{22}}{p_{11}p_{22}-p_{12}{}^2}\sum M_0\left(\frac{L-x}{L}\right)\frac{\Delta x}{EI}$$
$$+\frac{EI_C}{L}\frac{p_{12}}{p_{11}p_{22}-p_{12}{}^2}\sum M_0\left(\frac{x}{L}\right)\frac{\Delta x}{EI} \tag{3-8a}$$

and

$$M_{BA} = \frac{EI_C}{L}\left[\frac{p_{12}}{p_{11}p_{22}-p_{12}{}^2}\theta_{AB}+\frac{p_{22}}{p_{11}p_{22}-p_{12}{}^2}\theta_{BA}-\left(\frac{p_{12}+p_{11}}{p_{11}p_{22}-p_{12}{}^2}\right)\psi_{AB}\right]$$
$$-\frac{EI_C}{L}\frac{p_{12}}{p_{11}p_{22}-p_{12}{}^2}\sum M_0\left(\frac{L-x}{L}\right)\frac{\Delta x}{EI}$$
$$+\frac{EI_C}{L}\left(\frac{p_{11}}{p_{11}p_{22}-p_{12}{}^2}\right)\sum M_0\left(\frac{x}{L}\right)\frac{\Delta x}{EI} \tag{3-8b}$$

If [1]

$$\left.\begin{array}{l}k_{AA} = \dfrac{p_{22}}{p_{11}p_{22}-p_{12}{}^2}\\[2ex]k_{AB} = \dfrac{p_{12}}{p_{11}p_{22}-p_{12}{}^2}\\[2ex]k_{BB} = \dfrac{p_{11}}{p_{11}p_{22}-p_{12}{}^2}\end{array}\right\} \tag{3-9}$$

then, we see that if $\theta_{AB}=\theta_{BA}=\psi_{AB}=0$, Equations (3-8a) and (3-8b) become

$$M_{AB} = -\frac{EI_C}{L}k_{AA}\sum M_0\left(\frac{L-x}{L}\right)\frac{\Delta x}{EI}+\frac{EI_C}{L}k_{AB}\sum M_0\left(\frac{x}{L}\right)\frac{\Delta x}{EI} \tag{3-10a}$$

$$M_{BA} = -\frac{EI_C}{L}k_{AB}\sum M_0\left(\frac{L-x}{L}\right)\frac{\Delta x}{EI}+\frac{EI_C}{L}k_{BB}\sum M_0\left(\frac{x}{L}\right)\frac{\Delta x}{EI} \tag{3-10b}$$

which (because $\theta_{AB}=\theta_{BA}=\psi_{AB}=0$) are essentially fixed-end moments due to the lateral loads. These are designated $M_{F_{AB}}$ and $M_{F_{BA}}$. Physically, the fixed-end moments are the moments which would be present at the ends of any span, due to the lateral loads in that span (or due to relative lateral movement of the ends of the span) if the

[1] For $I=I_c=$ constant, $i=1$ and

$$p_{11} = \frac{1}{L}\int_0^L\left(\frac{L-x}{L}\right)^2 dx$$
$$p_{12} = \frac{1}{L}\int_0^L\left(\frac{L-x}{L}\right)\left(\frac{x}{L}\right)dx, \quad p_{22} = \frac{1}{L}\int_0^L\left(\frac{x}{L}\right)^2 dx.$$

ends were built-in. Thus, we obtain finally, from Equations (3-8a) and (3-8b), the *slope deflection equations* as follows: For EI variable in the span

$$M_{AB} = \frac{EI_C}{L}[k_{AA}\theta_{AB} + k_{AB}\theta_{BA} - (k_{AA} + k_{AB})\psi_{AB}] + M_{F_{AB}} \quad (3\text{-}11a)$$

$$M_{BA} = \frac{EI_C}{L}[k_{AB}\theta_{AB} + k_{BB}\theta_{BA} - (k_{AB} + k_{BB})\psi_{AB}] + M_{F_{BA}} \quad (3\text{-}11b)$$

If EI is constant in the span, these become

$$M_{AB} = \frac{2EI_C}{L}[2\theta_{AB} + \theta_{BA} - 3\psi_{AB}] + M_{F_{AB}} \quad (3\text{-}12a)$$

$$M_{BA} = \frac{2EI_C}{L}[\theta_{AB} + 2\theta_{BA} - 3\psi_{AB}] + M_{F_{BA}} \quad (3\text{-}12b)$$

Various fixed-end moments, for beams of constant EI, are shown in Fig. 3.4.

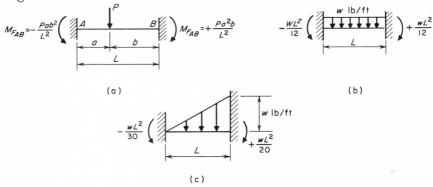

(a)   (b)

(c)

Fig. 3.4

3-3   The use of tables for solving variable moment of inertia structures

The solution of the variable moment of inertia structure requires computing the k's and fixed-end moments for each end of each span. This is a very laborious procedure in general. However, there are tables available in a handbook[2] from which these constants can be obtained for a large variety of shapes commonly used in engineering structures.

Because the constants of the handbook were obtained for a purpose different from that used in this book, the notation for the two sets of

[2] *Handbook of Frame Constants*, Portland Cement Association, 33 West Grand Avenue, Chicago 10, Ill., 1947.

constants is not identical. However, the connection between them is very simple and direct and is shown in the tabulation.

Our Notation	Equivalent Handbook Notation
k_{AA}	k_{AB}
k_{BB}	k_{BA}
k_{AB}	$C_{AB}k_{AB}$
k_{BA}	$C_{BA}k_{BA}$
$M_{F_{AB}}$	M_{AB}
$M_{F_{BA}}$	M_{BA}

In Art. 3-9, the k's and fixed-end moments for a typical variable inertia beam will be computed using the formulas of this chapter. These will then be compared to the values of the handbook and it will be shown that the agreement is good. Because the solution of the variable inertia structure is similar in every way to the solution for the constant inertia section (except that the k's and fixed-end moments are obtained differently), we shall not completely solve a variable inertia structure except as noted above. The solutions for the constant section structures will serve as typical examples.

3-4 Procedure for solving problems using the slope deflection equations

The general procedure to be used in solving problems using the slope deflection equations will now be given. Following this, several different typical illustrative beam and frame problems will be solved.

In practically all problems, the solution will be obtained most expeditiously by proceeding as follows:

1. Determine the k's for each span using the handbook if the span is of variable moment of inertia. If each span is of constant moment of inertia (the moment of inertia may vary from span to span), determine $K(=EI/L)$ for each span.

2. Note which θ's are zero, and determine relative support lateral movement (and therefore ψ) for each span.

3. Determine fixed-end moments for each end of each span, using the handbook if the moment of inertia is variable, otherwise use Fig. 3.4.

4. Apply the slope deflection Equation (3-11) or Equation (3-12) to each end of each span.

5. Now apply equations of statics and consistent deformations which in general are

    a. A balance of moments at each joint.

    b. A balance of shear forces in the case of rigid frames.

    c. Because, in general, the beams are continuous at all joints, at any joint K, $\theta_{KJ} = \theta_{KL}$.

Steps 1-5 will invariably give as many simultaneous equations as there are unknown slopes and relative support movements. These may then be solved for and the moments obtained from Equations (3-11) and Equations (3-12). Having the moments, we may obtain the shears and reactions by statics. After this, the signs of the moments may be converted to the ordinary moment sign convention and the shear and moment diagrams may be drawn.

3-5 Illustrative beam problem, constant I

Example:

Fig. 3.5 shows a continuous beam, of constant moment of inertia, all supports immovable. We wish to draw the shear and moment diagrams.

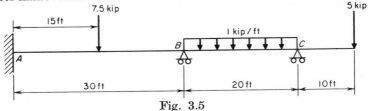

Fig. 3.5

Solution: The slope-deflection equation, for constant moment of inertia within the span becomes, in terms of general variables, M and N,

$$M_{MN} = 2K_{MN}[2\theta_{MN} + \theta_{NM} - 3\psi_{MN}] + M_{F_{MN}} \qquad (3\text{-}13)$$

Hence (the numbering below conforms to the procedure numbering of Art. 3-4),

1. $K_{AB} = \dfrac{EI}{30} = 1$ (this may be taken as unity, since relative values only of K are needed) and

$$K_{BC} = \frac{EI}{20} = 1.5$$

2. $$\left.\begin{array}{l} \theta_A = 0 \\ \psi_{AB} = \psi_{BC} = 0 \\ \theta_{BA} = \theta_{BC} \end{array}\right\} \text{by inspection}$$

3. From Fig. 3.4,

$$\left.\begin{array}{l} M_{F_{AB}} = -\dfrac{Pab^2}{L^2} = -\dfrac{7.5 \times 15 \times 15^2}{30^2} = -28.1 \text{ kip-ft} \\[3mm] M_{F_{BA}} = +\dfrac{Pa^2b}{L^2} = +\dfrac{7.5 \times 15^2 \times 15}{30^2} = +28.1 \text{ kip-ft} \\[3mm] M_{F_{BC}} = -\dfrac{wL^2}{12} = -\dfrac{1 \times 20^2}{12} = -33.3 \text{ kip-ft} \\[3mm] M_{F_{CB}} = +\dfrac{wL^2}{12} = +\dfrac{1 \times 20^2}{12} = +33.3 \text{ kip-ft} \end{array}\right\} \qquad (3\text{-}14)$$

4.
$$M_{AB} = K_{AB}[4\theta_{AB}+2\theta_{BA}-6\psi_{AB}]+M_{F_{AB}}$$
$$= 1[2\theta_{BA}]-28.1$$
$$M_{BA} = 1[4\theta_{BA}]+28.1$$
$$M_{BC} = 1.5[4\theta_{BC}+2\theta_{CB}]-33.3$$
$$M_{CB} = 1.5[4\theta_{CB}+2\theta_{BC}]+33.3$$
(3-15)

5. At point B (see Fig. 3.5a), $M_{BA}+M_{BC}=0$,

Fig. 3.5a. Unknown moments assumed in positive direction

and at joint C, $M_{CB}-50=0$, or
$$4\theta_{BA}+28.1+6\theta_{BC}+3\theta_{CB}-33.3 = 0$$
and
$$6\theta_{CB}+3\theta_{BC}+33.3-50.0 = 0$$
(3-16)

Also
$$\theta_{BC} = \theta_{BA}$$

These may be solved for θ_{BC} and θ_{CB} to give
$$\theta_{BC} = \theta_{BA} = -0.365$$
and
$$\theta_{CB} = +2.9$$
(3-17)

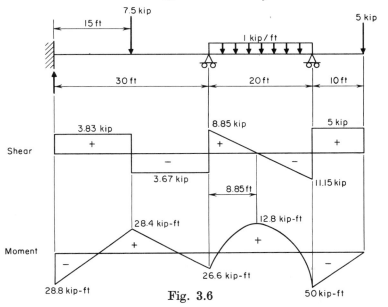

Fig. 3.6

Now going back to Equations (3-15) and using Equations (3-17), we obtain

$$\left.\begin{array}{l} M_{AB} = -2 \times 0.365 - 28.1 = -28.8 \text{ kip-ft} \\ M_{BA} = +26.6 \text{ kip-ft} \\ M_{BC} = -26.6 \text{ kip-ft} \\ M_{CB} = +50 \text{ kip-ft} \end{array}\right\} \quad (3\text{-}18)$$

Using these values of moments, the reactions may be found.   They are

$$\left.\begin{array}{l} R_A = 3.83 \text{ kip} \uparrow \\ R_B = 12.5 \text{ kip} \uparrow \\ R_C = 16.16 \text{ kip} \uparrow \end{array}\right\} \quad (3\text{-}19)$$

The shear and moment diagrams are now drawn as shown in Fig. 3.6.

3-6   Illustrative frame problem

The method is now applied to a rigid frame.   The frame and loading are shown in Fig. 3.7.

Example:

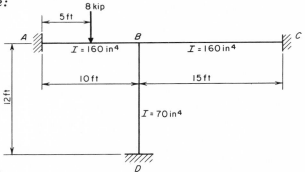

Fig. 3.7

Solution: Proceed with the solution, as before.

1.
$$K_{AB} = \frac{160E}{10}$$

$$K_{BC} = \frac{160E}{15}$$

$$K_{BD} = \frac{70E}{12}$$

2.
$$\theta_A = \theta_C = \theta_D = 0$$

$$\psi_{AB} = \psi_{BC} = \psi_{BD} = 0$$

3.
$$\left.\begin{array}{l} M_{F_{AB}} = -\dfrac{8 \times 5 \times 5^2}{10^2} = -10 \text{ kip-ft} \\ M_{F_{BA}} = +10 \text{ kip-ft} \end{array}\right\} \quad (3\text{-}20)$$

4.
$$M_{AB} = \frac{2E(160)}{10}\,\theta_B - 10$$

$$M_{BA} = \frac{2E(160)}{10}\,(2\theta_B) + 10$$

$$M_{BC} = \frac{2E(160)}{15}\,(2\theta_B)$$

$$M_{CB} = \frac{2E(160)}{15}\,\theta_B$$ (3-21)

$$M_{DB} = \frac{2E(70)}{12}\,\theta_B$$

$$M_{BD} = \frac{2E(70)}{12}\,(2\theta_B)$$

5.
$$M_{BD} + M_{BC} + M_{BA} = 0$$

from which,
$$\theta_B = -\frac{0.0769}{E}$$

Therefore,

$$\begin{aligned}
M_{AB} &= -12.5 \\
M_{BA} &= +5 \\
M_{BC} &= -3.34 \\
M_{CB} &= -1.66 \\
M_{DB} &= -0.833 \\
M_{BD} &= -1.66
\end{aligned}$$ (3.22)

Now, using statics, we obtain the shears and direct loads.   All are shown
in Fig. 3.8.

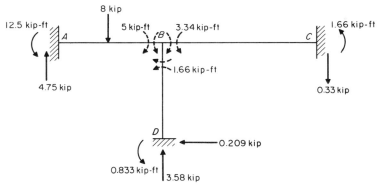

Fig. 3.8

3-7 Illustrative frame problem—sidesway

In the illustrative problem of the previous section, there was no relative lateral movement of the end joints of each span. In other words, there was no *sidesway* of the structure.

This will always be true for frames of the type shown in Fig. 3.7 and also for ordinary portal frames if the structure and loading are symmetrical about a center line. Thus, in Fig. 3.9, the case (a) will have zero sidesway (as shown), but cases (b) and (c) will have sidesway (as shown). The deflected structure is shown dotted in all cases.

In the general case of frame loading, the sidesway, which introduces a ψ term in the slope-deflection equation, must be considered.

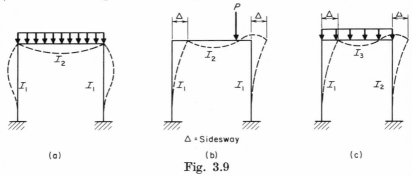

Δ = Sidesway

(a)   (b)   (c)

Fig. 3.9

Example:

To illustrate, we now solve the problem shown in Fig. 3.10.

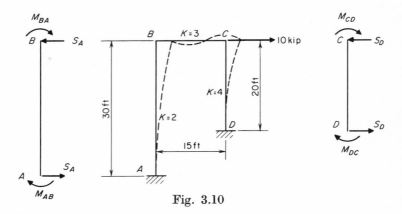

Fig. 3.10

Solution: 1. The K's are as shown on the figure. These are relative values computed from the I/L of each member.

2.
$$\theta_A = \theta_D = 0$$

$$\psi_{AB} = \frac{\Delta}{30} \qquad \Delta \text{ assumed positive}$$

$$\psi_{CD} = \frac{\Delta}{20}$$

3. Fixed-end moments are zero for all ends of all spans.

4.
$$M_{AB} = 2(2)\left[\theta_B - 3\frac{\Delta}{30}\right] = 4\theta_B - \frac{\Delta}{2.5}$$

$$M_{BA} = 2(2)\left[2\theta_B - 3\frac{\Delta}{30}\right] = 8\theta_B - \frac{\Delta}{2.5}$$

$$M_{DC} = 2(4)\left[\theta_C - 3\frac{\Delta}{20}\right] = 8\theta_C - 1.2\Delta \qquad (3\text{-}23)$$

$$M_{CD} = 2(4)\left[2\theta_C - 3\frac{\Delta}{20}\right] = 16\theta_C - 1.2\Delta$$

$$M_{BC} = 2(3)[2\theta_B + \theta_C] = 12\theta_B + 6\theta_C$$

$$M_{CB} = 2(3)[2\theta_C + \theta_B] = 12\theta_C + 6\theta_B$$

5. Joint equilibrium requires that

$$\left. \begin{array}{c} M_{BA} + M_{BC} = 0 \\ M_{CD} + M_{CB} = 0 \end{array} \right\} \qquad (3\text{-}24)$$

Now consider AB and CD as free bodies, subjected to end moments and shears. Writing the equation $\Sigma H = 0$ (see Fig. 3.10), we obtain

$$\frac{M_{AB} + M_{BA}}{30} + \frac{M_{CD} + M_{DC}}{20} + 10 = 0 \qquad (3\text{-}25)$$

Equations (3-24) become, upon substituting the values from Equations (3-23),

$$\left. \begin{array}{c} 8\theta_B - 0.4\Delta + 12\theta_B + 6\theta_C = 0 \\ 16\theta_C - 1.2\Delta + 12\theta_C + 6\theta_B = 0 \end{array} \right\} \qquad (3\text{-}24a)$$

In the same way, from Equation (3-25), we obtain

$$8.0\theta_B + 24\theta_C - 2.933\Delta = -200 \qquad (3\text{-}25a)$$

Thus, for determining the three unknown quantities, θ_B, θ_C, Δ, there are three equations (3-24a) and (3-25a). These are easily solved to give

$$\left. \begin{array}{c} \theta_B = +0.81 \\ \theta_C = +4.38 \\ \Delta = +106.1 \end{array} \right\} \qquad (3\text{-}26)$$

and therefore, from Equation (3-23),

$$\left. \begin{array}{c} M_{AB} = -39.26 \\ M_{BA} = -36.02 \\ M_{DC} = -92.2 \\ M_{CD} = -57.1 \end{array} \right\} \qquad (3\text{-}27)$$

Now using the equations of statics, we find the horizontal and vertical components of the reactions. These are as shown in Fig. 3.11, in which the moment diagram is also shown.

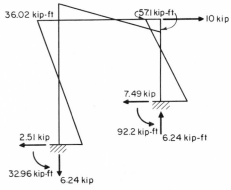

Fig. 3.11

3-8   Illustrative skew-frame problem

A typical skew frame is shown in Fig. 3.12. The complicating factor in problems of this type is the determination of the Δ terms for the various members. These can always be determined from the geometry of the figure. Two facts which must be remembered in this connection and which follow from the assumption of small deflections are

1. The lengths of all spans, in the deflected condition, are assumed equal to the original undeflected lengths.

2. The lateral movements of the ends of all spans are assumed to be in directions perpendicular to the original undeflected positions.

The use of these relations is illustrated in the problem of Fig. 3.12.

Example:

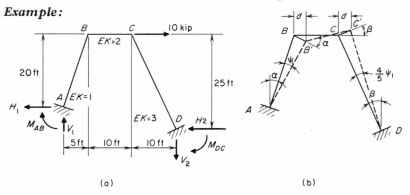

Fig. 3.12

Solution: 1. The K's are as shown on the figure.   These are given values.

2.
$$\theta_A = \theta_D = 0$$

$$\psi_{AB} = \frac{d}{20.6 \cos \alpha} = +\psi_1$$

$$\psi_{CD} = \frac{d}{26.9 \cos \beta} = +\frac{4}{5}\psi_1 \qquad \left.\begin{array}{l} \text{as shown on} \\ \text{Fig. 3-12} \end{array}\right.$$

$$\psi_{BC} = \frac{d \tan \alpha + d \tan \beta}{10} = -\frac{13}{10}\psi_1$$

3. Fixed-end moments are zero for each end of each span.

4.
$$M_{AB} = 2(1)(\theta_B - 3\psi_1) = 2\theta_B - 6\psi_1$$
$$M_{BA} = 2(1)(2\theta_B - 3\psi_1) = 4\theta_B - 6\psi_1$$
$$M_{BC} = 2(2)\left(2\theta_B + \theta_C + \frac{3(13)}{10}\psi_1\right) = 8\theta_B + 4\theta_C + 15.6\psi_1$$
$$M_{CB} = 2(2)\left(2\theta_C + \theta_B + \frac{3(13)}{10}\psi_1\right) = 8\theta_C + 4\theta_B + 15.6\psi_1 \qquad (3\text{-}28)$$
$$M_{CD} = 2(3)\left(2\theta_C - \frac{3(4)}{5}\psi_1\right) = 12\theta_C - 14.4\psi_1$$
$$M_{DC} = 2(3)\left(\theta_C - \frac{3(4)}{5}\psi_1\right) = 6\theta_C - 14.4\psi_1$$

5.
$$\left.\begin{array}{l} M_{BA} + M_{BC} = 0 \\ M_{CB} + M_{CD} = 0 \end{array}\right\} \qquad (3\text{-}29)$$

For member AB,
$$M_{AB} + M_{BA} + H_1(20) + V_1(5) = 0$$

For member CD,
$$M_{DC} + M_{CD} + H_2(25) + V_2(10) = 0$$

For member BC,
$$H_1 + H_2 - 10 = 0$$
$$V_1 = V_2$$
$$M_{BC} + M_{CB} + V_1(10) = 0$$

$\qquad\qquad\qquad\qquad\qquad\qquad\qquad\qquad\qquad\qquad\qquad\qquad\quad (3\text{-}30)$

The five equations (3-30) are equivalent to

$$5M_{AB} + 5M_{BA} + 4M_{DC} + 4M_{CD} - 6.5M_{BC} - 6.5M_{CB} = +1000 \qquad (3\text{-}30a)$$

The completion of this problem is left as an exercise for the student. The steps in the solution are as follows:

a. Substitute Equation (3-28) into Equations (3-29) and (3-30a).   This gives three equations in terms of three unknowns, θ_B, θ_C and ψ_1.

b. Solve for θ_B, θ_C and ψ_1.

c. Using Equation (3-28) obtain all moments.

d. Using Equation (3-30) obtain all shears and direct loads.

e. Draw shear and moment diagrams.

3-9   Illustrative variable moment of inertia solution

In this section we shall obtain the values of k and the fixed-end moment for a variable moment of inertia beam (a haunched beam), using the equations and methods derived in this chapter. These results will then be compared with the values obtained from the *Handbook of Frame Constants*.[3]

Example: The beam and loading are as shown in Fig. 3.13. The beam is divided into 10 equal sections of 2-ft length each, as shown. For convenience, the equations used in obtaining the solutions are listed below.

$$p_{11} = \frac{1}{L} \sum \frac{\Delta x}{i} \left(\frac{L-x}{L}\right)^2 \tag{3-6b}$$

$$p_{12} = \frac{1}{L} \sum \frac{\Delta x}{i} \left(\frac{L-x}{L}\right)\left(\frac{x}{L}\right) \tag{3-6c}$$

$$p_{22} = \frac{1}{L} \sum \frac{\Delta x}{i} \left(\frac{x}{L}\right)^2 \tag{3-6d}$$

$$\left. \begin{aligned} k_{AA} &= \frac{p_{22}}{p_{11}p_{22} - p_{12}{}^2} \\ k_{AB} &= \frac{p_{12}}{p_{11}p_{22} - p_{12}{}^2} \\ k_{BB} &= \frac{p_{11}}{p_{11}p_{22} - p_{12}{}^2} \end{aligned} \right\} \tag{3-9}$$

Solution: The complete solution is shown in the tabular form and computations which follow.

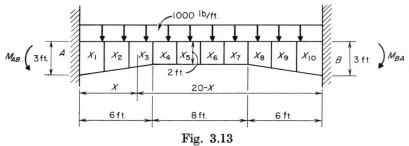

Fig. 3.13

Let $\Delta x = \dfrac{20}{10} = 2$

$I_C = \dfrac{1 \times 2^3}{12} = \dfrac{2}{3}$

$I_x = \dfrac{1 \times d^3}{12}$

[3] *Ibid.*

$$i = \frac{I_x}{I_C} = \left(\frac{d}{2}\right)^3$$

$$M_{0_{\frac{1}{10}}} = \frac{wL^2}{2}\left(\frac{1}{20}\right)\left(\frac{19}{20}\right) = 9.5 \text{ kip-ft}$$

$$\frac{\Delta x}{L} = \frac{2}{20} = \frac{1}{10}$$

Sec.	$\frac{1}{i}$	$\frac{x}{L}$	$\frac{1}{i}\frac{x}{L}$	$\frac{1}{i}\frac{x^2}{L^2}$	$\frac{L-x}{L}$	M_0 kip-ft	$M_0\left(\frac{\Delta x}{i}\right)\left(\frac{L-x}{L}\right)$	$M_0\left(\frac{\Delta x}{i}\right)\left(\frac{x}{L}\right)$	$\frac{1}{i}\left(\frac{x}{L}\right)\left(\frac{L-x}{L}\right)$
1	0.356	$\frac{1}{20}$	0.0178	0.00089	$\frac{19}{20}$	9.5	6.5	0.338	0.0169
2	0.513	$\frac{3}{20}$	0.0770	0.01157	$\frac{17}{20}$	25.5	22.3	3.9	0.0655
3	0.781	$\frac{5}{20}$	0.1950	0.04870	$\frac{15}{20}$	37.5	43.8	14.6	0.1465
4	1.000	$\frac{7}{20}$	0.3500	0.12230	$\frac{13}{20}$	45.5	59.2	31.8	0.2275
5	1.000	$\frac{9}{20}$	0.4500	0.20250	$\frac{11}{20}$	49.5	54.4	44.6	0.2475
6	1.000	$\frac{11}{20}$	0.5500	0.30250	$\frac{9}{20}$	49.5	44.6	54.4	0.2475
7	1.000	$\frac{13}{20}$	0.6500	0.42200	$\frac{7}{20}$	45.5	31.8	59.2	0.2275
8	0.781	$\frac{15}{20}$	0.5860	0.43900	$\frac{5}{20}$	37.5	14.6	43.8	0.1465
9	0.513	$\frac{17}{20}$	0.4370	0.37100	$\frac{3}{20}$	25.5	3.9	22.3	0.0655
10	0.356	$\frac{19}{20}$	0.3400	0.32300	$\frac{1}{20}$	9.5	0.338	6.5	0.0169
Σ	7.300		3.653	2.243			281.4	281.4	1.4078

Then,

$$\sum \frac{\Delta x}{i} = 2(7.3) = 14.6$$

$$\sum \frac{\Delta x}{i}\frac{x}{L} = 2(3.653) = 7.306$$

$$\sum \frac{\Delta x}{i}\frac{x^2}{L^2} = 2(2.243) = 4.486$$

and by symmetry, $\sum \frac{1}{i}\left(\frac{L-x}{L}\right)^2 = \sum \frac{1}{i}\frac{x^2}{L^2}$.   Therefore,

$$k_{AA} = \frac{\frac{1}{L}(4.486)}{\frac{1}{L}\left[(4.486)\left(\frac{1}{L}\right)(4.486)\right] - \frac{2}{L^2}(1.408((2)(1.408))} = 7.32$$

$$k_{AB} = \frac{20(2)(1.4078)}{12.27} = 4.59$$

$$k_{BB} = \frac{20(2.243)(2)}{12.27} = 7.32$$

From Equations (3.10a) and (3.10b),

$$M_{F_{AB}} = -7.32\left(\frac{1}{20}\right)(281.4) + 4.59\left(\frac{1}{20}\right)(281.4) = -38.5 \text{ kip-ft}$$

$$M_{F_{BA}} = +38.5 \text{ kip-ft}$$

The handbook solution is obtained as follows:

As pointed out in Art. 3-3, the values are related by

Our value	Handbook value
k_{AA}	k_{AB}
k_{BB}	k_{BA}
k_{AB}	$C_{AB}k_{AB}$
$M_{F_{AB}}$	M_{AB}
$M_{F_{BA}}$	M_{BA}

Referring to the handbook, Table 29,[4] $r_A = 0.4$,

$$k_{AB} = 6.79$$
$$k_{BA} = 7.17$$
$$C_{AB} = 0.634$$
$$M_{AB} = 0.0921 W L^2$$
$$M_{BA} = 0.0989 W L^2$$

and from Table 34,[5] $r_A = 0.6$,

$$k_{AB} = 7.86$$
$$k_{BA} = 7.49$$
$$C_{AB} = 0.622$$
$$M_{AB} = 0.1008 W L^2$$
$$M_{BA} = 0.0939 W L^2$$

Interpolating, to obtain the value corresponding to $r_A = 0.5$, we obtain (also shown are the computed values, for comparison),

Table	Computed
$k_{AB} = 7.31$	7.32
$k_{BA} = 7.33$	7.32
$C_{AB} k_{AB} = 0.628(7.31) = 4.59$	4.59
$M_{AB} = 38.5$ kip-ft	38.5 kip-ft

This indicates a very close check between the tabulated and computed values.

Problems

All of the following problems are to be solved using the slope-deflection method.

1. Complete the skew-frame problem of Art. 3-8. Draw shear and moment diagrams.

[4] *Ibid.*, p. 14.   [5] *Ibid.*, p. 16.

2. Draw shear and moment diagrams for the beam of Fig. 3.14.

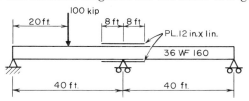

3. Draw shear and moment diagrams for the frames of Fig. 3.15 through Fig. 3.25.

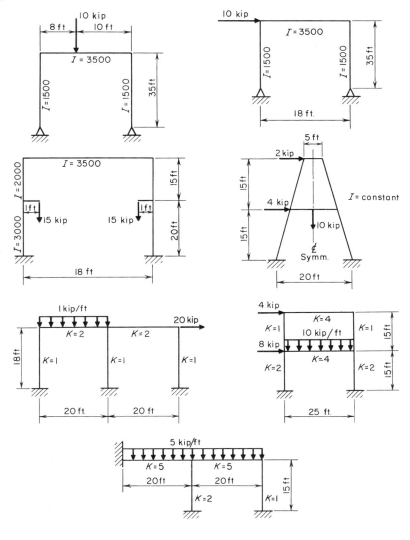

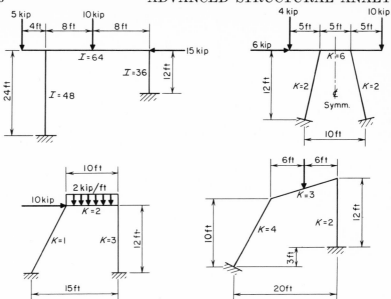

4. Determine the k's and the fixed-end moments for the beams of Figs. 3.26 through 3.28 using the analytical methods developed in this chapter and also the tables of the *Handbook of Frame Constants*.

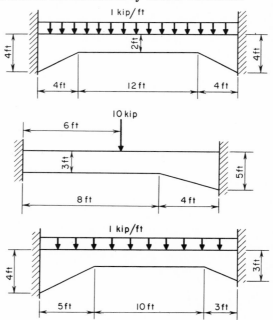

References

The following references contain some discussion of the slope-deflection method—generally restricted to structures containing uniform members. The list does not contain all the references on this subject. However, the ones given are representative.

1. Maugh, L. C., *Statically Indeterminate Structures*, John Wiley and Sons, New York, 1946.
2. Parcel, J. I. and Maney, G. A., *An Elementary Treatise on Statically Indeterminate Structures*, 2nd Ed., John Wiley and Sons, New York, 1936.
3. Wang, C. K., *Statically Indeterminate Structures*, McGraw-Hill Book Company, New York, 1953.
4. Wilbur, J. B. and Norris, C. H., *Elementary Structural Analysis*, McGraw-Hill Book Company, New York, 1948.
5. A useful handbook of rigid frame formulas is Kleinlogel, A., *Rigid Frame Formulas*, translation of the 11th German Edition, Ungar Publishing Company, New York, 1952.

Chapter 4

THE MOMENT DISTRIBUTION METHOD

4-1 Introduction

Moment distribution is a method of solving for the moments in continuous beams and frames by successive approximations. It became generally known to structural engineers through the publication of Hardy Cross' classic paper in 1932.[1] There has been much discussion as to just how the moment distribution method fits into the general theory of numerical analysis. It appears to be fairly generally agreed that moment distribution is a particular application of the general procedure of *relaxation*[2] which is so useful throughout all of mathematical physics.[3]

For our purposes, we may describe the moment distribution method as a solution by successive approximations of the slope-deflection equations described in the previous chapter.

In order to apply properly the moment distribution method, it is necessary that certain basic terms and defined quantities be clearly understood. In the next article, we shall define two of these: *stiffness factor* and *distribution factor*. In Arts. 4-3 and 4-4 we shall define "carry-over factor" and the sign convention. Before we proceed to illustrative problems, all of these will be summarized in diagram form in Art. 4-5.

4-2 Basic concepts: stiffness and distribution factors

Consider the frame of Fig. 4.1 with members of constant section in which the joint X is a rigid joint. A moment, M_0, is applied at the joint producing a clockwise rotation, θ_X.

---

[1] Hardy Cross, "Analysis of Continuous Beams and Frames by Distributing Fixed-End Moments," *Transactions*, ASCE, 1932, p. 1. See also H. Cross and N. D. Morgan, *Continuous Frames of Reinforced Concrete*, John Wiley and Sons, New York, 1932.

[2] See Chapter 6 in which various numerical methods of analysis, including relaxation, are applied to typical structural problems.

[3] The pioneer and great developer of relaxation methods and techniques is R. V. Southwell. His major contributions in these fields are given in his books, *Relaxation Methods in Engineering Science*, Oxford, The Clarendon Press, 1940. *Relaxation Methods in Theoretical Physics*, Oxford, The Clarendon Press, 1946.

We define the term

$$K = \frac{4EI}{L} \tag{4-1}$$

as the *stiffness factor* of a beam and determine this for each member of the structure of Fig. 4.1.

It is seen from the slope-deflection equations, Equation (3-12), that the stiffness factor, as defined, is the moment that must be applied at one end of a constant section member (which is on unyielding supports at both ends) to produce a unit rotation of that end when the other end is fixed.

Using the terminology of Chapter 3, we write the equilibrium equation of joint X as

$$M_{XA} + M_{XB} + M_{XC} + M_0 = 0 \tag{4-2a}$$

where

$$M_{XA} = K_{XA}[\theta_X + \tfrac{1}{2}\theta_A] \tag{4-2b}$$

$$M_{XB} = K_{XB}\theta_X \tag{4-2c}$$

$$M_{XC} = K_{XC}\theta_X \tag{4-2d}$$

But

$$M_{AX} = K_{XA}[\tfrac{1}{2}\theta_X + \theta_A] = 0 \tag{4-2e}$$

from which

$$\theta_A = -\tfrac{1}{2}\theta_X$$

and

$$M_{XA} = K_{XA}(\tfrac{3}{4}\theta_X) \tag{4-2f}$$

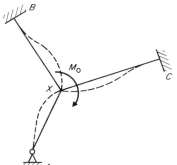

Fig. 4.1

Using these values in Equation (4-2a), we can find the joint rotation θ_X, as follows

$$K_{XA}(\tfrac{3}{4}\theta_X) + K_{XB}\theta_X + K_{XC}\theta_X = -M_0$$

or

$$\theta_X = -\frac{M_0}{\tfrac{3}{4}K_{XA} + K_{XB} + K_{XC}} \tag{4-2g}$$

Substituting θ_X back into the equations for the moments, we obtain

$$M_{XA} = -\frac{\tfrac{3}{4}K_{XA}}{\tfrac{3}{4}K_{XA} + K_{XB} + K_{XC}} M_0 \tag{4-3a}$$

$$M_{XB} = -\frac{K_{XB}}{\tfrac{3}{4}K_{XA} + K_{XB} + K_{XC}} M_0 \tag{4-3b}$$

$$M_{XC} = -\frac{K_{XC}}{\tfrac{3}{4}K_{XA} + K_{XB} + K_{XC}} M_0 \tag{4-3c}$$

We define the stiffness factor ratios of Equations (4-3) as the *distribution factors*. Thus, for example,

$$D_{XA} = \frac{\frac{3}{4}K_{XA}}{\frac{3}{4}K_{XA}+K_{XB}+K_{XC}}$$

is the distribution factor for end X of beam XA and is a measure of the portion of the applied external moment at X which is taken by beam XA at end X. Then

$$M_{XA} = -D_{XA}M_0 \qquad (4\text{-}4a)$$

$$M_{XB} = -D_{XB}M_0 \qquad (4\text{-}4b)$$

$$M_{XC} = -D_{XC}M_0 \qquad (4\text{-}4c)$$

4-3 Carry-over factors

The moments M_{AX}, M_{BX}, and M_{CX} are (in terms of the slope-deflection equations)

$$M_{AX} = \tfrac{1}{4}K_{AX}[4\theta_A + 2\theta_X] = 0 \qquad (4\text{-}5a)$$

$$M_{BX} = \tfrac{1}{4}K_{BX}(2\theta_X) = \tfrac{1}{2}M_{XB} \qquad (4\text{-}5b)$$

$$M_{CX} = \tfrac{1}{4}K_{CX}(2\theta_X) = \tfrac{1}{2}M_{XC} \qquad (4\text{-}5c)$$

The ratios of the far end moments to the rigid-joint moments are defined as *carry-over factors* and are denoted by the letter C. Thus,

$$C_{XA} = \frac{M_{AX}}{M_{XA}} = 0 \qquad (4\text{-}6a)$$

$$C_{XB} = \frac{M_{BX}}{M_{XB}} = \tfrac{1}{2} \qquad (4\text{-}6b)$$

$$C_{XC} = \frac{M_{CX}}{M_{XC}} = \tfrac{1}{2} \qquad (4\text{-}6c)$$

For members of constant moment of inertia the carry-over factor to a built-in end will always be $\tfrac{1}{2}$ and, to a pin-connected end, it will always be 0. For the time being we will limit ourselves to beams and frames of constant cross section.

4-4 Sign convention

It is convenient to establish clearly a sign convention for moments. As in the case of any sign convention the choice is arbitrary, the opposite sign convention to that chosen could readily be used. Our convention will be the following: *If the internal bending moment about a joint is counterclockwise it is a positive moment.* By this convention an externally applied moment is positive if it is counter clockwise.

4-5 Summary of basic defined quantities—moment distribution method for members of constant cross section

The basic definitions are those for stiffness factors, distribution factors, and carry-over factors. The meaning of these factors can best be illustrated by the summary Fig. 4.2 and the discussion which follows it.

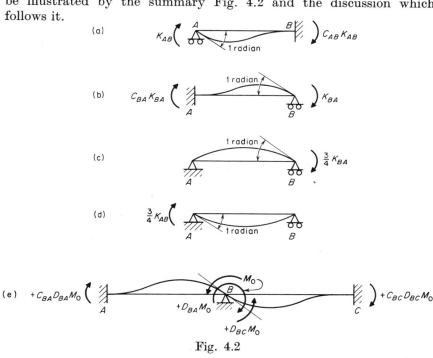

Fig. 4.2

In Figs. 4.2a and 4.2b, note that the applied moments are equal to K_{AB} and K_{BA} and produce unit rotations at the ends. Hence, as defined in Art. 4-2, these are *stiffness factors*. The carry-over factors (for the far end built-in) determine the moments at the built-in ends. In accordance with the sign convention, the applied external moments are negative—for then, at the joints, $\sum M = 0$ as required.

Figs. 4.2c and 4.2d are similar to the previous two figures except that now the far end is hinged. From Equation (4-2f) it follows that the stiffness factors for these cases are always given by

$$K = \frac{3}{4}\left(\frac{4EI}{L}\right)$$

as shown. The carry-over factors are zero and the far end moments are also zero, as required for a hinged end. The applied external moments are negative.

In Fig. 4.2e the applied external moment M_0 is a negative moment. The moments M_{BA} and M_{BC} are positive and are given by the values shown. The moments at the built-in ends are also positive and are obtained from the moments at joint B simply by multiplying these by the carry-over factors.

In addition to the terms defined and given above, the moment distribution method also utilizes the concept of *fixed-end moments*. These were previously defined in Art. 3-2, and the same definition applies here. We shall use the abbreviation F.E.M. to represent this term.

4-6 Continuous beam problems

Example: Determine the moments at A and B for the beam and loading of Fig. 4.3.

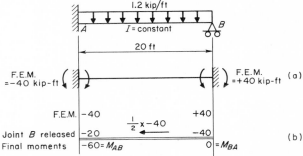

Fig. 4.3

Solution: In the illustrative example of Fig. 4.3, we consider joint B to be initially locked against rotation. The fixed-end moments are then

$$\mp \frac{1.2 \times (20)^2}{12} = \mp 40 \text{ kip-ft}$$

The minus sign is used for the fixed-end moment at A since the internal F.E.M. at the joint is clockwise. The plus sign is used for the F.E.M. at B because the internal fixed-end moment at joint B is counterclockwise. These values are shown in Fig. 4.3b. If joint B is released, it will rotate until the moment becomes zero. This is equivalent to applying an external moment at B, of value $+40$ kip-ft (and hence an internal, joint, moment of -40 kip-ft). But a moment of -40 kip-ft applied at joint B produces a moment at A of one half that amount. The carry-over factor times the change in moment is $-40 \times \frac{1}{2} = -20$ kip-ft. These values are shown beneath the diagram. The final moments are obtained by adding the values in the two columns as shown.

Example: Solve for the moments at A, B, and C for the beam and loading shown in Fig. 4.4.

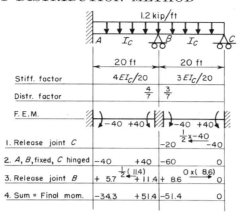

	$4EI_C/20$		$3EI_C/20$	
Stiff. factor	$4EI_C/20$		$3EI_C/20$	
Distr. factor	$\frac{4}{7}$		$\frac{3}{7}$	
F.E.M.	−40	+40	−40	+40
1. Release joint C			−20 $(\frac{1}{2}\times -40)$	−40
2. A, B, fixed, C hinged	−40	+40	−60	0
3. Release joint B	+5.7 $\frac{1}{2}(11.4)$	+11.4	+8.6 $0\times(8.6)$	0
4. Sum = Final mom.	−34.3	+51.4	−51.4	0

Fig. 4.4

Solution: The beam of this example differs from that of the previous one in that it contains an additional joint. The stiffness and distribution factors are calculated in accordance with the principles of Art. 4-5 (see Fig. 4.2) and the various steps involved in the solution are explained on the diagram. For Step 3, in which joint B is released, note that there is initially an unbalanced moment of -20 kip-ft. The change in moment, when we allow rotation, is of the opposite sign, or

$$M_{BA} = +D_{BA}(20) = +\tfrac{4}{7}\times 20 = +11.4 \text{ kip-ft}$$
$$M_{BC} = +D_{BC}(20) = +\tfrac{3}{7}\times 20 = +8.6 \text{ kip-ft}$$

These moments carry over to supports A and C as indicated under Step 3.

	A	B	B	C	C	D
K	$4EI_C/20$		$12EI_C/20$		$3EI_C/20$	
Relative K		4	12	12	3	0
Distr. factor		$\frac{4}{16}=\frac{1}{4}$	$\frac{3}{4}$	$\frac{4}{5}$	$\frac{1}{5}$	
F.E.M	−40	+40	0	0	−60	0
Release C			+24 ← +48	+12	
Release B	− 8 ← −16	−48 → −24			
" C			+ 9.6 ← +19.2	+4.8	
" B	−1.2 ← −2.4	−7.2 → −3.6			
" C			+1.4 ← +2.9	0.7	
" B	−0.2 ← −0.3	−1.1 → −0.5			
" C			+0.2 ← +0.4	+0.1	
" B			−0.2			
Final moments	−49.4	+21.3	−21.3	+42.4	−42.4	0

Fig. 4.5

It will be noted that the solution is dependent upon one rotation, that of joint B; therefore the answers given in Step 4 are exact.

Example: Solve for the moments at joints A, B, C, and D for the beam and loading shown in Fig. 4.5.

Solution: The beam in this problem is a three-span continuous beam. For this case the approximations are successive, and joints B and C must be alternately locked and released. This procedure is arbitrarily stopped when the final moments are known to three significant figures (i.e., when the carry-over moments become less than 0.1). After each distribution at a joint, the distributed moments are underlined indicating that the joint moments, at this point, are balanced (in equilibrium).

4-7   Rigid frames, no sidesway

Example: Solve for the joint moments in the rigid frame shown in Fig. 4.6.

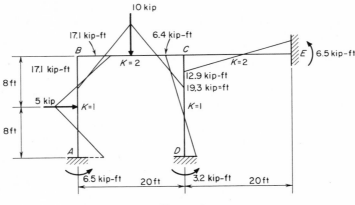

Fig. 4.6

Solution: The frame is horizontally tied at E so that joints B and C cannot translate horizontally. Moment distribution can be applied to this type of frame using exactly the same procedures as for the continuous beams. Computations are tabulated for clarity in Table 4.1, although some computers prefer to arrange their calculations directly on the diagram. The final results and moment diagrams are indicated on the figure.

4-8   Rigid frames with sidesway

Example: Determine the joint moments and support reactions for the unsymmetrical frame and loading shown in Fig. 4.7.

Solution: The frame shown is subject to horizontal translation (sidesway) of joints B and C through the same distance Δ (if axial elongation of members is ignored).

TABLE 4.1

Joint	A	B		C			D	E
D.F.		A $\frac{1}{3}$	C $\frac{2}{3}$	B $\frac{2}{5}$	D $\frac{1}{5}$	E $\frac{2}{5}$		
F.E.M. Release C	− 10	+ 10	− 25 − 5	+ 25 − 10	− 5	− 10	− 2.5	− 5
Release B	+ 3.3	+ 6.7	+ 13.3	+ 6.7				
Release C			− 1.4	− 2.7	− 1.3	− 2.7	− 0.7	− 1.4
Release B	+ 0.2	+ 0.4	+ 1.0	+ 0.5				
Release C			− 0.1	− 0.2	− 0.1	− 0.2	− 0.0	− 0.1
Release B		+ 0.	+ 0.1					
Sum	− 6.5	+ 17.1	− 17.1	+ 19.3	− 6.4	− 2.9	− 3.2	− 6.5

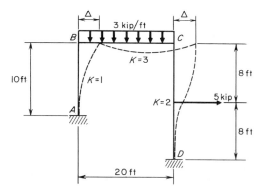

Fig. 4.7

From the slope-deflection equations, it is seen that changes in moment accompany sidesway. This effect must be taken into consideration in the solution. There are several ways of accomplishing this, but only one method will be given here. This is, in outline:

1. Hold the frame at either B or C, so that sidesway is prevented.
2. Distribute moments due to the given loads following usual moment distribution procedure.
3. From the conditions of equilibrium, calculate the holding force necessary to prevent sidesway.
4. Find the moments due to applying a force equal and opposite to the holding force.
5. Add the moments due to steps 2 and 4 to obtain the final moments.

The procedure will be illustrated using the problem of Fig. 4.7 as an example: The F.E.M.'s are

$$M_{F_{BC}} = -\frac{3(20)^2}{12} = -100 \text{ kip-ft} = -M_{F_{CB}}$$

$$M_{F_{DC}} = -\frac{5(16)}{8} = -10 \text{ kip-ft} = -M_{F_{CD}}$$

The distribution factors, as well as the primary moment distribution of Step 2 above, are shown on Fig. 4.8.

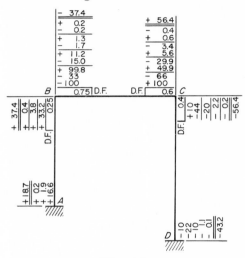

Fig. 4.8

The holding force must next be computed. To do this we must first find the horizontal reactions at A and D.

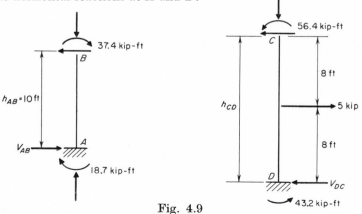

Fig. 4.9

These are obtained by taking moments about points B and C using the free bodies of the columns of Fig. 4.9. Thus,

$$V_{AB} = +\frac{M_{AB}+M_{BA}}{h_{AB}} = +\frac{18.7+37.4}{10} = +5.6 \text{ kip}$$

The plus sign indicates that V_{AB} acts from left to right as shown in Fig. 4.10. Similarly,

$$V_{DC} = \frac{M_{CD}+M_{DC}+5 \times 8}{h_{CD}} = \frac{+56.4+43.2+40}{16} = +7.11 \text{ kip}$$

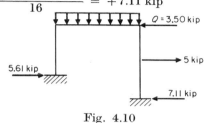

V_{DC} acts from right to left as shown. The holding force Q, Fig. 4.10, is found from the equilibrium of the frame,

$$Q = +5+5.61-7.11 = 3.50 \text{ kip}$$

This holding force does not act on the actual frame and must be eliminated. To do so, we will apply a force equal and opposite to Q to the frame. The

Fig. 4.10

effects of such a force are found by solving the problem of Fig. 4.11.

In Fig. 4.11 there are no F.E.M.'s due to transverse loads directly. However, there are F.E.M.'s due to lateral translation of the ends of the vertical members and these are the initial moments introduced into the structure. They are obtained as follows:

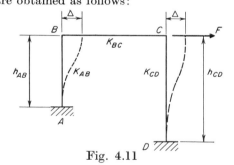

Fig. 4.11

Translate the frame by an amount Δ at the same time locking joints B and C against rotation (see Fig. 4.11). The moments developed will be

$$M_{F_{AB}} = M_{F_{BA}} = \frac{3}{2} K_{AB} \frac{\Delta}{h_{AB}} \qquad (4\text{-}7a)$$

$$M_{F_{CD}} = M_{F_{DC}} = \frac{3}{2} K_{CD} \frac{\Delta}{h_{CD}} \qquad (4\text{-}7b)$$

These equations follow directly from the slope-deflection equations. They are fixed-end moments because $\theta_B=\theta_C=0$, both joints having been locked against rotation. The ratio of the fixed-end moments can be found from Equations (4-7), as

$$\frac{M_{F_{AB}}}{M_{F_{CD}}} = \frac{K_{AB}}{K_{CD}} \frac{h_{CD}}{h_{AB}} \qquad (4\text{-}8)$$

For a specific problem it is sufficient to calculate this ratio, assign an arbitrary value to $M_{F_{CD}}$ and calculate $M_{F_{AB}}$. Then distribute moments in accordance with the usual procedure of allowing each joint to rotate in succession. In effect, we have assigned an arbitrary value to Δ, applied a force F of unknown magnitude to prevent any further sidesway, and calculated the joint moments corresponding to this arbitrary value of Δ. We can then find the force F which is preventing return of the frame to its original, undeflected position. This will be done for our problem.

$$\frac{h_{CD}}{h_{AB}}\ \frac{K_{AB}}{K_{CD}} = \frac{1}{2} \times \frac{16}{10} = 0.8$$

Then, if $M_{F_{CD}}$ is taken as -100 kip-ft,

$$M_{F_{AB}} = -\tfrac{1}{2} \times 100 \times 1.6 = -80 \text{ kip-ft}$$

After the F.E.M.'s are known, moment distribution is accomplished as shown on Fig. 4.12.

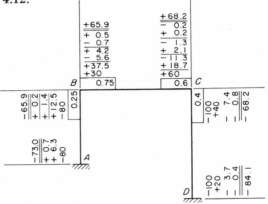

Fig. 4.12

The horizontal reactions are, as before,

$$V_{AB} = \frac{73.0 + 65.9}{10} = 13.89 \text{ kip}$$

$$V_{DC} = \frac{84.1 + 68.2}{16} = 9.67 \text{ kip}$$

The holding force F must then be

$$F = V_{AB} + V_{DC} = 13.89 + 9.67 = 23.56 \text{ kip}$$

We originally had a holding force of 3.50 kip (see Fig. 4.10). Fig. 4.12 shows the effects of a force $F = 23.56$ kip. Since the laws of superposition hold, when we multiply the results of Fig. 4.12 by a ratio $\dfrac{Q}{F} = \dfrac{+3.50}{23.56} = +0.148$

we will have the moments produced by a force of 3.50 kip pushing to the right. These values are shown in Fig. 4.13.

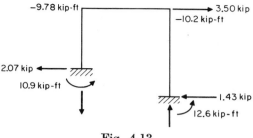

Fig. 4.13

The superposition of the results as shown on Fig. 4.13 with those shown on Figs. 4.8 and 4.10 is the solution of the original problem. The final result is shown in Fig. 4.14, which represents the solution to the problem.

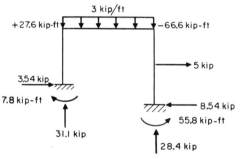

Fig. 4.14

4-9   Frames with inclined members: one story

Translation of one-story frames with inclined members results in sidesway as indicated by the dash lines of Fig. 4.15a. The relative value of the sidesway for each member is found by the construction

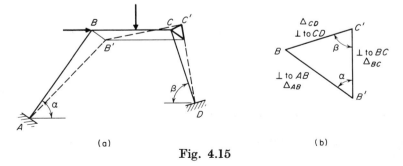

(a)   (b)

Fig. 4.15

of a Williot type diagram (Fig. 4.15b). The procedure involved in solving such a frame is to introduce a holding force Q at one of the joints normally free to translate, such as B or C, in order to prevent sidesway. Solve by moment distribution and, from the equilibrium conditions, find the force Q. Then find the effects of applying a force $-Q$ to the frame and add these to the results of the primary distribution to obtain the final results.

The relations between the sidesway quantities of Fig. 4.15b can be found by trigonometry. These are, from the sine law,

$$\Delta_{CD} = \Delta_{AB} \frac{\sin \alpha}{\sin \beta} \tag{4-9a}$$

$$\Delta_{BC} = \Delta_{AB} \frac{\sin (180 - \alpha - \beta)}{\sin \beta} \tag{4-9b}$$

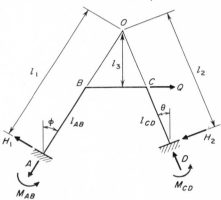

Fig. 4.16

The equilibrium condition which enables one to solve for Q is obtained by taking moments about point O (see Fig. 4.16)

$$Ql_3 = H_1 l_1 + H_2 l_2 - M_{AB} - M_{CD} \tag{4-10a}$$

where

$$H_1 = \frac{M_{AB} + M_{BA}}{l_{AB}} \tag{4-10b}$$

$$H_2 = \frac{M_{CD} + M_{DC}}{l_{CD}} \tag{4-10c}$$

The typical procedure is illustrated by the following problem.

Example: By moment distribution, determine the moments for the frame of Fig. 4.17a.

Solution: The F.E.M.'s are

$$\text{F.E.M.}_{BC} = -\frac{100 \times 12 \times 8^2}{20^2} = -192 \text{ kip-ft}$$

$$\text{F.E.M.}_{CB} = +\frac{100 \times 8 \times 12^2}{20^2} = +288 \text{ kip-ft}$$

The results of the primary distribution are given in Table 4.2.

TABLE 4.2

	A	B		C		D
	B	A	C	B	D	C
D.F.	0	0.25	0.75	0.60	0.40	0
F.E.M.	+34.8		−192.0	+288.0		−57.7
	+ 3.9		− 86.4	−172.7	−115.3	−20.9
	+ 0.4	+69.7	+208.7	+104.4		− 2.4
			− 31.2	− 62.5	−41.9	− 0.2
		+ 7.8	+ 23.4	+ 11.7		
			− 3.5	− 7.0	− 4.7	
		+ 0.9	+ 2.6	+ 1.3		
			− 0.4	− 0.8	− 0.5	
		+ 0.1	+ 0.3	+ 0.1		
				− 0.1		
Σ	+39.1	+78.5	− 78.5	+162.4	−162.4	−81.2

The geometric relations for sidesway are (see Fig. 4.17b)

$$\Delta_{AB} = \frac{\Delta}{\cos 30} = \frac{\Delta}{0.866}$$

$$\Delta_{BC} = \frac{\Delta_{AB}}{2} = \frac{\Delta}{1.732}$$

H_1 and H_2, resulting from the primary distribution, are calculated from the equilibrium of the free bodies (Fig. 4.17c) and the holding force is found to be 16.27 kip, as follows

$$H_1 = \frac{39.1 + 78.5}{11.54} = \frac{117.6}{11.54} = 10.18 \text{ kip}$$

$$H_2 = \frac{162.4 + 81.2}{15} = \frac{243.6}{15} = 16.24 \text{ kip}$$

$$\sum M_I = 0$$

$$10.18 \times 51.54 + 100 \times 8 - 39.1 + 81.2 = 16.24 \times 49.6 + 34.6Q$$

$$525 + 800 + 81.2 - 39.1 - 806 = 34.6Q$$

$$Q = \frac{561.1}{34.6} = 16.27 \text{ kip}$$

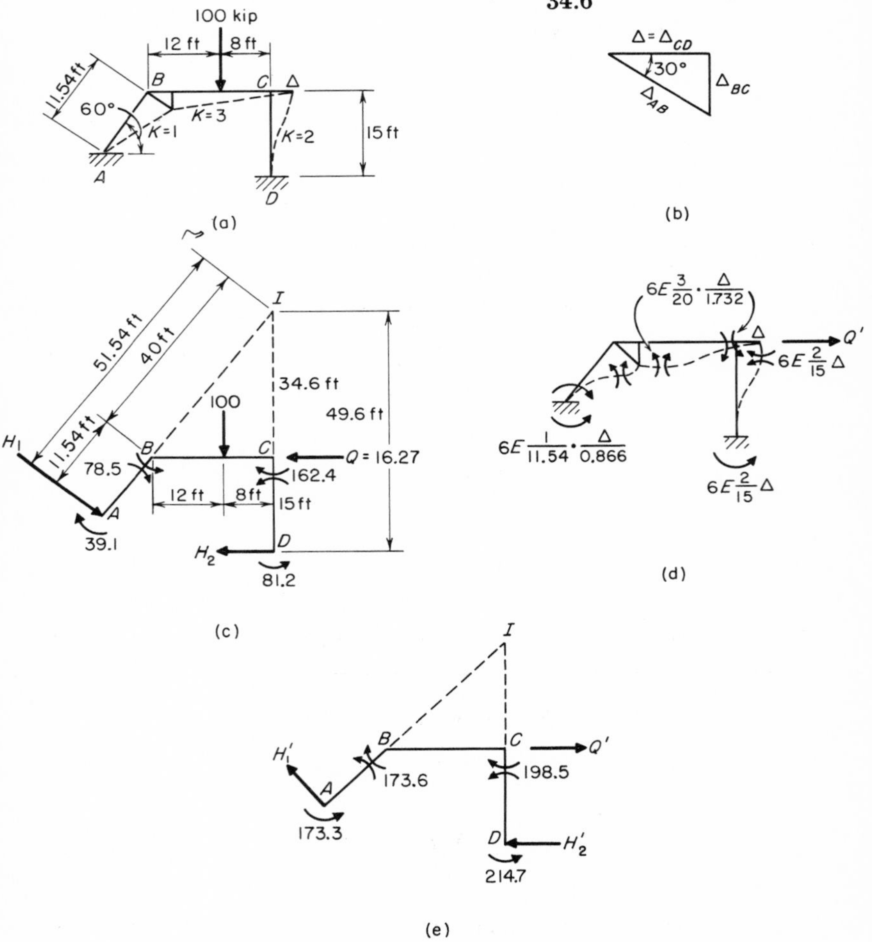

(a)

(b)

(c)

(d)

(e)

Fig. 4.17

The F.E.M.'s for an arbitrary sidesway are next calculated. The moment distribution is then shown in Table 4.3. A new holding force is found (Q'), the multiplying ratio Q/Q' is calculated, and the final moments (the last line of Table 4.3) are found. All this is as shown in the following.

Let
$$\Delta = \frac{1732}{6E}$$

$$M_{AB} = M_{BA} = -6E \times \frac{1}{11.54} \times \frac{1732}{6E} \times \frac{1}{0.866} = -173.2$$

$$M_{BC} = M_{CB} = +6E \times \frac{3}{20} \times \frac{1732}{6E} \times \frac{1}{1732} = +150.0$$

$$M_{CD} = M_{DC} = -6E \times \frac{2}{15} \times \frac{1732}{6E} = -231.0$$

TABLE 4.3

	A	B		C		D
	B	A	C	B	D	C
D.F.	0	0.25	0.75	0.60	0.40	0
F.E.M.	− 173.2	− 173.2	+ 150.0	+ 150.0	− 231.0	− 231.0
	− 0.1		+ 24.3	+ 48.6	+ 32.4	+ 16.2
		− 0.3	− 0.8	− 0.4		+ 0.1
			+ 0.2	+ 0.3	+ 0.1	
		− 0.1	− 0.1			
Σ	− 173.3	− 173.6	+ 173.6	+ 198.5	− 198.5	− 214.7
0.222 × Σ From Table 4.2	− 38.6 + 39.1	− 38.5 + 78.5	+ 38.5 − 78.5	+ 44.0 + 162.4	− 44.0 − 162.4	− 47.7 − 86.2
Final Mom.	+ 2.5	+ 40.0	− 40.0	+ 206.4	− 206.4	− 128.9

$$H_1' = \frac{346.9}{11.54} = 30.0 \text{ kip}$$

$$H_2' = \frac{413.2}{15} = 27.6 \text{ kip}$$

$$34.6Q' + 173.3 + 214.7 = 30.0 \times 51.54 + 27.6 \times 49.6$$

$$Q' = \frac{2528}{34.6} = 73.2 \text{ kip}$$

$$\frac{Q}{Q'} \text{ ratio} = \frac{16.26}{73.2} = 0.222$$

4-10 Two-stage frames

To determine the moments for the frame of Fig. 4.18a.

1. Prevent translation of joints C and F by applying holding forces Q_1 and Q_2 (see Fig. 4.18b); find F.E.M.'s. Solve, using moment distribution. Check the shear equation to find the holding forces Q_1 and Q_2.

2. Introduce sidesway Δ_1 (Fig. 4.18c), determine the corresponding F.E.M.'s, and distribute moments. Find Q_1' and Q_2' from the equilibrium equations.

3. Introduce sidesway Δ_2 (Fig. 4.18d). Find the corresponding F.E.M.'s, distribute the moments, and determine Q_1'', Q_2''.

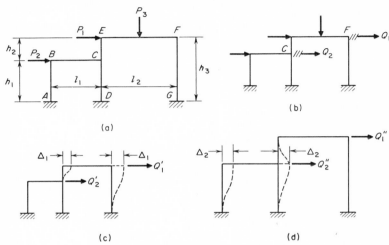

Fig. 4.18

4. Introduce factors m and n such that

$$mQ_1' + nQ_1'' + Q_1 = 0 \qquad (4\text{-}11a)$$

$$mQ_2' + nQ_2'' + Q_2 = 0 \qquad (4\text{-}11b)$$

Equations (4.11a) and (4.11b) are a system of simultaneous equations in two unknowns, m and n, which may be solved. Knowing m and n, obtain the final moments by adding to the moments due to Step 1, m times the moments due to Step 2, and n times the moments due to Step 3.

The next problem illustrates this procedure.

Example: Find the joint moments for the two-stage frame shown in Fig. 4.19a.

Solution: The solution is shown in Fig. 4.19b, c, d, and e, and in the following tables and computations. Refer to the general procedure given at the beginning of this article and illustrated in Fig. 4.18. Note the following:

1. In Step 1, for the present problem there are no F.E.M.'s. Hence, no moment distribution solution is necessary and Q_1 and Q_2 are given by the loading, 8 kip and 10 kip.

2. Step 2 is shown in Fig. 4.19b and c and in Table 4.4.

3. Step 3 is shown in Fig. 4.19d and e and in Table 4.5.

4. Step 4 is shown following Table 4.5.

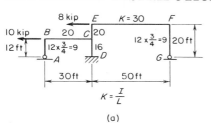

(a)

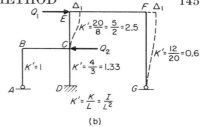

(b)

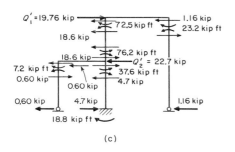

(c)

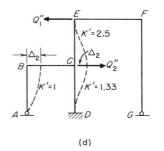

(d)

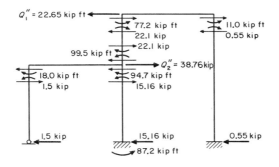

(e)

Figs. 4.19

Thus, $$\sum K' = 2.5 + 0.6 = 3.1$$

and the F.E.M.'s are given by

$$M_{EC} = M_{CE} = -6E\Delta_1 \frac{I}{L^2} = -6E\Delta_1(2.5)$$

$$M_{GF} = 0$$

$$M_{FG} = -3E\Delta_1 \frac{I}{L^2} = -3E\Delta_1(0.6)$$

so that

$$\sum M = -E\Delta_1[(12)(2.5) + (3)(0.6)]$$

and

$$M_{EC} = M_{CE} = \frac{-E\Delta_1(6)(2.5)}{E\Delta_1[(12)(2.5)+(3)(0.6)]} \times \sum M = \frac{15.0}{31.8} \sum M$$

$$M_{FG} = \frac{-E\Delta_1(3)(0.6)}{-E\Delta_1(31.8)} \sum M = \frac{1.8}{31.8} \sum M$$

Assume $\sum M = -318$. Then

$$M_{EC} = M_{CE} = -150$$
$$M_{GF} = 0$$
$$M_{FG} = -18$$

The moment distribution solution corresponding to these F.E.M.'s is shown in Table 4.4. From this table, solve for the forces Q'_1 and Q'_2 and find

$$Q'_1 = 19.76 \text{ kip}$$
$$Q'_2 = 22.7 \text{ kip}$$

TABLE 4.4

	B		D	C			E		F	
D.F.	A 0.31	C 0.69	C 0	B 0.357	D 0.286	E 0.357	C 0.40	F 0.60	E 0.77	G 0.23
F.E.M.						−150.0	−150.0			−18.0
		+21.4	+17.2			+ 30.0	+ 60.0	+90.0	+45.0	
	−6.6	−14.8	+ 1.4	+42.8	+34.4	+ 42.8	+ 21.4	−10.4	−20.8	− 6.2
		+ 1.7	+ 0.2	− 7.4		− 2.2	− 4.4	− 6.6	− 3.3	
	−0.5	− 1.2		+ 3.4	+ 2.8	+ 3.4	+ 1.7	+ 1.3	+ 2.5	+ 0.8
		+ 0.2		− 0.6		− 0.6	− 1.2	− 1.8	− 0.9	
	−0.1	− 0.1		+ 0.4	+ 0.4	+ 0.4	+ 0.2	+ 0.3	+ 0.7	+ 0.2
						− 0.1	− 0.2	− 0.3	− 0.1	
				+ 0.1					+ 0.1	
$\sum$	− 7.2	+ 7.2	+18.8	+38.6	+37.6	− 76.2	− 72.5	+72.5	+23.2	−23.2

Proceeding in the same way for sidesway Δ_2, we now find for the F.E.M.'s,

$$M_{AB} = 0$$
$$M_{BA} = -3E\Delta_2(1)$$
$$M_{CD} = M_{DC} = -6E\Delta_2(1.33)$$
$$M_{CE} = M_{EC} = +6E\Delta_2(2.5)$$
$$\sum M = E\Delta_2(-3 - 6 \times 1.33 + 6 \times 2.5)$$
$$= E\Delta_2(+4.02)$$

Thus,

$$M_{AB} = 0$$

$$M_{BA} = -\frac{3}{4.02}\sum M$$

$$M_{CD} = M_{DC} = -\frac{7.98}{4.02}\sum M$$

$$M_{CE} = M_{EC} = +\frac{15.00}{4.02}\sum M$$

Assume $\sum M = +40.2$. Then

$$M_{AB} = 0$$

$$M_{BA} = -30$$

$$M_{CD} = M_{DC} = -79.8$$

$$M_{CE} = M_{EC} = +150.0$$

The moment distribution solution corresponding to these F.E.M.'s is shown in Table 4.5. From this table, solve for the forces Q_1'' and Q_2'' and find

$$Q_1'' = 22.65 \text{ kip}$$

$$Q_2'' = 38.76 \text{ kip}$$

TABLE 4.5

	B		D	C			E		F	
	A	C	C	B	D	E	C	F	E	G
D.F.	0.31	0.69	0	0.357	0.286	0.357	0.40	0.60	0.77	0.23
F.E.M.	−30.0		−79.8		−79.8	+150.0	+150.0			
		− 7.1	− 5.8			− 30.0	−60.0	−90.0	−45.0	
	+11.5	+25.6	− 1.5	−14.3	−11.6	− 14.3	− 7.1	+17.3	+34.6	+10.4
		− 1.9	− 0.1	+12.8		− 2.0	− 4.1	− 6.1	− 3.0	
	+ 0.5	+ 1.4		− 3.8	− 3.1	− 3.8	− 1.9	+ 1.2	+ 2.4	+ 0.6
		− 0.1		+ 0.7		+ 0.1	+ 0.3	+ 0.4	+ 0.2	
		+ 0.1		− 0.3	− 0.2	− 0.3	− 0.1	− 0.1	− 0.2	
							+ 0.1	+ 0.1		
$\sum$	−18.0	+18.0	−87.2	− 4.9	−94.7	+99.5	+77.2	−77.2	−11.0	+11.0

Now solve for n and m as follows,

$$19.76m - 22.65n + 8 = 0$$

$$-22.70m + 38.76n + 10 = 0$$

from which

$$n = -1.51$$
$$m = -2.14$$

The final joint moments are now given by

$$M_{AB} = 0$$
$$M_{BA} = -7.2(-2.14) - 18.0(-1.51) = +42.6 \text{ kip-ft}$$
$$M_{BC} = -42.6 \text{ kip-ft}$$
$$M_{CB} = +38.6(-2.14) - 4.9(-1.51) = -75.2 \text{ kip-ft}$$
$$M_{CD} = +37.6(-2.14) - 94.7(-1.51) = +62.5 \text{ kip-ft}$$
$$M_{CE} = -76.2(-2.14) + 99.5(-1.51) = +12.7 \text{ kip-ft}$$
$$M_{EC} = -72.5(-2.14) + 77.2(-1.51) = +38.7 \text{ kip-ft}$$
$$M_{EF} = -38.7 \text{ kip-ft}$$
$$M_{FE} = +23.2(-2.14) - 11.0(-1.51) = -33.1 \text{ kip-ft}$$
$$M_{FG} = +33.1 \text{ kip-ft}$$
$$M_{GF} = 0$$
$$M_{DC} = +18.0(-2.14) - 87.2(-1.51) = +91.5 \text{ kip-ft}$$

4-11 Two-story bents

The bent of Fig. 4.20a will be analyzed by using auxiliary force systems Q_1', Q_1'', Q_2', Q_2'' as in the preceding problem. As in the usual procedure, find Δ_1', Δ_2', and Δ_3' in terms of Δ' in order to solve for the F.E.M.'s due to the translation without rotation shown in

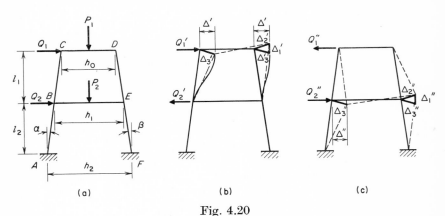

Fig. 4.20

Fig. 4.20b. Likewise we must express Δ_1'', Δ_2'', and Δ_3'' in terms of Δ'' (Fig. 4.20c). From the Williot type constructions, we obtain

$$\Delta_1' = \Delta'(\tan \alpha + \tan \beta) = \Delta'\left(\frac{h_1 - h_0}{l_1}\right) \tag{4-12a}$$

$$\Delta_2' = \frac{\Delta'}{\cos \beta} = \Delta'\frac{l_{DE}}{l_1} \tag{4-12b}$$

$$\Delta_3' = \frac{\Delta'}{\cos \alpha} = \Delta'\frac{l_{BC}}{l_1} \tag{4-12c}$$

$$\Delta_1'' = \Delta''\left(\frac{h_2 - h_1}{l_2}\right) \tag{4-12d}$$

$$\Delta_2'' = \Delta''\frac{l_{EF}}{l_2} \tag{4-12e}$$

$$\Delta_3'' = \Delta''\frac{l_{AB}}{l_2} \tag{4-12f}$$

The procedure is illustrated by the following problem.

Example: Find the joint moments in the unsymmetrical two-story bent shown in Fig. 4.21a.

Solution: The complete solution is shown in Tables 4.6 and 4.7, in Figs. 4.21b through g, and in the computations which follow. A detailed explanation of these will now be presented.

The various Δ terms corresponding to assumed deformations Δ' and Δ'' (see Figs. 4.21b and e) are given by

$$\text{Rotation of member } CB = \frac{\Delta_{CB}}{l_{CB}} = \frac{\Delta''}{l_2} = \frac{\Delta''}{12}$$

$$\text{Rotation of member } C'B' = \frac{\Delta_{C'B'}}{l_{C'B'}} = \frac{\Delta''}{l_2} = \frac{\Delta''}{12}$$

$$\text{Rotation of member } BB' = \frac{\Delta_2(\tan \phi_1 + \tan \phi_2)}{h_1} = \frac{\Delta''}{l_2}\frac{(h_2 - h_1)}{h_1} = \frac{\Delta''}{12} \times \frac{6}{12} = \frac{\Delta''}{24}$$

$$\text{Rotation of member } BA = \frac{\Delta_{AB}}{l_{AB}} = \frac{\Delta' - \Delta''}{\cos \phi_1} \times \frac{\cos \phi_1}{l_1} = \frac{\Delta' - \Delta''}{l_1} = \frac{\Delta' - \Delta''}{12}$$

$$\text{Rotation of member } B'A' = \frac{\Delta' - \Delta''}{\cos \phi_2} \times \frac{\cos \phi_2}{l_2} = \frac{\Delta' - \Delta''}{l_1} = \frac{\Delta' - \Delta''}{12}$$

$$\text{Rotation of member } AA' = \frac{\Delta_{AA'}}{l_{AA'}} = \frac{\Delta'(\tan \phi_1 + \tan \phi_2)}{h_0}$$

$$= \frac{\Delta'}{h_0}\frac{(h_1 - h_0)}{l_1} = \frac{\Delta'}{6} \times \frac{6}{12} = \frac{\Delta'}{12}$$

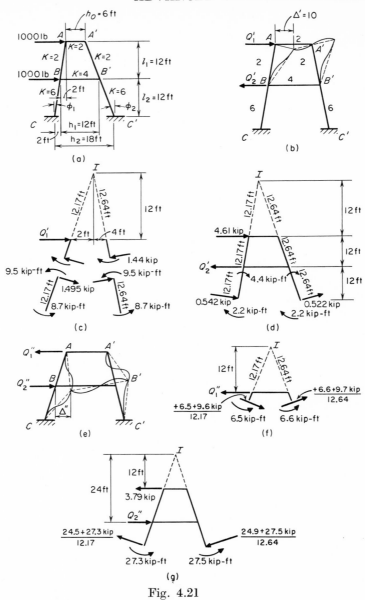

Fig. 4.21

If, now, we assume $\Delta'=10$, $\Delta''=0$ and take $E=1$, we find the following F.E.M.'s,

$$M_{BA} = M_{AB} = -(6)(2)\frac{(10)}{(12)} = -10.0$$

$$M_{B'A'} = M_{A'B'} = -(6)(2)\frac{(10)}{(12)} = -10.0$$

$$M_{AA'} = M_{A'A} = +(6)(2)\frac{(10)}{(12)} = +10.0$$

Solving the structure for these initial F.E.M.'s, we obtain Table 4.6. The last line in this table was filled in after m was obtained at the end of the solution.

TABLE 4.6

	C	B			A		A'		B'			C'
D.F.	B 0	C 0.50	B' 0.333	A 0.167	B 0.50	A' 0.50	A 0.50	B' 0.50	A' 0.167	B 0.333	C' 0.50	B' 0
F.E.M.				-10.0	-10.0	+10.0	+10.0	-10.0	-10.0			
	+2.5	+5.0	+3.3	+1.7	+0.8			+0.7		+1.7		+2.1
		-0.3	+1.4		-0.1	-0.2	-0.4	-0.3	+1.4	+2.8	+4.1	+0.1
		-0.7	-0.5	-0.2	-0.2	-0.3	-0.1		-0.1	-0.2		
					-0.1		+0.1			+0.1	+0.2	
		+0.1										
Σ	+2.2	+4.4	+4.3	-8.7	-9.5	+9.5	+9.5	-9.5	-8.7	+4.3	+4.4	+2.2
$\frac{m\times\Sigma}{1000}$	+0.75	+1.49	+1.46	-2.95	-3.22	+3.22	+3.22	-3.22	-2.95	+1.46	+1.49	+0.75

Now, solving for Q_1' and Q_2' (see Figs. 4.21b, c, and d), we obtain

$$12Q_1' = 2(9.5)+1.495(12.17)+1.44(12.44)$$
$$Q_1' = \frac{55.4}{12} = \overrightarrow{4.61} \text{ kip}$$

and

$$24Q_2' = 55.4+0.542(36.51)+0.522(37.92)-2.2-2.2$$
$$Q_2' = \overleftarrow{3.78} \text{ kip}$$

Now consider the deflection Δ'', see Fig. 4.21e. Assuming $\Delta''=10$, $\Delta'=0$, $E=1$, we obtain the following F.E.M.'s,

$$M_{AB} = M_{BA} = \frac{6K\Delta''}{12} = \frac{6(2)(10)}{12} = +10$$

$$M_{BC} = M_{CB} = -\frac{6(6)(10)}{12} = -30$$

$$M_{A'B'} = M_{B'A'} = \frac{6(2)(10)}{12} = +10$$

$$M_{B'C'} = M_{C'B'} = -\frac{6(6)(10)}{12} = -30$$

$$M_{B'B} = M_{BB'} = \frac{6(4)(10)}{24} = +10$$

Solving the structure for these initial F.E.M.'s, we get the data in Table 4.7. The last line in this table was filled in after n was obtained at the end of the solution.

TABLE 4.7

	C	B			A		A'		B'			C'
D.F.	B 0	C 0.50	B' 0.333	A 0.167	B 0.50	A' 0.50	A' 0.50	B' 0.50	A' 0.167	B 0.333	C' 0.50	B' 0
F.E.M.	− 30	− 30	+10	+10	+10	0	0	+10	+10	+10	−30	− 30
	+ 2.5	+ 5	+ 3.3	+ 1.7	+ 0.8		−2.7		− 1.8	+ 1.7		+ 2.5
	+0.2		+ 1.7	− 2.7	− 5.4	−5.4	−3.6	− 3.7	+ 1.7	+ 3.4	+ 5.0	
		+ 0.5	+ 0.3	+ 0.2	+ 0.1	−1.8	+0.2	+ 0.8	− 0.2	+ 0.1	+ 0.1	
				+ 0.4	+ 0.9	+0.8	−0.5	− 0.5				
						−0.2						
					+ 0.1	+0.1						
Σ	− 27.3	− 24.5	+15.3	+ 9.6	+ 6.5	−6.5	−6.6	+ 6.6	+ 9.7	+15.2	−24.9	−27.5
$\frac{n \times \Sigma}{1000}$	− 4.06	− 3.65	+ 2.28	+ 1.43	+ 0.97	−0.97	−0.98	+ 0.98	+ 1.45	+ 2.26	− 3.70	− 4.10

Now, solving for Q''_1 and Q''_2 (see Figs. 4.21 f and g), we find that

$$Q''_1 = \frac{6.5+6.6+16.1+16.3}{12}$$

$$= \overleftarrow{3.79} \text{ kip}$$

and

$$Q''_2 = \frac{3.79(12)+3(51.8)+3(52.4)}{24}$$

$$= \overrightarrow{15.34} \text{ kip}$$

To determine n and m, we have

$$mQ'_1+nQ''_1 = 1000 \text{ lb}$$
$$mQ'_2+nQ''_2 = 1000 \text{ lb}$$

which give

$$m = +339$$
$$n = +148.8$$

Having these we obtain the final joint moments, using the values in the last rows of Tables 4.6 and 4.7 (all values are in kip-ft).

$$M_{CB} = +0.75-4.06 = -3.31$$
$$M_{BC} = +1.49-3.65 = -2.16$$
$$M_{BB'} = +1.46+2.28 = +3.74$$
$$M_{BA} = -2.95+1.43 = -1.52$$
$$M_{AB} = -3.22+0.97 = -2.25$$

$$M_{AA'} = +3.22 - 0.97 = +2.25$$
$$M_{A'A} = +3.22 - 0.98 = +2.24$$
$$M_{A'B'} = -3.22 + 0.98 = -2.24$$
$$M_{B'A'} = -2.95 + 1.45 = -1.50$$
$$M_{B'B} = +2.26 + 1.46 = +3.72$$
$$M_{B'C'} = +1.49 - 3.70 = -2.21$$
$$M_{C'B'} = +0.75 - 4.10 = -3.35$$

4-12   Secondary stresses in trusses[4]

Although most trusses used in present-day engineering construction are gusseted (rigidly connected) at their joints, it is common practice (because of the ease and simplicity of the analysis) to analyze these as though they were pin connected.   The pin-connected stresses are the so-called *primary stresses*.

This procedure is safe and adequate for light trusses, such as are used in small homes, offices, or similar structures.   However, for heavy, massive highway, railroad, or building trusses, the rigid end connections introduce *secondary stresses* which are frequently of the same order of magnitude as the primary stresses.   These should therefore be considered in the design.   One procedure for obtaining these stresses approximately is the following:

1. Assume pin-connected joints and calculate the primary stresses in the members.

2. By use of the Williot—Mohr diagram, find the panel point deflections corresponding to the primary stresses of Step 1.

3. For any member, the components of its transverse end-point deflections will introduce (assuming completely rigid connections) F.E.M.'s due to translation as given in Equation (4-7).   Compute these.

4. Solve the truss by moment distribution using the F.E.M.'s of Step 3.

These final moments then cause additional joint deflections which cause additional moments, etc.   However, in most practical cases, the moments obtained in Step 4 above are sufficiently accurate and are used for computing the secondary stresses.

4-13   Moment distribution—variable moment of inertia

We obtained for the slope-deflection equations [Chapter 3, Equations (3-11a) and (3-11b)] for sections of variable inertia, $I = I_C \cdot i$,

[4] This subject is discussed in more detail in J. L. Parcel and G. A. Maney, *Statically Indeterminate Stresses*, John Wiley and Sons, New York, 1936.   The book includes additional references and contains an illustrative problem.

$$M_{AB} = \frac{EI_C}{L}[k_{AA}\theta_{AB} + k_{AB}\theta_{BA} - (k_{AA} + k_{AB})\psi_{AB}] + M_{F_{AB}}$$

$$M_{BA} = \frac{EI_C}{L}[k_{AB}\theta_{AB} + k_{BB}\theta_{BA} - (k_{AB} + k_{BB})\psi_{AB}] + M_{F_{BA}}$$

Following ordinary moment distribution procedure, for the rigid frame of Fig. 4.22, we obtain the following.

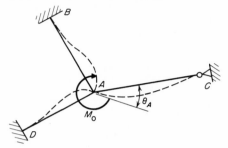

Fig. 4.22

If joint C is fixed,

$$\theta_A = -\frac{M_0}{\left(\dfrac{EI_C k_{AA}}{L}\right)_{AB} + \left(\dfrac{EI_C k_{AA}}{L}\right)_{AC} + \left(\dfrac{EI_C k_{AA}}{L}\right)_{AB}} \qquad (4\text{-}13a)$$

and

$$M_{AB} = -\left(\frac{EI_C k_{AA}}{L}\right)_{AB}\left[\frac{M_0}{\left(\dfrac{EI_C k_{AA}}{L}\right)_{AB} + \left(\dfrac{EI_C k_{AA}}{L}\right)_{AC} + \left(\dfrac{EI_C k_{AA}}{L}\right)_{AD}}\right]$$

$$(4\text{-}13b)$$

Expressions for M_{AC} and M_{AD} can be determined similarly. If joint C is hinged,

$$M_{CA} = 0 = \left(\frac{EI_C}{L}\right)_{AC}(k_{AC}\theta_A + k_{CC}\theta_C)$$

or

$$\theta_C = -\frac{k_{AC}}{k_{CC}}\theta_A$$

and

$$M_{AC} = \left(\frac{EI_C}{L}\right)_{AC}\left[\left(k_{AA} - \frac{k^2_{AC}}{k_{CC}}\right)\theta_A\right]$$

or

$$M_{AC} = \left(\frac{EI_C}{L}k_{AA}\right)_{AC}\left(1 - \frac{k_{AC}}{k_{AA}}\cdot\frac{k_{AC}}{k_{CC}}\right)\theta_A \qquad (4\text{-}14)$$

But, $k_{AC}/k_{AA}=C_{AC}=$ carry-over factor for A to C, and $k_{AC}/k_{CC}=C_{CA}$ = carry-over factor for C to A. Therefore,

$$M_{AC} = \left[\frac{EI_c}{L}k_{AA}(1-C_{AC}C_{CA})\right]_{AC}\cdot\theta_A \qquad (4\text{-}15a)$$

Thus the adjusted stiffness factor for the far end hinged is seen to be

$$k'_{AA} = \frac{EI_c}{L}k_{AA}(1-C_{AC}C_{CA}) \qquad (4\text{-}15b)$$

If I is constant, $C_{AC}=C_{CA}=\frac{1}{2}$ and $k'_{AA}=\frac{EI_c}{L}(\frac{3}{4}k_{AA})$ as before.

In some problems it is helpful to utilize the symmetry or anti-symmetry of the structure. In these cases the following relations hold.

Antisymmetry: For $\theta_C=\theta_A$, as occurs in all antisymmetric cases,

$$M_{AC} = \left(\frac{EI_c}{L}\right)_{AC}\left[(k_{AA}+k_{AC})\right]_{AC}\theta_A$$

$$= \left[\left(\frac{EI_c}{L}\right)k_{AA}\left(1+\frac{k_{AC}}{k_{AA}}\right)\right]_{AC}\theta_A$$

$$M_{AC} = \left[\frac{EI_c}{L}k_{AA}(1+C_{AC})\right]_{AC}\theta_A \qquad (4.16)$$

The adjusted stiffness factor in this case is

$$k''_{AA} = (EI_c/L)k_{AA}(1+C_{AC}) \qquad (4\text{-}17)$$

Symmetry: For $\theta_C=-\theta_A$, as occurs in symmetric cases the adjusted stiffness factor is obtained in a similar manner. It is

$$k'''_{AA} = (EI_c/L)k_{AA}(1-C_{AC}) \qquad (4\text{-}18)$$

The moment distribution procedure for structures of variable moment of inertia is identical to that used for constant sections. It consists of first calculating (or looking up in tables, see Chapter 3) the stiffness factors, the carry-over factors, and the fixed-end moment coefficients, and then distributing moments in the usual manner.

4-14 Continuous beams of variable section

As an illustration of the procedure to be used in solving structures with variable section, we shall solve the following problem.

Example: Solve, by moment distribution, the continuous beam with variable inertia of Fig. 4.23, using the Portland Cement *Handbook of Frame Constants* to obtain the stiffness and carry-over factors and the fixed-end moments. Exclude the weight of the beam from the calculations.

Solution: As the first step, the various coefficients for the two spans,

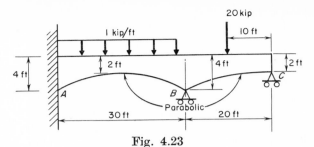

Fig. 4.23

AB and BC, are obtained from the Portland Cement Handbook. These are shown below for the two spans in question,

<table>
<tr><td>Span AB</td><td>Span BC</td></tr>
<tr><td>$a_A = a_B = 0.5$</td><td>$a_B = 1, a_C = 0$</td></tr>
<tr><td>$r_A = r_B = 1$</td><td>$r_B = 1 \quad r_C = 0$</td></tr>
<tr><td>$C_{AB} = C_{BA} = 0.694$</td><td>$C_{BC} = 0.334, C_{CB} = 0.910$</td></tr>
<tr><td>$M_{F_{AB}} = -(0.1025)(1)(30)^2$</td><td>$M_{F_{BC}} = 0.2138\ PL$</td></tr>
<tr><td>$= -92.25$</td><td>$= -85.52$</td></tr>
<tr><td>$M_{F_{BA}} = +(0.1025)(1)(30)^2$</td><td>$M_{F_{CB}} = 0.0742 PL$</td></tr>
<tr><td>$= +92.25$</td><td>$= +29.69$</td></tr>
<tr><td>$k_{AB} = k_{BA} = 12.03$</td><td>$k_{BC} = 14.62, k_{CB} = 5.36$</td></tr>
</table>

Now proceed in the usual way and set up the solution in a tabular form as follows:

TABLE 4.8

	A		B			C
k/L	0	12.03/30 = 0.401	0.731	= 14.62/20		
D.F.	0		0.354	0.646		1
C.O.F.	—		0.694	0.334		0.910
F.E.M.	− 92.3		+ 92.3	− 85.5		+ 29.7
	+ 5.0	×.694		− 27.0	×.910	− 29.7
	+ 0.7		+ 7.2	+ 13.0	×.334	+ 4.4
	+ 0.2			− 4.0	×.910	− 4.4
			+ 1.4	+ 2.6		+ 0.9
				− 0.8		− 0.9
			+ 0.3	+ 0.5		+ 0.2
						− 0.2
Σ	− 86.4		+ 101.2	− 101.2		0

The final moments are

$$M_{AB} = -86.4 \text{ kip-ft} \qquad M_{BC} = -101.2 \text{ kip-ft}$$
$$M_{BA} = +101.2 \text{ kip-ft} \qquad M_{CB} = 0$$

4-15 General solution of the three-span continuous beam with variable moment of inertia

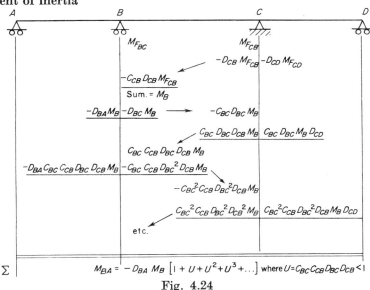

Fig. 4.24

The general solution of the problem of a three-span continuous beam with variable moment of inertia leads to an interesting result.

Denoting fixed-end moments by M_F, distribution factors by D, and carry-over factors by C, we obtain the following final results (see Fig. 4.24 for the complete solution):

If

$$U = C_{BC}C_{CB}D_{BC}D_{CB} \tag{4-19}$$

and

$$M_B = M_{F_{BC}} - C_{CB}D_{CB}M_{F_{CB}} \tag{4-20}$$

we have

$$M_{BA} = -D_{BA}M_B[1 + U + U^2 + \cdots U^n] \tag{4-21}$$

The factor U is necessarily less than unity; so the solution for M_{BA}, Equation (4-21), is an infinite series which converges to the value

$$M_{BA} = \frac{-D_{BA}M_B}{1-U} \tag{4-22a}[1]$$

---

[1] Similar convergent geometric series solutions are derived for continuous beams up to and including four spans (symmetric about the center.) See Continuous Concrete Bridges, Portland Cement Association.

Thus, the final solution becomes

$$M_{BA} = \frac{-D_{BA}(M_{F_{BC}} - C_{CB}D_{CB}M_{F_{CB}})}{1 - U} \qquad (4\text{-}22\text{b})$$

$$M_{BC} = \frac{(1 - D_{BC})(M_{F_{BC}} - C_{CB}D_{CB}M_{F_{CB}})}{1 - U} \qquad (4\text{-}22\text{c})$$

$$M_{CB} = \frac{(1 - D_{CB})(M_{F_{CB}} - C_{BC}D_{BC}M_{F_{BC}})}{1 - U} \qquad (4\text{-}22\text{d})$$

$$M_{CD} = \frac{-D_{CD}(M_{F_{CB}} - C_{BC}D_{BC}M_{F_{BC}})}{1 - U} \qquad (4\text{-}22\text{e})$$

In the above solution $C_{CD} = C_{BA} = 0$ and K_{CD} and K_{BA} are adjusted for hinges at A and D.

Equations (4-22b) through (4-22e) are the final exact solutions of this particular problem. These values will be used in solving the rigid frame problems which follow.

4-16 Rigid frames with variable moment of inertia

The general technique used in solving the rigid frame of variable cross section is the same as that used for constant cross section. The solution for a single-span, two-hinged symmetric frame with un-symmetrical loading will be obtained in general form, as follows:

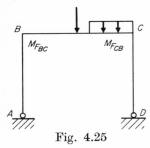

Fig. 4.25

For the two-hinged frame of Fig. 4.25, with sidesway prevented, the results of a primary moment distribution are given in terms of the fixed-end moments at B and C by Equations (4-22b) through (4-22e).

The horizontal reactions at A and D corresponding to this primary distribution can be calculated and are called H'_{AB} and H'_{DC}. These are held in equilibrium by the holding force Q preventing sidesway.

Now introduce sidesway and calculate the corresponding horizontal reactions H''_{AB} and H''_{DC}. From equilibrium

$$H'_{AB} + H'_{DC} + H''_{AB} + H''_{DC} = 0 \qquad (4\text{-}23)$$

and

$$M'_{BA} + M'_{CD} + M''_{BA} + M''_{CD} = 0 \qquad (4\text{-}24)$$

But for a frame symmetric about the center line

$$M''_{BA} = M''_{CD} = -\frac{M'_{BA} + M'_{CD}}{2} \qquad (4\text{-}25)$$

Then the final moment

$$M_{BA} = M'_{BA} + M''_{BA}$$

$$= M'_{BA} - \frac{M'_{BA} + M'_{CD}}{2}$$

or

$$M_{BA} = \frac{M'_{BA} - M'_{CD}}{2} \tag{4-26}$$

and the final moment M_{CD} is

$$M_{CD} = M'_{CD} - \tfrac{1}{2}(M'_{BA} + M'_{CD})$$

or

$$M_{CD} = \frac{-M'_{BA} + M'_{CD}}{2} \tag{4-27}$$

Also, from symmetry

$$C_{BC} = C_{CB}, \quad D_{BC} = D_{CB}, \quad D_{BA} = D_{CD}$$

Thus, from Equations (4-22b) through (4-22e),

$$M'_{BA} = \frac{-D_{BA}(M_{F_{BC}} - C_{BC}D_{BC}M_{F_{CB}})}{1-U}$$

$$M'_{BC} = \frac{(1-D_{CB})(M_{F_{BC}} - C_{BC}D_{BC}M_{F_{CB}})}{1-U}$$

$$M'_{CB} = \frac{(1-D_{CB})(M_{F_{CB}} - C_{BC}D_{BC}M_{F_{BC}})}{1-U}$$

$$M'_{CD} = \frac{-D_{CD}(M_{F_{CB}} - C_{BC}D_{BC}M_{F_{BC}})}{1-U}$$

and using these values in Equation (4-26) and Equation (4-27) we obtain finally

$$M_{BA} = \frac{D_{BA}(1 + C_{BC}D_{BC})(-M_{F_{BC}} + M_{F_{CB}})}{2(1-U)} \tag{4-28}$$

$$M_{CD} = -M_{BA}$$

These are the final moments, the effect of sidesway included.

The following illustrative problem will show the use of these equations.

4-17 Symmetric one-span frame

Example: Moments and thrusts are to be determined on the vertical and horizontal sections at the haunch and at the crown of the frame of Fig. 4.26a. For this purpose values should be determined for points 0, 1, and 5.

(a) Assuming a 9-in. pavement on the structure, determine the dead load moments.

(b) Assuming an H20 live loading,[5] determine the maximum live load moments.

Use *Continuous Concrete Bridges* for carry-over and distribution factors and fixed-end moment coefficients.

Solution:

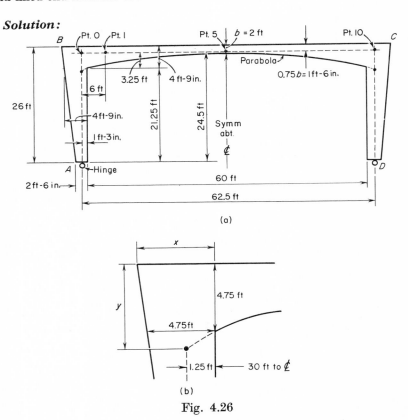

Fig. 4.26

From Fig. 4.26b, the following values are obtained for x and y,

$$\frac{y}{4.75} = \frac{31.25^2}{30^2}$$

or

$$y = 5.16 \text{ ft}, \ y - 2.0 = 3.16 \text{ ft}$$

---

[5] See *Standard Specifications for Highway Bridges*, American Association of State Highway Officials (AASHO), 1949. Also *Continuous Concrete Bridges*, Portland Cement Association, 33 West Grand Avenue, Chicago 10, Ill., 1947.

Similarly,

$$x = 4.75 + \frac{3.25}{21.25} \text{ (3.5)}$$

or

$$x = 5.285 \text{ ft}$$

Then, for the horizontal beam, from the charts in *Continuous Concrete Bridges*,

$$r_{BC} = r_{CB} = \frac{3.16}{2.0} = 1.58$$

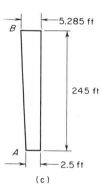

$$C_{BC} = C_{CB} = 0.755$$

$$k_{BC} = k_{CB} = 18.0$$

$$K_{BC} = \frac{kEI_C}{L} = \frac{18E(b)\dfrac{(2^3)}{12}}{62.5}$$

$$= 0.192bE$$

In the same way, for the column (see Fig. 4.26c) we have, $r_A = 0$, $\alpha_A = 0$, $r_B = \dfrac{2.785}{2.5} = 1.113$, $\alpha_B = 1$

so that
$$C_{AB} = 0.869, \quad k_{AB} = 7.16$$
$$C_{BA} = 0.279, \quad k_{BA} = 22.43$$

Fig. 4.26

$$K_{BA} = \frac{kEI}{L} = \frac{22.43\dfrac{(2.5^3)}{12}}{24.5} bE(1 - C_{AB}C_{BA}) = 0.903bE$$

The distribution factors may now be obtained for the two conditions of loading—symmetrical and unsymmetrical. The computations for these are shown below.

$$D_{BC} = \frac{0.192bE}{(0.192 + 0.903)bE}$$

$$= 0.175$$

and

$$D_{BA} = 0.825$$

The solution for the dead load is obtained as follows,

$$M_{BA} = \frac{D_{BA}(1 + C_{BC}D_{BC})(-M_{F_{BC}} + M_{F_{CB}})}{2(1 - U)}$$

where

$$U = C_{BC}C_{CB}D_{BC}D_{CB}$$

Thus,

$$M_{BA} = \frac{0.825(1+0.755\times0.175)(-M_{F_{BC}}+M_{F_{CB}})}{2(1-0.755\times0.175\times0.755\times0.175)}$$

$$= 0.476(-M_{F_{BC}}+M_{F_{CB}})$$

Also,

$$M_{BC} = -M_{BA}$$

Now, the dead load, assuming a 9-in. roadway slab in addition to the arch weight, is as shown in Fig. 4.26d.

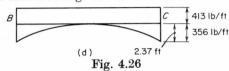

(d)   2.37 ft

Fig. 4.26

The F.E.M. coefficients are (see Fig. 17 of *Continuous Concrete Bridges*):

for uniform load, $-0.1075wL^2$
for parabolic load, $-(0.0172+0.0025)wL^2 = -0.0197wL^2$

Therefore,

$$M_{F_{BC}} = -0.1075(413)(62.5)^2 - 0.0197(356)(62.5)^2$$

$$= -201.4 \text{ kip-ft}$$

and (see Fig. 4.26e) the final dead load moment at point 0 is

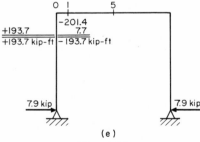

(e)

Fig. 4.26

$$-M_{BC} = +M_{BA} = +193.7 \text{ kip-ft}$$

The dead load moments may now be obtained at points 1 and 5 (the underlined factors used below come from Fig. 17a in *Continuous Concrete Bridges*).

$$M_{D.L.\,1} = -193{,}700 + 413/2\ (62.5)^2(0.1)(0.9) + \underline{(0.0102} + \underline{0.002})(62.5)^2(356)$$

$$= -104 \text{ kip-ft}$$

$$M_{D.L.\,5} = -193{,}700 + 413/2\ (62.5)^2(0.5)(0.5) + \underline{(0.0125} + \underline{0.0125})(62.5)^2(356)$$

$$= +43.1 \text{ kip-ft}$$

The *H*20 live loads are shown in Fig. 4.26f. Using these loadings, we obtain the following moments (see Fig. 4.26g, h, i):

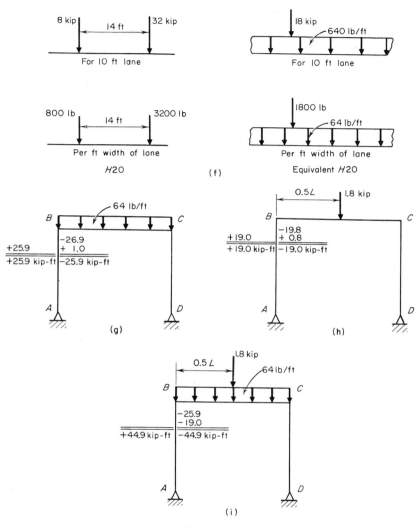

Figs. 4.26

for $w = 64$ lb/ft,

$$\text{F.E.M.} = -\underline{0.1075}(64)(62.5)^2 = -26.9 \text{ kip-ft}$$

and

$$M_{BA} = -M_{BC} = 0.476[-(-26.9)+26.9] = +25.9 \text{ kip-ft}$$

For a concentrated load, 1800 lb, at $0.5L$ for maximum haunch moment (see Figs. 7 and 15 of *Continuous Concrete Bridges*),

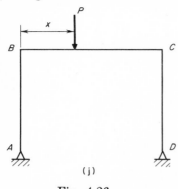

(j)

Fig. 4.26

F.E.M. $= -0.176PL = -19.8$ kip-ft

and now

$$M_{BA} = -M_{BC}$$
$$= 0.476[-(-19.8)+19.8] = +19.0$$

Therefore, for both acting, we have

$$M_{BA} = -M_{BC} = 44.9 \text{ kip-ft}$$

as shown in Fig. 4.26i.

The live load haunch moments for movable load P, see Fig. 4.26j, are obtained using the charts in *Continuous Concrete Bridges* and these are as follows (coefficients are underlined):

for load at $x = 0.1L$, $M_{BA} = -M_{BC} = 0.476(62.5)(P)(\underline{0.0936+0.0046})$

$$= 2.95P$$

$$= 2950 \text{ for } P = 1000$$

for load at $x = 0.2L$, $M_{BA} = -M_{BC} = 5720$

for load at $x = 0.3L$, $M_{BA} = -M_{BC} = 8130$

for load at $x = 0.4L$, $M_{BA} = -M_{BC} = 9920$

for load at $x = 0.5L$, $M_{BA} = -M_{BC} = 10{,}570$

Using these values, we can construct moment diagrams, as shown in Fig. 4.26k, for various positions of the load P. Then we may construct moment influence lines (using the diagrams of Fig. 4.26k). These are shown on Figs. 4.26l and m and represent the influence lines for moments at the haunch point 0, and at points 1 and 5 of Fig. 4.26a.

To illustrate the use of these influence lines, let us determine the maximum moments at points 1 and 5 using the $H20$ truck train loads. (See the AASHO Specifications and pp. 10–11 of *Continuous Concrete Bridges*.) The loading is shown in Fig. 4.26n.

For the maximum at point 1, place one truck on the span, with the 3200-lb load at midspan. Then, from the influence line Fig. 4.26m,

$$M_1 = -[3.2(7.7)+0.8(3.1)] = -27.2 \text{ kip-ft}$$

If we use the equivalent loading, we get

$$M_1 = -25.9+(64/2)(62.5)^2(0.1)(0.9)-1.8(7.7)$$

$$= -28.52 \text{ kip-ft}$$

For the maximum moment at point 5, place two trucks on the span, with the 3200-lb load at midspan. Then, from the influence line Fig. 4.26m,

$$M_5 = [0.8(1.0)+3.2(5.1)+0.8(0.7)] = +17.68 \text{ kip-ft}$$

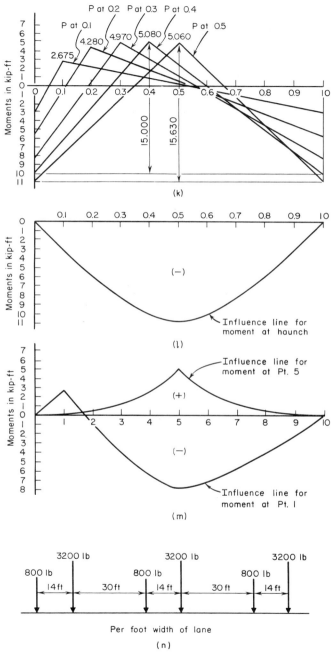

Fig. 4.26

If we use equivalent loading, we get

$$M_5 = -25.9 + 64/2 \ (62.5)^2(0.5)(0.5) + 1.8(5.1) = +14.48 \text{ kip-ft}$$

4-18   Cambered rigid frames—approximate method of solution

Many rigid frame bridges have cambered horizontal members, i.e., curved center lines for the horizontal beam portions of the frames as shown in Fig. 4.27.

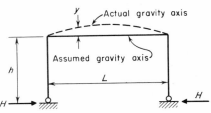

Fig. 4.27

An approximate procedure for including the effect of the curvature is given in the following step-by-step outline of the method of solution.

STEP 1.   Solve the rigid frame assuming a straight line gravity axis for the cambered member. H will be the horizontal reaction for this case.

STEP 2.   Let the true horizontal reaction be $H' = H - \Delta H$.   The approximate corrections necessary to be applied to Step 1 are moments of value $H'y$, which may be assumed as produced by a fictitious uniform loading w_C such that

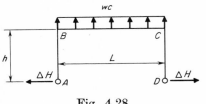

Fig. 4.28

$$\frac{w_C L^2}{8} = H'y_{\max} = (H - \Delta H)y_{\max}$$

from which

$$w_C = \frac{8(H - \Delta H)}{L^2} y_{\max} \quad (4\text{-}29)$$

STEP 3.   Solve by moment distribution the structure of Fig. 4.28. First, find the F.E.M.'s,

$$M_{F_{BC}} = \text{(tabulated coefficient) } w_C L^2$$
$$= \text{(tabulated coefficient) } (y_{\max})(H - \Delta H)(8)$$

Then

$$\Delta H = \frac{-D_{BA}M_{F_{BC}}}{h} = -\frac{D_{BA} \text{ (tabulated coefficient)}(8y_{\max})(H - \Delta H)}{h}$$

or

$$\Delta H = -\frac{8D_{BA} \text{ (tabulated coefficient)}y_{\max}H}{h + 8D_{BA} \text{ (tabulated coefficient)}y_{\max}} \quad (4\text{-}30)$$

All quantities on the right-hand side of Equation (4-31) are known. Thus, a first-order approximation to the correction to H, given by ΔH, may be obtained. Knowing ΔH, the first-order corrected moments are then equal to

$$M_0 + (\Delta H)(h + y)$$

where M_0 are those moments obtained in Step 1.

Problems

1. Solve by moment distribution.

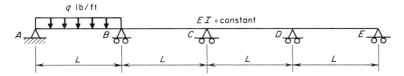

2. Same as problem 1 except the uniform load is on span BC.
3. Obtain the solution of the beam of problem 1 if the load is continuous over all four spans by superposition of the solutions of problems 1 and 2.
4. Solve by moment distribution.

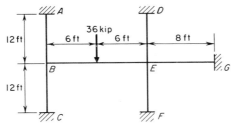

EI is the same for all members

5. Solve by moment distribution. Take advantage of symmetry.

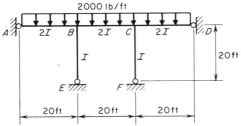

6. Solve by moment distribution.

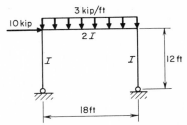

7. Solve by moment distribution.

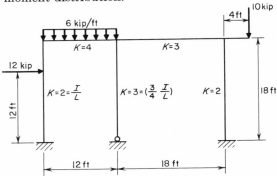

8. Solve by moment distribution.   Use antisymmetric relations.

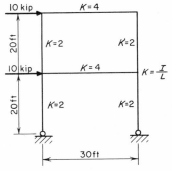

9. Solve by moment distribution.

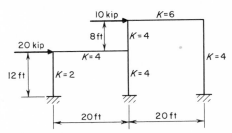

10. Solve by moment distribution.

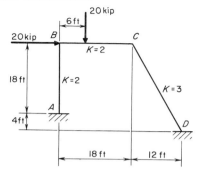

11. Solve by moment distribution.

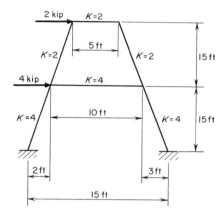

12. Dimensions are same as for problem 10. Solve by moment distribution.

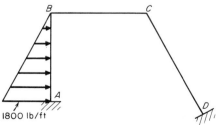

13. Solve by moment distribution. Hint: For sidesway relationships, show

$$x = \frac{\Delta_2 \cos \alpha_2 + \Delta_1 \cos \alpha_1 \left[\cos (\alpha_1 + \alpha_2)\right]}{\sin (\alpha_1 + \alpha_2)} + \Delta_1 \sin \alpha_1$$

$$y = \frac{\Delta_1 \cos \alpha_1 + \Delta_2 \cos \alpha_2 \left[\cos (\alpha_1 + \alpha_2)\right]}{\sin (\alpha_1 + \alpha_2)} + \Delta_2 \sin \alpha_2$$

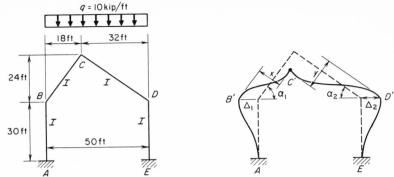

14. Solve for the moment at B using moment distribution.

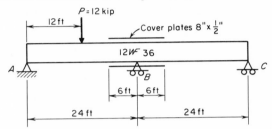

15. Determine the moment diagram for the continuous beam with parabolic haunches shown.

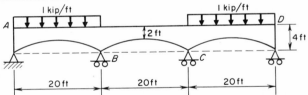

16. Determine the change in end moment that will be produced in the beam of problem 15 if support B settles an amount $\Delta = \frac{1}{8}$ in.

17. Solve by moment distribution.

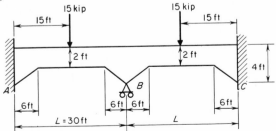

18. For the two-hinged concrete frame shown:

(a) Assuming a 9-in. pavement on the structure determine the dead load moments.

(b) Determine the moments for a 10-kip load at the 0.2 span, 0.4 span, and midspan.

(c) Calculate the end moments for a temperature drop of 80°F. The coefficient of linear thermal expansion is $6 \times 10^{-6}/°F$ and $E = 2.5 \times 10^6$ lb/in.^{2}.

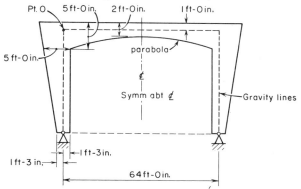

19. Find the moment at B and at the center of span BC for a load of 10 kips at: (a) the center of span BC; (b) the point E.

Calculate the dead load moments if the frame is made of concrete weighing 150 lb/cu ft.

Calculate the end moments for all members for a temperature rise of 60°. Use temperature coefficient and modulus of elasticity values given in problem 18.

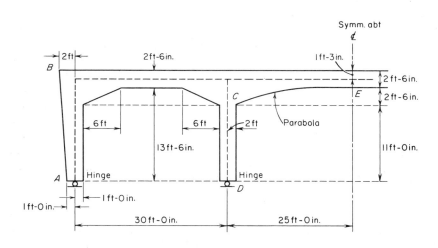

Chapter 5

THE ELASTIC ARCH

5-1 Introduction

The arch is a fundamental structural unit, and as such it is used in structures in all engineering fields. First, we will discuss the general approximate analysis of arches considering them as essentially thick curved beams. The unit load and elastic center methods of arch analysis will then be described and, as illustrative examples, fixed-ended and two-hinged arches will be solved. Finally, the more exact *deflection theory* of arch analysis will be discussed.

5-2 General theory of arch analysis

Let us consider the effect of a load P applied to an elastic arch with built-in support conditions at the abutments. The reactions are shown in Fig. 5.1a and the arch is evidently statically indeterminate to the third degree.

In order to derive the energy equations used in determining the reactions, shears, and moments, it is necessary to set up the equilibrium and deformation equations for a thick curved bar. The theory of curved bars was developed by Winkler in 1858. An outline of this theory follows.

It will be assumed in developing the thick curved bar equations that Navier's hypothesis holds, i.e., that a plane section before bending remains plane after bending, that the cross section of the arch is symmetric with respect to the loading plane, that Hooke's Law applies, and that the deformations are small enough so that the values of the stresses and moments are not materially affected by these deformations.

As shown in Fig. 5.1c, the normal force N is positive if tensile, the moment M is positive if tension is on the inside of the bar, and the shear V is positive if it produces clockwise moment about any point within the free body. ρ is the radius to the centroidal axis of the cross section. Due to the load N, the face DE rotates through an angle $\dfrac{\Delta ds}{\rho}$. Due to the moment M, this face rotates through an angle

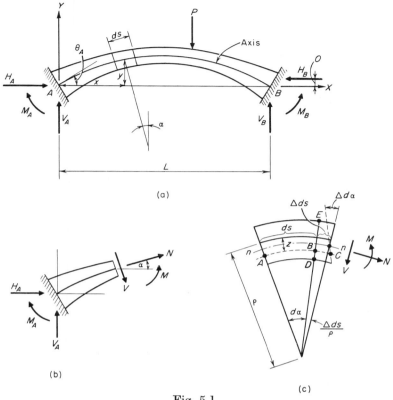

Fig. 5.1

$\Delta d\alpha$ in the opposite direction. z is assumed positive when measured inward toward the center of curvature of the member.

A fiber AB has an original length given by

$$AB = (\rho - z)d\alpha$$

The increase in length of fiber AB due to the loads shown is

$$BC = (\rho - z)\frac{\Delta ds}{\rho} + z\Delta d\alpha$$

Using Hooke's Law, the stress on the element AB is given by

$$\sigma = E(\text{unit strain}) = E\left(\frac{\text{change in length of } AB}{\text{original length of } AB}\right)$$

That is,

$$\sigma = E\frac{\dfrac{\rho - z}{\rho}\Delta ds + z\Delta d\alpha}{(\rho - z)d\alpha}$$

or

$$\sigma = \frac{E}{\rho}\frac{\Delta ds}{d\alpha} + \frac{Ez}{\rho - z}\frac{\Delta d\alpha}{d\alpha} \tag{5-1}$$

Then

$$M = \int_{\text{area}} \sigma z dA \tag{5-2}$$

and

$$N = \int_{\text{area}} \sigma dA \tag{5-3}$$

Substituting the expression for σ in the integral Equation (5-2), we obtain

$$M = \int_A \left[\frac{E}{\rho}\frac{\Delta ds}{d\alpha} + \frac{Ez}{\rho - z}\frac{\Delta d\alpha}{d\alpha}\right] z dA$$

If we take out of the integral those factors which do not vary with z,

$$M = \frac{E}{\rho}\frac{\Delta ds}{d\alpha}\int_A z dA + E\frac{\Delta d\alpha}{d\alpha}\int_A \frac{z^2}{\rho - z}dA$$

But $\int_A z dA = 0$, since z is measured from an axis through the center of gravity of the cross section; hence,

$$\frac{\Delta d\alpha}{d\alpha} = \frac{M}{E\int_A \dfrac{z^2}{\rho - z}dA} \tag{5-2a}$$

from which

$$\Delta d\alpha = \frac{M ds}{E\rho\int_A \dfrac{z^2}{\rho - z}dA} \tag{5-2b}$$

Since

$$\frac{z^2}{\rho - z} = -z + \frac{\rho z}{\rho - z}$$

it follows that

$$\int_A \frac{z^2}{\rho - z}dA = -\int_A z dA + \rho\int_A \frac{z}{\rho - z}dA = \rho\int_A \frac{z}{\rho - z}dA$$

Then substituting this in Equation (5-2a), we obtain

$$\frac{\Delta d\alpha}{d\alpha} = \frac{M}{E\rho\int_A \dfrac{z}{\rho - z}dA} \tag{5-2c}$$

Solving for the thrust N in the same way, we find that

$$N = \int_A \sigma dA = \int_A \left[\frac{E}{\rho} \frac{\Delta ds}{d\alpha} + \frac{Ez}{\rho - z} \frac{\Delta d\alpha}{d\alpha} \right] dA$$

or

$$N = \frac{E}{\rho} \frac{\Delta ds}{d\alpha} \int_A dA + E \frac{\Delta d\alpha}{d\alpha} \int_A \frac{z}{\rho - z} dA$$

or

$$N = \frac{EA}{\rho} \frac{\Delta ds}{d\alpha} + E \frac{\Delta d\alpha}{d\alpha} \int_A \frac{z}{\rho - z} dA$$

Substituting Equation (5-2c) into the above gives

$$N = \frac{EA}{\rho} \frac{\Delta ds}{d\alpha} + \frac{M}{\rho}$$

from which

$$\frac{\Delta ds}{d\alpha} = \frac{N\rho}{EA} - \frac{M}{EA} \tag{5-3a}$$

or

$$\Delta ds = \left(\frac{N}{EA} - \frac{M}{EA\rho} \right) ds \tag{5-3b}$$

Using Equations (5-2a) and (5-3a) in Equation (5-1), we obtain for the stress on any fiber

$$\sigma = \frac{N}{A} - \frac{M}{\rho A} + \frac{Ez}{\rho - z} \cdot \frac{M}{E \int_A \frac{z^2}{\rho - z} dA}$$

or

$$\sigma = \frac{N}{A} - \frac{M}{\rho A} + \frac{Mz}{(\rho - z)I'} \tag{5-4}$$

where

$$I' = \int_A \frac{z^2}{\rho - z} dA \tag{5-5}$$

At the centroid of the area $(z = 0)$

$$\sigma = \frac{N}{A} - \frac{M}{\rho A} \tag{5-4a}$$

If $N = 0$, then $\sigma = -M/\rho A$. This shows that the stress is not zero at the centroid due to a pure bending load. Furthermore, the variation of σ with z is not linear but is hyperbolic in accordance with Equation (5-4). Also, the neutral axis $n - n$ for the pure bending case (line of $\sigma = 0$) is closer to the center of curvature than the centroidal axis (see Fig. 5.1c).

The strain energy of an element of an elastic curved bar, neglecting shear deformations (see Fig. 5.1c), is

$$dV = \frac{1}{2}\left[N \cdot \Delta ds - M \cdot \left(\frac{\Delta ds}{\rho} - \Delta d\alpha\right)\right]$$

But Δds is the elongation of the middle fiber of the bar, which equals the stress at the middle fiber times ds/E. Using Equation (5-4a), this gives

$$\Delta ds = \left(\frac{N}{A} - \frac{M}{\rho A}\right)\frac{ds}{E} = \left(N - \frac{M}{\rho}\right)\frac{ds}{AE}$$

and

$$\frac{\Delta d\alpha}{ds} = \frac{1}{\rho}\frac{\Delta d\alpha}{d\alpha} = \frac{1}{\rho}\frac{M}{EI'}$$

Substituting these in the expression for dV, we obtain

$$dV = \frac{1}{2}\left[\left(N^2 - 2\frac{NM}{\rho} + \frac{M^2}{\rho^2}\right)\frac{ds}{AE} + \frac{M^2}{\rho EI'}\,ds\right] \qquad (5\text{-}6)$$

The total strain energy of the bar is obtained by integrating Equation (5-6) with respect to s

$$V = \frac{1}{2}\int_s\left[\left(N^2 - 2\frac{NM}{\rho} + \frac{M^2}{\rho^2}\right)\frac{1}{AE} + \frac{M^2}{\rho EI'}\right]ds \qquad (5\text{-}6a)$$

When the radius exceeds five times the depth of the bar which is almost always the case for the structural arch, the following approximations can be made.

$$\rho I' = \rho \int_A \frac{z^2}{\rho - z}\,dA \approx \int_A z^2 dA = I \qquad (5\text{-}7)$$

or

$$\sigma = \frac{N}{A} + \frac{Mz}{I} \qquad (5\text{-}8)$$

and

$$V = \frac{1}{2}\int_s\left(\frac{N^2}{EA} + \frac{M^2}{EI}\right)ds \qquad (5\text{-}9)$$

Equation (5-9) is seen to be the same as the one used in the rigid frame analysis and it may be used to solve the problem of the statically indeterminate elastic arch, using any of the applicable methods described in Chapter 2. One such method is discussed in the following article.

5-3   The statically indeterminate arch

The resultant axial force N, shear V, and internal bending moment M acting on any section through the arch are shown in Fig. 5.1b.

Applying the superposition procedure of Chapter 2 to the horizontal, vertical, and rotational displacements of the support A, we can write three simultaneous equations in terms of the unknown redundant reactions M_A, H_A, and V_A. If we use the dummy load procedure of applying unit horizontal and vertical loads and unit moment at A and ignoring shear deformations, these equations become

$$H_A\left[\int y^2\frac{ds}{EI}+\int\frac{u^2ds}{AE}\right]+V_A\left[\int xy\frac{ds}{EI}+\int\frac{uvds}{AE}\right]$$

$$+M_A\left[\int y\frac{ds}{EI}+\int\frac{uds}{AE}\right]+\left[\int\frac{M_Pyds}{EI}+\int\frac{N_Puds}{AE}\right]=0 \quad (5\text{-}9a)$$

$$H_A\left[\int xy\frac{ds}{EI}+\int\frac{uvds}{AE}\right]+V_A\left[\int x^2\frac{ds}{EI}+\int\frac{v^2ds}{AE}\right]$$

$$+M_A\left[\int x\frac{ds}{EI}+\int\frac{vds}{AE}\right]+\left[\int\frac{M_Pxds}{EI}+\int\frac{N_Pvds}{AE}\right]=0 \quad (5\text{-}9b)$$

$$H_A\left[\int y\frac{ds}{EI}+\int\frac{uds}{AE}\right]+V_A\left[\int x\frac{ds}{EI}+\int\frac{vds}{AE}\right]$$

$$+M_A\left[\int\frac{ds}{EI}+\int\frac{ds}{AE}\right]+\left[\int\frac{M_Pds}{EI}+\int\frac{N_Pds}{AE}\right]=0 \quad (5\text{-}9c)$$

where

M_P = moment at any section due to the given loads, with redundants removed.

N_P = axial thrust at any section due to the given loads, with redundants removed.

u = axial thrust at any section due to a unit horizontal load at $A\leftarrow$.

v = axial thrust at any section due to a unit vertical load at $A\uparrow$.

A = area of any section.

I = moment of inertia of any section, about the neutral (centroidal) axis.

E = modulus of elasticity of the material.

For arches with low rise to span ratios (so-called flat arches), the reactions can be determined with sufficient accuracy by neglecting the terms in Equations (5-9) containing v, and u can be taken as unity.

For the two-hinged arch, the problem reduces to a statically indeterminate structure of the first degree. If H_A is taken as the redundant, it may be found by solving the equation

$$H_A\cdot\left[\int y^2\frac{ds}{EI}+\int\frac{u^2ds}{AE}\right]+\left[\int\frac{M_Pyds}{EI}+\int\frac{N_Puds}{AE}\right]=0 \quad (5\text{-}10)$$

In Equations (5-9) and (5-10), the variation in the coordinates x and y of any point on the axis of the arch due to the deflection of the arch under load is ignored. When this assumption leads to serious errors, it is necessary to consider the deflections in setting up the superposition equations. This will be considered in the latter part of this chapter when the Deflection Theory of Arches will be presented.

5-4 Elastic center analysis, flat arches

By shifting the origin of coordinates to the elastic center of the arch (see Chapter 2), Equations (5-9) are greatly simplified and become, for unit loads applied as shown in Figs. 5.2a, b, c,

$$H\left[\int y^2 \frac{ds}{EI} + \int \frac{\cos^2\alpha\, ds}{AE}\right] + \int \frac{M_P y\, ds}{EI} = 0 \qquad (5\text{-}11a)$$

$$V\int \frac{x^2 ds}{EI} + \int M_P x \frac{ds}{EI} = 0 \qquad (5\text{-}11b)$$

$$M\int \frac{ds}{EI} + \int \frac{M_P ds}{EI} = 0 \qquad (5\text{-}11c)$$

In the above equations, terms containing N and v have been omitted because the effect of these terms is small. Note that $u = \cos \alpha$.

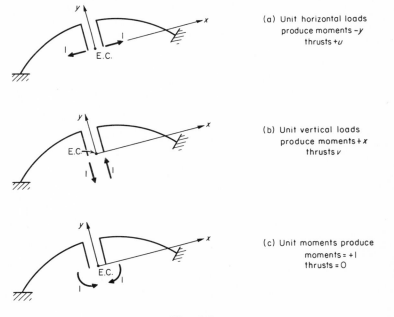

(a) Unit horizontal loads produce moments $-y$ thrusts $+u$

(b) Unit vertical loads produce moments $+x$ thrusts v

(c) Unit moments produce moments $= +1$ thrusts $= 0$

Fig. 5.2

In the development of the superposition Equations (5-9), the redundants could have been considered the thrust N, the shear V, and the moment M at the crown. The deflection components would then be the tangential separation, the transverse (shear) separation, and the relative rotations between the two sections. If pairs of unit tangential and transverse loads and a pair of opposite unit moments are used, equations identical to Equations (5-9) would result. This demonstration is left to the student. In the elastic center procedure, Equations (5-11) result from using unit loads at the elastic center as shown in Figs. 5.2a, b, c. The redundants found by the elastic center method will be oriented the same as the unit loads if positive, opposite if negative.

For a symmetric arch, the principal axes will be vertical and horizontal and consequently V_A and H_A will be vertical and horizontal.

5-5 Flat arches—evaluation of integrals

In the usual practical case, exact evaluation of the integrals of Equations (5-11) becomes impossible, since A and I vary and M_P is usually a function of both x and y. Use of an approximate numerical procedure therefore becomes necessary. The usual method is to divide the arch into a finite number of sections each of length Δs, to evaluate the contribution to each integral of each section, and to add the results. The larger the number of subdivisions, the closer will the summations approach the integral. An illustration of this procedure is given in Art. 5-7.

5-6 Influence lines for vertical loads

Influence lines for H_A, V_A, and M_A (or H_B, V_B, and M_B) will enable the designer to calculate arch reactions for any specified load or combinations thereof. Fig. 5.3 shows an arch with unit loads applied at the elastic center. The influence lines for H_B, V_B, and M_B are obtained as follows.

By the Law of Reciprocal Deflections one may verify the relations shown in Fig. 5.3. Let

$$\eta_H = +\delta_{XW}, \quad \eta_V = +\delta_{YW}, \quad \eta_M = +\theta_W$$

Writing the superposition equations for the fixed arch (Fig. 5.3e), we obtain:

$$H\delta_{XH} + \delta_{XW} = 0$$
$$V\delta_{YV} + \delta_{YW} = 0$$
$$M\theta_M + \theta_W = 0$$

from which

$$H = -\frac{\delta_{XW}}{\delta_{XH}} = -\frac{\eta_H}{\delta_{XH}}$$

$$V = -\frac{\delta_{YW}}{\delta_{YV}} = -\frac{\eta_V}{\delta_{YV}} \left.\right\} \qquad (5\text{-}12)$$

$$M = -\frac{\theta_W}{\theta_M} = -\frac{\eta_M}{\theta_M}$$

where

$$\delta_{XH} = \int y^2 \frac{ds}{EI} + \int \frac{ds}{AE} = I_{X'X'} + \int \frac{ds}{AE} \qquad (5\text{-}12a)$$

$$\delta_{YV} = \int x^2 \frac{ds}{EI} = I_{Y'Y'} \qquad (5\text{-}12b)$$

$$\theta_M = \int \frac{ds}{EI} \qquad (5\text{-}12c)$$

The student should note particularly that the signs of all quantities are consistent in Fig. 5.3 and Equations (5-12).

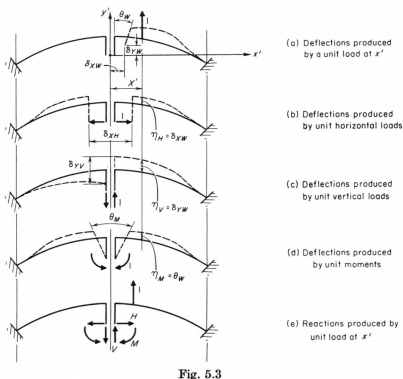

(a) Deflections produced by a unit load at x'

(b) Deflections produced by unit horizontal loads

(c) Deflections produced by unit vertical loads

(d) Deflections produced by unit moments

(e) Reactions produced by unit load at x'

Fig. 5.3

It is seen that the terms in Equations (5-12) are properties of the ds/EI areas which can be computed by the incremental procedure outlined in Art. 5-5 and illustrated in the next article. To compute the influence ordinates η_H, η_V, η_M, the use of the conjugate beam is convenient. That this method may be used is shown in the following:

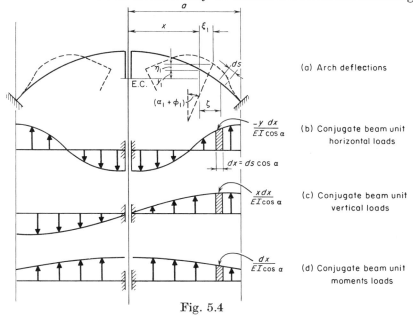

(a) Arch deflections

(b) Conjugate beam unit horizontal loads

(c) Conjugate beam unit vertical loads

(d) Conjugate beam unit moments loads

Fig. 5.4

Let any point on the arch axis be located by coordinates x_1 and y_1, as shown on Fig. 5.4a. Let α_1 be the vertical angle to this point. After loads are applied, let ξ_1 and η_1 be the horizontal and vertical displacements of the point in question. Let ϕ_1 be the change in vertical angle due to the bending deformations. The rotational deformation of a differential element of length ds is (see Equations (5-2b) and (5-7))*

$$\Delta d\alpha - \frac{\Delta ds}{\rho} = \frac{m}{EI'}\, d\alpha - \frac{\Delta ds}{\rho} = \frac{mds}{EI'\rho} - \frac{\Delta ds}{\rho} \approx \frac{mds}{EI} \qquad (5\text{-}13)$$

from which the approximate total rotational deformation of a normal to the elastic curve at point x_1, y_1 is

$$\sum(\Delta d\alpha) = \phi_1 = \int_{x_1}^{a} \frac{mds}{EI} \qquad (5\text{-}13\text{a})$$

---

* In Equation (5-13), the final form is obtained by assuming that the rotation of the cross-section due to the normal load is much less than the rotation due to the moment.

or $\sum(\Delta d\alpha)$ = area under the $\dfrac{m}{EI \cos \alpha}$ diagram between x_1 and a

= shear in the conjugate beam at x_1.

The vertical displacement of point x_1, y_1, due to the bending deformation of a single element ds located a distance ζ from the point is

$$d\eta_1 = \zeta d\phi = \zeta \frac{mds}{EI}$$

Then

$$\eta_1 = \int_0^{a-x_1} \frac{\zeta m dx}{EI \cos \alpha}$$

Since $\zeta = x - x_1$, then $d\zeta = dx$ and

$$\eta_1 = \int_0^{a-x_1} \frac{\zeta m d\zeta}{EI \cos \alpha} \tag{5-14}$$

or η_1 = moment of area of $\dfrac{m}{EI \cos \alpha}$ diagram about point x_1, y_1. This is the moment in the conjugate beam at x_1, y_1.

Thus, to find the influence ordinates η_H, η_V, η_M, we see that we need only find the moment in each of the conjugate beams of Fig. 5.4b, c, and d. For this purpose the conjugate beam loads can be replaced by a series of concentrated loads usually obtained by dividing the span of the conjugate beam into a number of increments of length Δx. The loads will then be the average ordinate times Δx and will yield an approximate solution. If a closer approximation is desired, better results can be obtained by using Simpson's Parabolic Rule.[1]

5-7 Illustrative problem—symmetrical arch analysis by elastic center method

The equation of the axis of a symmetrical arch is $\left(\dfrac{x}{40}\right)^2 + \left(\dfrac{y}{20}\right)^2 = 1$.
Assuming that the depth of the arch varies uniformly with x from 2 feet at the crown to 4 feet at either abutment, find the influence lines for the moment and the vertical and horizontal reactions at A. For computations, divide the arch into 8 segments of equal horizontal projection.

[1] See S. Timoshenko and D. H. Young, *Theory of Structures*, McGraw-Hill Book Company, New York, 1945, p. 451.

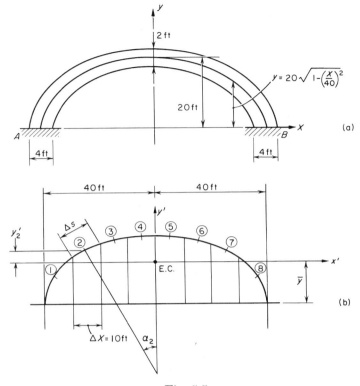

Fig. 5.5

It will first be necessary to locate the elastic center and to calculate the sectional properties. We have

$$I_{X'X'} = \int y'^2 \frac{ds}{EI} \doteq \sum y'^2 \frac{\Delta x}{EI \cos \alpha}$$

$$I_{Y'Y'} = \int x^2 \frac{ds}{EI} \doteq \sum x^2 \frac{\Delta x}{EI \cos \alpha}$$

$$\int \frac{ds}{EI} \doteq \sum \frac{\Delta x}{EI \cos \alpha}$$

$$\int \frac{ds}{AE} \doteq \sum \frac{\Delta x}{AE \cos \alpha}$$

By symmetry, the elastic center is on the y axis, and the principal axis x' is at right angles to it or parallel to the x axis. Computations will be made for an arch strip one foot wide. The vertical angle α will be computed for a point on the axis in the middle of each

TABLE 5.1

Col.	1	2	3	4	5	6	7	8	9	10	11
Point	$x = x'$, ft	y, ft	α	I, ft^4	$\dfrac{\Delta x}{I \cos \alpha} = \dfrac{\Delta s}{I}$	$y\dfrac{\Delta s}{I}$	$y' = y - \bar{y}$	$y'^2\dfrac{\Delta s}{I}$	$x'^2\dfrac{\Delta s}{I}$	A	$\dfrac{\Delta s}{A}$
1	−35	9.6825	42°–6.2′	4.406	3.0592	29.6207	−7.8090	186.5512	3747.5200	3.750	3.593
2	−25	15.6124	21°–49.0′	2.861	3.7648	58.7776	−1.8791	13.2935	2353.0000	3.250	3.314
3	−15	18.5404	11°–26.1′	1.740	5.8617	108.6782	1.0489	6.4490	1318.8825	2.750	3.709
4	−5	19.8431	3°–36′	0.949	10.5585	209.5133	2.3516	58.3885	263.9625	2.250	4.452
5	5	19.8431	−3°–36′	0.949	10.5585	209.5133	2.3516	58.3885	263.9625	2.250	4.452
6	15	18.5404	−11°–26.1′	1.740	5.8617	108.6782	1.0489	6.4490	1318.8825	2.750	3.709
7	25	15.6124	−21°–49.0′	2.861	3.7648	58.7776	−1.8791	13.2935	2353.0000	3.250	3.314
8	35	9.6825	−42°–6.2′	4.406	3.0592	29.6207	−7.8090	186.5512	3747.5200	3.750	3.593
Σ					46.4884	813.1636		529.3644	15366.73		30.136

$$\bar{y} = \frac{813.1636}{46.4884} = 17.4915$$

TABLE 5.2

(Structure Symmetrical about Center Line)

1	2	3	4*	5	6	7	8*	9	10	11	12*	13
		Unit Horizontal Load				Unit Vertical Load				Unit Moment		
Point	$-y'\dfrac{\Delta s}{I}$	$\phi_i = \sum 2$	$\Delta\eta_H = \phi_i\Delta x$	$\eta_H = \sum 4$	$x\dfrac{\Delta s}{I}$	$\phi_i = \sum 6$	$\Delta\eta_{IV} = \phi_i\Delta x$	$\eta_{IV} = \sum 8$	$\dfrac{\Delta s}{I}$	$\phi_i = \sum 10$	$\Delta\eta_M = \phi_i\Delta x$	$\eta_M = \sum 12$
8	23.8892	0	119.50	0	107.0720	0	535.35	0	3.0592	0	15.296	0
		23.89		119.50		107.07		535.35		3.06		15.29
7	7.0744		274.25		94.1200		1541.30		3.7648		49.416	
		30.96		393.75		201.19		2076.65		6.82		64.71
6	− 6.1483		278.89		87.9255		2451.55		5.8617		97.548	
		24.82		672.65		289.12		4528.20		12.69		162.26
5	−24.8293		124.10		52.7925		3155.15		10.5585		179.649	
		0		796.75		341.91		7683.35		23.24		341.91

* Incremental areas calculated by trapezoidal rules.

increment Δs. These points are labeled 1, 2, 3, etc., in Fig. 5.5b. The coordinates of these points are shown in Table 5.1. To get α,

$$\tan \alpha = \text{slope of ellipse} = -\frac{x}{80} \frac{1}{\sqrt{1 - \left(\dfrac{x}{40}\right)^2}}$$

Since E is constant throughout and cancels, it is left out of all the computations.

Table 5.1 is a tabular computation for the section properties described above. The various column headings are self-explanatory.

We now use the conjugate procedure outlined in Art. 5-4 to obtain the influence lines for the redundants at the elastic center. The computations are shown in Table 5.2.

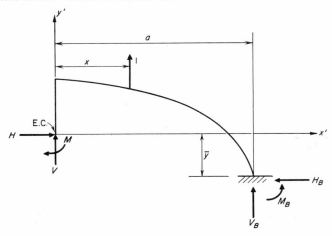

Fig. 5.6

With η_H, η_V, and η_M known from Table 5.2, H, V, and M can be calculated for a unit load at points 5, 6, 7, and 8. The reactions H_B, V_B, and M_B are then known from the equations of equilibrium (see Fig. 5.6).

$$H_B = H \tag{5-15}$$

$$V_B = -V, \quad \text{(load to left of E.C.)} \tag{5-16a}$$

$$V_B = -V - 1, \quad \text{(load to right of E.C.)} \tag{5-16b}$$

$$M_B = M + Va + H\bar{y}, \quad \text{(load to left of E.C.)} \tag{5-17a}$$

$$M_B = M + Va + H\bar{y} + 1(a - x), \quad \text{(load to right of E.C.)} \tag{5-17b}$$

Computations for H, V, M, H_B, V_B, and M_B are shown in Table 5.3, in which

$$H_B = -\frac{\eta_H}{\delta_{XH}}, \quad V = -\frac{\eta_V}{\delta_{YV}}, \quad M = -\frac{\eta_M}{\theta_M}$$

$$\delta_{YV} = \sum \frac{x^2 \Delta s}{I} = 15366.73$$

$$\delta_{XH} = \sum y'^2 \frac{\Delta s}{I} + \sum \frac{\Delta s}{A} = 559.50$$

$$\theta_M = \sum \frac{\Delta s}{I} = 46.4884$$

TABLE 5.3

Point	$a - x$	$H = H_B$	V	V_B	M	$+ Va$	$+ H\bar{y}$	M_B
	0	0	0	-1.00	0	0	0	0
8								
	10	-0.2135	-0.0348	-0.9652	-0.3289	-1.392	-3.734	$+4.544$
7								
	20	-0.7037	-0.1351	-0.8649	-1.3919	-5.404	-12.309	$+0.895$
6								
	30	-1.2022	-0.2946	-0.7054	-3.4903	-11.784	-21.028	-6.306
5								
	40	-1.4240	0.5000	-0.5000	-7.3548	$+20.00$	-24.908	-12.262
4								
	50	-1.2022	0.2946	-0.2946	-3.4903	$+11.784$	-21.028	-12.734
3								
	60	-0.7037	0.1351	-0.1351	-1.3919	$+5.404$	-12.309	-8.296
2								
	70	-0.2135	0.0348	-0.0348	-0.3289	$+1.392$	-3.734	-2.671
1								
	80	0	0	0	0	0	0	0

Influence lines for H_B, M_B, and V_B may now be plotted and are shown in Fig. 5.7. These represent the solution to the problem.

Note that the signs of the curves correspond to a vertical load acting upward. If the load acts downward, the opposite sign must be used.

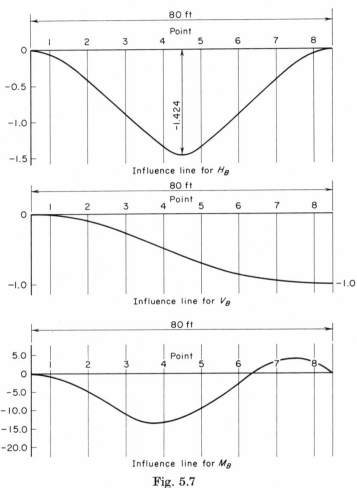

Fig. 5.7

5-8 Shear, thrust, and moment at any section of the arch

The vertical force F_X, horizontal force H_X, and the moment M_X at any section of the arch can now be found for any given load.

Referring to Fig. 5.8, we obtain by applying the equations of equilibrium.

$$H_X = H_B \tag{5-18}$$

$$F_X = -V_B - \sum(\text{loads acting on free body, positive load up}) \tag{5-19}$$

$F_X = -V_B + wx$,   (if the loading is uniform downward)   (5-20)

$M_X = M_B + V_B x - H_B y +$ (moment of loads)   (5-21)

$M_X = \left[M_B + V_B x - H_B y - \dfrac{wx^2}{2} \right]$,   (if loading is uniform)   (5-22)

To find H_B, V_B, and M_B, we use the influence lines previously obtained. Having obtained these, calculate H_X, F_X, and M_X. Then the shear at any section is given by

$$V_X = F_X \cos \alpha + H_X \sin \alpha$$
$$(5\text{-}23)$$

and the thrust at any section is given by

$$N_X = +H_X \cos \alpha - F_X \sin \alpha$$
$$(5\text{-}24)$$

To illustrate all of the above we consider the following problem.

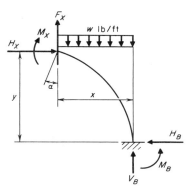

Fig. 5.8

Example: For the arch analyzed in Art. 5-5, determine the moment diagram produced by a dead load of 1500 lb/ft.

Solution:

$$M_X = M_B + V_B x - H_B y - \frac{wx^2}{2}$$

Determine

$$M_B = \sum w \cdot \Delta x \cdot [-\text{moment influence ordinate}]$$
$$V_B = \sum w \cdot \Delta x \cdot [-\text{vertical reaction influence ordinate}]$$
$$H_B = \sum w \cdot \Delta x \cdot [-\text{horizontal reaction influence ordinate}]$$

in which the influence ordinates are determined from Fig. 5.7. The computations for M_X are shown in Table 5.4. The moment ordinates determined in Table 5.4 are plotted in Fig. 5.9, which is, therefore, the solution to the problem.

5-9   Analysis of the two-hinged flat arch

It was pointed out (Art. 5-3) that the two-hinged arch is statically indeterminate to the first degree and that if we treat H_A as the redundant for flat arches, it is given by

$$H_A = \frac{-\displaystyle\int M_P y \, \frac{ds}{EI}}{\displaystyle\int y^2 \, \frac{ds}{EI} + \int \frac{\cos^2 \alpha \, ds}{AE}} = -\frac{\delta_{XW}}{\delta_{XH}}$$

TABLE 5.4

	1	2	3	4	5	6	7	8	9
Point	x	y	Moment Influence Ordinate	Vertical Reaction Influence Ordinate	Horizontal Reaction Influence Ordinate	V_Bx	$-H_By$	$-\dfrac{wx^2}{2}$	M_X kip-ft
A									+538
1	75	9.6825	− 1.0	−0.02	−0.11	+4500	− 809	−4220	+ 9
2	65	15.6124	− 5.3	−0.08	−0.46	+3900	−1306	−3170	− 38
3	55	18.5404	−11.0	−0.21	−0.95	+3300	−1542	−2270	+ 26
4	45	19.8431	−13.0	−0.40	−1.31	+2700	−1660	−1520	+ 58
5	35	19.8431	− 9.7	−0.60	−1.31	+2100	−1660	− 920	+ 58
6	25	18.5404	− 2.5	−0.78	−0.95	+1500	−1543	− 469	+ 26
7	15	15.6124	+ 3.0	−0.92	−0.46	+ 900	−1307	− 169	− 38
8	5	9.6825	+ 3.7	−0.99	−0.11	+ 300	− 810	− 19	+ 9
B									+538

$$\sum \qquad -35.8 \qquad -4.00 \qquad -5.66$$

$M_B = w \cdot \Delta x \cdot \sum (-\text{moment influence ordinate}) = 1.5(10)(35.8) = 538 \text{ kip-ft}$

$V_B = w \cdot \Delta x \cdot \sum (-\text{vertical reaction influence ordinate}) = 1.5(10)(4.00) = 60.0 \text{ kip}$

$H_B = w \cdot \Delta x \cdot \sum (-\text{horizontal reaction influence ordinate}) = 1.5(10)(5.66) = 84.9 \text{ kip}$

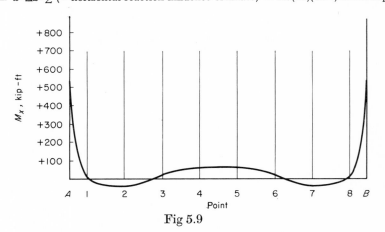

Fig 5.9

An influence line for H_A may now be obtained by applying a unit load at A (Fig. 5.10b), in which case the deflection of the axis at any point is $\eta_H = \delta_{XW}$ by the Law of Reciprocal Deflections (see Fig. 5.10a).

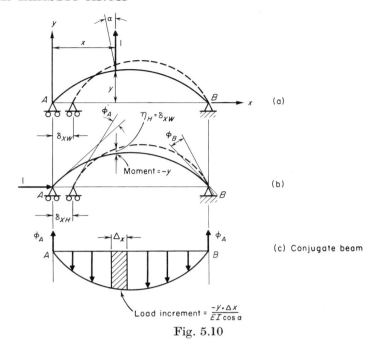

Fig. 5.10

We can then find $\eta_H =$ bending moment of a conjugate beam loaded with an M/EI diagram equal to the moment produced by a unit horizontal load applied at A divided by EI. An approximate numerical solution for η_H is made by using an incremental procedure identical to that for the fixed-end arch.

5-10 Illustrative problem—two-hinged arch

For the elliptical arch of Art. 5-7, determine the influence line for H_A if the arch is hinged at both ends.

Computations for η_H are arranged and presented in Table 5.5 and η_H is plotted in Fig. 5.11 for an upward unit load.

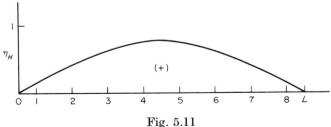

Fig. 5.11

TABLE 5.5

Col.	1	2	3	4	5	6	7	8	9*
Point	x	y	α	I	$-\dfrac{y\Delta x}{I \cos \alpha}$	$\sum \text{col. 5}$	$\phi_i = \phi_A + \text{col. 6}$	$\phi_i \Delta x$	$\eta_H = \dfrac{\sum \phi_i \Delta x}{\delta_{XH}}$
1	5	9.6825	42°–6.2′	4.406	– 29.6207	0	–406.5896	–2033	–0.138
2	15	15.6124	21°–49.0′	2.861	– 58.7776	– 29.6207	–376.9689	–3770	–0.393
3	25	18.5404	11°–26.1′	1.740	–108.6782	– 88.3983	–318.1913	–3182	–0.609
4	35	19.8431	3°–36.0′	0.949	–209.5133	–197.0765	–209.5131	–2095	–0.751
5	45	19.8431	–3°–36.0′	0.949	–209.5133	–406.5898	0	0	–0.751
6	55	18.5404	–11°–26.1′	1.740	–108.6782	–616.1031	–209.5131	–2095	–0.609
7	65	15.6124	–21°–49.0′	2.861	– 58.7776	–724.7813	–318.1913	–3182	–0.393
8	75	9.6825	–42°–6.2′	4.406	– 29.6207	–783.5589	–376.9689	–3770	–0.138
						–813.1796	–406.5896	–2033	

$$\sum = -813.1796$$

$$\phi_A = +\frac{813.1796}{2} = +406.5898$$

5-11   Deflection theory of arches

The basic curved bar equations of Art. 5-2 were developed assuming that the deformations were small enough that the stresses, shears, moments, and thrusts were not materially affected if these deformations were ignored.   This is not so in the case of long-span arch bridges.[2] Serious increases in stresses can occur as a consequence of the displacement of the arch.   These increases can be so large that, if ignored, structural failures may occur.   For a complete discussion of this subject see the reference[2].   A theory which includes the effects of the deformations is called a *deflection theory*.   Any such theory is usually found to be nonlinear—that is, if an applied load is doubled, the resulting displacements and stresses are not twice the original value. Hence, the superposition methods do not apply.   There is, at present, no method of obtaining an exact solution to such a nonlinear problem. Approximations can be made following two possible general procedures:

(a) A Rayleigh-type solution can be obtained by assuming a displacement curve that satisfies the boundary conditions and by minimizing the total energy of the system (see Chapter 6).   This would lead to a result similar to the one given by Beskin, described in Art. 5-14.

(b) Using the reactions, shears, thrusts, and moments obtained by solving the linear superposition equations as previously described, determine, as a first approximation, the displacements and recalculate the shears, thrusts, and moments, considering the loads and the arch in this displaced position.   Continue the procedure until convergence is apparently assured.   A simple solution of this type for a rigid frame, was discussed in Art. 4-18.

5-12   Effect of deflections for fixed arch

In the elastic analysis, the conditions for equilibrium of a fixed arch were found to be in terms of the reactions at A,

$$H_X = H_A \tag{5-18a}$$

$$F_X = V_A - \sum wx \tag{5-19a}$$

$$M_X = M_A + V_A x - H_A y - \text{(moment of loads)} \tag{5-21a}$$

$$V_X = F_X \cos \alpha - H_X \sin \alpha \tag{5-23a}$$

$$N_X = +H_X \cos \alpha + F_X \sin \alpha \tag{5-24a}$$

[2] "Rainbow Arch Bridge Symposium," *Transactions*, ASCE, Paper No. 2236, Vol. 110, 1945, pp. 1–178.

A method for determining the effect of arch deformations on the stresses by means of interaction diagrams is described by H. A. Miklofsky and O. J. Sotillo, "Design of Flexible Steel Arches by Interaction Diagrams," *Proceedings*, ASCE (Structural Division, Paper No. 1190, March, 1957).

where Equations (5-23a) and (5-24a) are the shear and thrust, respectively, on a particular section of the arch, and H_X and F_X are the horizontal and vertical components of the shear and thrust.

When the effects of displacement are included, we obtain

$$H_{X\Delta} = H_A + \Delta H_A \qquad (5\text{-}25a)$$

$$F_{X\Delta} = V_A + \Delta V_A - \sum w(x + \xi) \qquad (5\text{-}25b)$$

$$M_{X\Delta} = M_A + \Delta M_A + (V_A + \Delta V_A)(x + \xi)$$
$$- (H_A + \Delta H_A)(y + \eta) - (M_{\text{loads}} + \Delta M_{\text{loads}}) \qquad (5\text{-}25c)$$

in which ΔH_A, ΔV_A, ΔM_A are the changes in the reactions at A due to the deflections ξ and η in the x and y directions, respectively.

Expanding Equation (5-25c) and omitting higher-order terms, we obtain

$$M_{X\Delta} = M_A + \Delta M_A + V_A(x + \xi) + \Delta V_A x - H_A(y + \eta)$$
$$- \Delta H_A y - (M_{\text{loads}} + \Delta M_{\text{loads}}) \qquad (5\text{-}26)$$

Then the change in moment

$$\Delta M_X = \Delta M_A + V_A \xi + \Delta V_A x - H_A \eta - \Delta H_A y - \Delta M_{\text{loads}} \qquad (5\text{-}27)$$

If the terms depending upon ξ are ignored we obtain

$$\Delta M_X = \Delta M_A - H_A \eta - \Delta H_A y \qquad (5\text{-}27a)$$

At this point we must consider the displacement expressions for the arch. These are best given in the form of differential equations and are derived in the next article.

5-13 Differential equations for the displacements of curved bars

The instantaneous radius of curvature of the axis of the arch is expressed in terms of polar coordinates r, α as

$$\rho = \frac{[r^2 + (r')^2]^{3/2}}{r^2 - rr'' + 2(r')^2} \qquad (5\text{-}28)$$

where

$$r' = \frac{dr}{d\alpha} \quad \text{and} \quad r'' = \frac{d^2 r}{d\alpha^2}$$

The curvature is given by

$$\frac{1}{\rho} = \frac{r^2 - rr'' + 2(r')^2}{[r^2 + (r')^2]^{3/2}} \qquad (5\text{-}28a)$$

Let u and v be the radial and tangential components of displacement of any point on the axis of the unloaded arch.

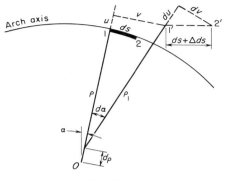

Fig. 5.12

Let us choose the origin so that for the arch point in question, $\rho = r$. Then, after the arch becomes displaced due to the specified loads, the radius of curvature becomes

$$\rho_1 \doteq \rho - d\rho + u + v\,d\alpha \approx \rho + u$$

and

$$\rho_1' = \frac{d}{d\alpha}(\rho + u) = \rho' + u'$$

(The prime designates differentiation with respect to α.) Also,

$$\rho_1'' = \rho'' + u''$$

Hence, from Equation (5-28a),

$$\frac{1}{\rho_1} = \frac{(\rho+u)^2 - (\rho+u)(\rho''+u'') + 2(\rho'+u')^2}{[(\rho+u)^2 + (\rho'+u')^2]^{3/2}} \qquad (5\text{-}29)$$

If u' is very much less than ρ, and ρ is very nearly constant with α, then ρ', ρ'', and u' may be neglected in Equation (5-29) and

$$\frac{1}{\rho_1} \approx \frac{(\rho+u)^2 - (\rho+u)u''}{(\rho+u)^3} \qquad (5\text{-}30)$$

or

$$\frac{1}{\rho_1} = \frac{1}{\rho+u} - \frac{u''}{(\rho+u)^2}$$

The change in curvature as point 1 deflects to 1' (see Fig. 5.12) is

$$\frac{1}{\rho_1} - \frac{1}{\rho} = \frac{1}{\rho+u} - \frac{u''}{(\rho+u)^2} - \frac{1}{\rho} = -\frac{u}{\rho(\rho+u)} - \frac{u''}{(\rho+u)^2}$$

If we make the further approximation here that

$$\rho(\rho + u) \doteq (\rho + u)^2 \doteq \rho^2$$

then

$$\frac{1}{\rho_1} - \frac{1}{\rho} = -\frac{(u + u'')}{\rho^2}$$

or

$$\frac{1}{\rho_1} = \frac{1}{\rho} = -\left[\frac{1}{\rho^2}\frac{d^2 u}{d\alpha^2} + \frac{u}{\rho^2}\right] \tag{5-31}$$

But $\rho \, d\alpha = ds$, so that

$$\frac{1}{\rho_1} - \frac{1}{\rho} = -\left[\frac{d^2 u}{ds^2} + \frac{u}{\rho^2}\right] \tag{5-32}$$

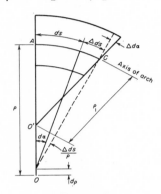

Fig. 5.13

The relations between the change in length of a fiber of length ds along the axis of an arch and the consequent changes in rotation and radius of curvature are shown in Fig. 5.13. The center of curvature shifts from 0 to 0′ and the radius changes from ρ to ρ_1, as the element ds changes by Δds. The angle AOC is changed to

$$d\alpha + \frac{\Delta ds}{\rho} + \Delta d\alpha = \frac{ds + \Delta ds}{\rho_1}$$

Noting that $d\alpha = ds/\rho$ and solving for $\Delta d\alpha$, we obtain

$$\Delta d\alpha = \frac{ds + \Delta ds}{\rho_1} - \frac{ds + \Delta ds}{\rho}$$

$$= \left(\frac{1}{\rho_1} - \frac{1}{\rho}\right)\left(\frac{1 + \Delta ds}{ds}\right)ds$$

$$\frac{\Delta d\alpha}{ds} = \left(\frac{1}{\rho_1} - \frac{1}{\rho}\right)\left(1 + \frac{\Delta ds}{ds}\right) \tag{5-33}$$

Substituting Equation (5-32) for $\left(\dfrac{1}{\rho_1}-\dfrac{1}{\rho}\right)$, we obtain

$$\frac{\Delta d\alpha}{ds} = -\left(\frac{d^2u}{ds^2}+\frac{u}{\rho^2}\right)\left(1+\frac{\Delta ds}{ds}\right) \qquad (5\text{-}33\text{a})$$

From Art. 5-1, Equations (5-2a) and (5-3b),

$$\frac{\Delta d\alpha}{ds} = \frac{1}{\rho}\frac{\Delta d\alpha}{d\alpha} = \frac{1}{\rho}\frac{M}{EI'}$$

and

$$\frac{\Delta ds}{ds} = \frac{N}{EA}-\frac{M}{EA\rho}$$

Substituting these in Equation (5-33a), we obtain

$$\frac{1}{\rho}\frac{M}{EI'} = -\left(\frac{d^2u}{ds^2}+\frac{u}{\rho^2}\right)\left(1+\frac{N}{EA}-\frac{M}{EA\rho}\right) \qquad (5\text{-}34)$$

If we assume that for the arch $\Delta ds/ds$ is small enough in comparison to unity to ignore, Equation (5-34) becomes

$$\frac{d^2u}{ds^2}+\frac{u}{\rho^2} = -\frac{M}{\rho EI'} \approx -\frac{M}{EI} \qquad (5\text{-}35)$$

Referring again to Fig. 5.12, in considering the displacement of an element of length ds from points 1–2 on the axis of the arch to points 1′–2′, the component in the 0–1 direction of the displacement between point 1′ and point 2′ is

$$\Delta_N = (\rho+u+du)\cos d\alpha - (v+dv)\sin d\alpha - (\rho+u)$$

For small angles $\cos d\alpha \doteq 1$, $\sin d\alpha \doteq d\alpha$, or

$$\Delta_N = (\rho+u+du)-(v+dv)d\alpha-\rho+u$$

$$\Delta_N = du - v\,d\alpha \quad \text{(neglecting higher-order terms)} \qquad (5\text{-}36)$$

In a direction tangent to 0–1, the separation between 1′ and 2′ is

$$\Delta_T = (\rho+u+du)\sin d\alpha + (v+dv)\cos d\alpha - v$$

$$\Delta_T = \rho\,d\alpha + u\,d\alpha + dv \quad \text{(neglecting higher-order terms)} \qquad (5\text{-}37)$$

The length of the element 1′–2′ is $ds+\Delta ds$, where

$$ds+\Delta ds = \left[\sqrt{\left(\rho+u+\frac{dv}{d\alpha}\right)^2+\left(\frac{du}{d\alpha}-v\right)^2}\,\right]d\alpha$$

Obtaining the first few terms by the binomial expansion, we have

$$\frac{ds}{d\alpha}+\frac{\Delta ds}{d\alpha} = \left(\rho+u+\frac{dv}{d\alpha}\right)+\frac{1}{2}\frac{\left(\dfrac{du}{d\alpha}-v\right)^2}{\rho+u+\dfrac{dv}{d\alpha}}+\cdots$$

But

$$\frac{ds}{d\alpha} = \rho, \quad \left(\frac{du}{d\alpha}-v\right)^2 = \left(\frac{du}{d\alpha}\right)^2 - 2\frac{du}{d\alpha}v+v^2$$

If $du/d\alpha$ and v are small, with respect to ρ', then the second and higher terms of the series may be ignored and

$$\rho+\frac{\Delta ds}{d\alpha} = \rho+u+\frac{dv}{d\alpha}$$

But $d\alpha=ds/\rho$; therefore

$$\rho\,\frac{\Delta ds}{ds} = u+\rho\,\frac{dv}{ds} \qquad (5\text{-}38)$$

From Equation (5-3b),

$$\frac{\Delta ds}{ds} = \frac{N}{EA}-\frac{M}{EA\rho}$$

Therefore, dividing Equation (5-38) by ρ and substituting Equation (5-3b), we obtain

$$\frac{u}{\rho}+\frac{dv}{ds} = \frac{N}{EA}-\frac{M}{EA\rho} \qquad (5\text{-}39)$$

Also

$$\frac{d^2u}{ds^2}+\frac{u}{\rho^2} = -\frac{M}{\rho EI'} \approx -\frac{M}{EI} \qquad (5\text{-}35)$$

These are the two differential equations of a curved bar subject to the assumptions made in their derivations.

5-14   Applications of the deflection theory

Equations (5-39) and (5-35) can be used to calculate the deflections produced in an arch. Then procedure (b) of Art. 5-11 may be applied to give an approximate deflection-theory solution.

For a circular bar, the radius of curvature is constant and Equation (5-35) can be solved by direct integration provided that I is constant. For such a solution, the reader is referred to Timoshenko.[3] For parabolic, elliptical, and other arches, numerical solutions can be obtained using the methods of Chapter 6.

[3] S. Timoshenko, *Strength of Materials*, Vol. I, D. Van Nostrand Company, Princeton, N.J., 1956.

According to Beskin,[4]

1. An error of about 4% occurs in the value of the bending moments when the term u/ρ^2 is neglected in Equation (5-35).

2. For a two-hinged arch, if we assume $\Delta H_A = 0$, $\xi = 0$ and noting that $M_A = \Delta M_A = 0$, Equation (5-27a) becomes

$$\Delta M_X = -H_A \eta = Nu$$

or the moment at any section of the arch, $M_{X\Delta}$, is given by

$$M_{X\Delta} = M_{XE} + Nu \tag{5-40}$$

where M_{XE} = arch moments as computed from the elastic theory neglecting deformations. Ignoring the term u/ρ^2, Equation (5-35) becomes

$$EI \frac{d^2u}{ds^2} = -M_{XE} - Nu = -M_{X\Delta} \tag{5-41}$$

If I is constant, Equation (5-41) can be solved as follows: Assume

$$M_{XE} = M_0 \sin \frac{2\pi s}{L}$$

where L is the free span (arc length) of the arch and M_{XE} satisfies the boundary conditions of the arch.

Then

$$\frac{d^2u}{ds^2} + \frac{N}{EI} u = -\frac{M_0}{EI} \sin \frac{2\pi s}{L}$$

If N is assumed constant and if $k^2 = N/EI$, then a solution in terms of constants A, B, C is

$$u = A \cos ks + B \sin ks - CM_0 \sin \frac{2\pi s}{L}$$

When

$$\begin{aligned} s &= 0, u = 0 \qquad \text{gives } A = 0 \\ s &= L, u = 0 \qquad \text{gives } \sin kL = 0, (B \neq 0) \end{aligned}$$

or

$$kL = n\pi, \qquad n = 1, 2, 3, 4 \cdots$$

For $n = 1$,

$$kL = \sqrt{\frac{N_{Cr}}{EI}} L = \pi, \text{ where } N_{Cr} = \frac{\pi^2 EI}{L^2} = \text{ a critical column type load.}$$

For $B = 0$,

$$u = CM_0 \sin \frac{2\pi s}{L} \tag{5-42}$$

$$u' = CM_0 \frac{2\pi}{L} \cos \frac{2\pi s}{L}$$

$$u'' = -CM_0 \frac{4\pi^2}{L^2} \sin \frac{2\pi s}{L}$$

[4] Beskin on Rainbow Arch Bridge, *Transactions*, ASCE, Vol. 110, 1945.

Substituting in the differential equation, we obtain

$$-4CM_0 \frac{\pi^2}{L^2} \sin \frac{2\pi s}{L} + \frac{N}{EI} C \frac{M_0}{EI} \sin \frac{2\pi s}{L} = -\frac{M_0}{EI} \sin \frac{2\pi s}{L}$$

or

$$C = \frac{1}{\dfrac{4\pi^2 EI}{L^2} - N}$$

and

$$u'' = -\frac{\pi^2}{L^2} \frac{M_0}{N_{\text{Cr}}} \left(\frac{1}{1 - \dfrac{N}{4N_{\text{Cr}}}} \right) \sin \frac{2\pi s}{L} \qquad (5\text{-}43)$$

But from Equation (5-41), $M_{X\triangle} = -EI \dfrac{d^2 u}{ds^2}$. Using Equation (5-43), we obtain

$$M_{X\triangle} = \frac{\pi^2 EI}{L^2 N_{\text{Cr}}} \left(\frac{1}{1 - \dfrac{N}{4N_{\text{Cr}}}} \right) M_0 \sin \frac{2\pi s}{L} \qquad (5\text{-}44)$$

or

$$M_{X\triangle} = \left(\frac{1}{1 - \dfrac{N}{4N_{\text{Cr}}}} \right) M_{XE} \qquad (5\text{-}44\text{a})$$

Thus, $M_{X\triangle}$ is almost a linear function of M_{XE} subject to the assumptions made.

The above results are in reasonable agreement with experimental values given in the Rainbow Arch Bridge Symposium for both two-hinged and fixed arches (providing that for the fixed arch $0.7L$ is used in place of L in calculating the critical load). It is therefore suggested that Equation (5-44a) can be used to estimate the moments that result from the deflection theory if the moments M_{XE}, obtained from the analysis disregarding displacements, are known. The result, Equation (5-44a) is similar to the one obtained in an analogous manner for beams.[5] It can be extended by considering M_{XE} to consist of additional sine terms.[6] See Chapter 6 for a more complete discussion of this method.

---

[5] S. Timoshenko, *Strength of Materials*, Vol. 2, D. Van Nostrand Company, Princeton, N.J., 1956.

[6] M. Hupner, "Application des Series Trigonometriques a l'etude du flambement des arcs," *Annales des Ponts et Chaussees*, November 1935, p. 754.

The approximate normal stresses in an arch section, according to the deflection theory, are then given by

$$\sigma_{XD} = -\frac{N}{A} \pm \frac{zM_{XE}}{I} \left[\frac{1}{1 - \frac{N}{4N_{Cr}}}\right] \qquad (5\text{-}45)$$

5-15   Criterion for use of the deflection theory

Computations have indicated that arches with a factor of safety against buckling below 3 should probably be investigated by the deflection theory.   The factor of safety is defined by

$$\text{F.S.} = \frac{N_{Cr}}{N} = \frac{\dfrac{\pi^2 EI}{L^2}}{N} \qquad (5\text{-}46)$$

where L is the arc length of a two-hinged arch and where $L =$ approximately 0.7 times the arc length if used for the fixed arch.

Problems

1. A circular concrete arch with built-in supports carries a fill as shown in the diagram.

(a) Find the influence lines for the moment and vertical and horizontal reactions at A.

(b) Using the influence lines, determine the moment diagram and the thrust at any section due to dead load.

In the computations, divide the arch into 10 equal segments.

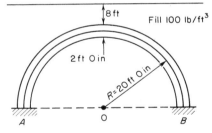

2. Rework problem 1 assuming the arch is now a parabolic arch of constant thickness (2 ft 0 in.) with a span of 40 ft 0 in. and a rise of 20 ft 0 in.   (The equation of the parabola is $y = 20 - \dfrac{x^2}{20}$ with the origin of coordinates through point O.)

Chapter 6

NUMERICAL AND APPROXIMATE METHODS OF BEAM DEFLECTION ANALYSIS

6-1 Introduction

In this chapter we shall discuss several different numerical and approximate methods for determining beam shears, moments, and deflections. In particular, the discussion will cover (1) the finite difference method, (2) the relaxation method, (3) a numerical procedure, (4) an approximate trigonometric method. We shall not discuss at this time the most useful and most generally used numerical procedure for solving redundant beams, the moment distribution method. This was presented in Chapter 4.

It should be noted that although the methods discussed in this chapter are useful in the determination of beam quantities, these methods do have a much greater field of application. The general principles discussed are fundamental and find application in all the fields of applied mechanics and physics. We shall tie the discussion in with the beam, since this is the field of primary interest in this text. The extension to other fields can be made with little difficulty.[1]

6-2 Finite difference method

In the finite difference method, we replace differential quantities with *difference* quantities. For example, consider the beam shown in Fig. 6.1.

The slope at any point, such as 3 is given by

$$\text{Slope} = \left(\frac{dy}{dx}\right)_3$$

[1] Following are some of the references to the material covered in this chapter. Additional references will be found in these.

T. v. Karman and M. A. Biot, *Mathematical Methods in Engineering*, McGraw-Hill Book Company, New York, 1940. Contains a chapter on finite differences.

D. N. de G. Allen, *Relaxation Methods*, McGraw-Hill Book Company, New York, 1954. For treatment of finite difference and relaxation methods.

N. M. Newmark, "Numerical Procedure for Computing Deflections, Moments and Buckling Loads," *Transactions*, ASCE, Vol. 69, 1943, p. 1161.

S. Timoshenko, *Strength of Materials*, Vol. 2, D. Van Nostrand Company, Princeton, N.J., 1956. Discussion of trigonometric methods.

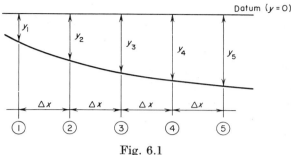

Fig. 6.1

This is approximated, in finite difference notation, by the quantity

$$\text{Slope} = \left(\frac{\Delta y}{\Delta x}\right)_3 = \frac{y_4 - y_3}{\Delta x} \tag{6-1}$$

The second differential d^2y/dx^2 is approximated, in a similar way, by

$$\left(\frac{d^2y}{dx^2}\right)_3 = \left[\frac{\Delta\left(\frac{\Delta y}{\Delta x}\right)}{\Delta x}\right]_3 = \frac{(y_4 - y_3) - (y_3 - y_2)}{(\Delta x)^2}$$

or

$$\left(\frac{d^2y}{dx^2}\right)_3 = \frac{y_4 - 2y_3 + y_2}{(\Delta x)^2} \tag{6-2}$$

and similarly for the higher-order differential quantities. For our purposes the above expressions are all that are needed for the beam analyses.

In finite difference notation, the Bernoulli--Euler beam differential equation

$$\frac{d^2y}{dx^2} = \frac{M}{EI}$$

becomes

$$y_{n+1} - 2y_n + y_{n-1} = \frac{M}{EI}(\Delta x)^2 \tag{6-3}$$

In applying the method to a particular problem, we divide the beam into an equal number of parts. (The equal lengths are not necessary but simplify the numerical computation and usually can be done without difficulty.) Equation (6-3) is then applied to the various stations along the beam. If M is known at all points along the beam then we obtain a series of simultaneous equations in terms of unknown y's. There will be as many unknowns as there are equations, and the solution to the problem requires solving the simultaneous equations.

In practice, if there are more than three simultaneous equations, computing machines or similar devices should be used to solve the equations. However, in theory, the method will give the solution to any problem, of constant or variable moment of inertia, provided M/EI is known at all points.

Also, as would be expected, the smaller we choose Δx, the more accurate the solution. However, the smaller we choose Δx, the larger is the number of simultaneous equations.

We shall illustrate the method by solving two problems. The first will be a simple deflection problem; the second, a redundant beam. The more complicated cases, involving variable I or loading, are handled in a similar manner.

Example: Determine the deflections for the centrally loaded, simply supported beam of constant stiffness, EI.

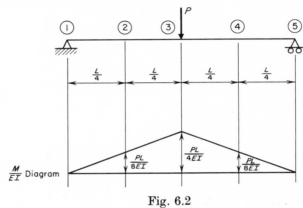

Fig. 6.2

Solution: Divide the beam into four equal spaces as shown. Then

$$\Delta x = \frac{L}{4}$$

Boundary conditions require that

$$y_1 = y_5 = 0$$

Now apply the finite difference Equation (6-3) to the points 2, 3, and 4 in turn, using for M/EI the value of this quantity at the point.[2] This gives

$$-2y_2 + y_3 = \left(\frac{PL}{8EI}\right)\left(\frac{L^2}{16}\right)$$

---

[2] If desired, an average or weighted value of this quantity can be used, since it does vary from point to point. There are various ways of performing this averaging. In this illustrative problem, this is not done, since we wish merely to fix ideas and illustrate methods.

$$y_2 - 2y_3 + y_4 = \left(\frac{PL}{4EI}\right)\left(\frac{L^2}{16}\right)$$

$$y_3 - 2y_4 = \left(\frac{PL}{8EI}\right)\left(\frac{L^2}{16}\right)$$

These are three equations in three unknowns y_2, y_3, and y_4. Solving for the deflections, we find

$$y_4 = y_2 = \frac{-PL^3}{64EI} \left(\text{vs.} -\frac{(\frac{11}{12})PL^3}{64EI}, \text{exact}\right)$$

and

$$y_3 = \frac{-PL^3}{42.7EI} \left(\text{vs.} \frac{-PL^3}{48EI}, \text{exact}\right)$$

It will be seen that the values obtained are somewhat larger than the exact engineering values. If a weighted M/EI had been used, the computed values would have been closer to the exact values. Also, greater accuracy could have been obtained if more sections had been used.

The next illustrative problem indicates the method of application to a redundant beam and also indicates the application of the method to the built-in beam case.

Example: Determine the reaction R_R for the redundant beam. *EI* is constant.

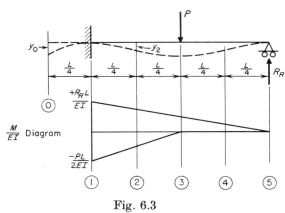

Fig. 6.3

Solution: As before we divide the beam into four equal parts. The M/EI diagram (in terms of the load P and reaction R_R) is drawn by parts as shown in Fig. 6.3.

Now consider conditions at the left support. The beam is built in here—i.e., has zero slope at this point. Physically this means that, if we consider a fictitious piece of beam of length $L/4$ extending into the fixed-end wall, and label this end "O", then

$$\begin{cases} y_1 = 0 & \text{(6-4a)} \\ y_O = y_2 & \text{(6-4b)} \end{cases}$$

Equation (6-4b) is the statement of the zero slope boundary condition in finite difference form.

Now apply Equation (6-3) to the points 1, 2, 3, and 4 in turn. This gives, after using Equation (6-4) and also the condition that $y_5 = 0$, four equations in terms of four unknowns, y_2, y_3, y_4, and R_R. These four equations may then be solved for the unknowns. Thus,

$$y_0 - 2y_1 + y_2 = \left(R_R L - \frac{PL}{2} \right) \frac{L^2}{16EI}$$

$$y_1 - 2y_2 + y_3 = \left(\frac{3R_R L}{4} - \frac{PL}{4} \right) \frac{L^2}{16EI}$$

$$y_2 - 2y_3 + y_4 = \left(\frac{R_R L}{2EI} \right) \left(\frac{L^2}{16} \right)$$

$$y_3 - 2y_4 + y_5 = \left(\frac{R_R L}{4EI} \right) \left(\frac{L^2}{16} \right)$$

Solving these, we find

$$R_R = \tfrac{7}{22} P \text{ (vs. } \tfrac{5}{16} P \text{, exact)}$$

6-3   The relaxation method

The relaxation method is essentially a systematic procedure for solving finite difference equations. The method can perhaps best be described by considering a specific problem.

Example: Let us consider once more the simply supported, centrally loaded, constant stiffness beam of length L. We divide this beam into four equal parts as before, see Fig. 6.2.

Solution: According to Equation (6-3), the solution to the problem requires that for any point,

$$y_{n-1} - 2y_n + y_{n+1} = \frac{M}{EI} (\Delta x)^2 \tag{6-3}$$

Otherwise stated, we require that at all points

$$y_{n-1} - 2y_n + y_{n+1} - \frac{M}{EI} (\Delta x)^2 = 0 \tag{6-5}$$

and a measure of the inaccuracy of any assumed solution is the amount which this expression differs from zero. We call the left-hand side of Equation (6-5) the *residual*, R, and observe that since

$$y_{n-1} - 2y_n + y_{n+1} - \frac{M}{EI} (\Delta x)^2 = R \tag{6-6}$$

it shall be the purpose of the relaxation solution to alter the y's and to thereby reduce the residual to zero (or very nearly zero) at all points of the beam.

However, it is important also to note that if the value of y at any point, n has changed, then according to Equation (6-6), the residual is changed at adjacent points, the change (in this case at points y_{n-1} and y_{n+1}) being equal to the change in the value of y_n.

To illustrate, consider any four adjacent points as in Fig. 6.4. Any assumed values of y are initially chosen for the points. These are shown to the left of the vertical line at each point (3 at i, 2 at j etc.). Assume the moments and stiffnesses are known at each point and therefore R at each point can be determined. These are shown to the right of vertical lines (-6 at i, $+4$ at j, etc.).

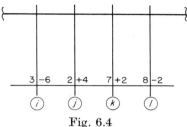

Fig. 6.4

To make the residual at $i=$zero, y_i should be changed by $R/2$ [see Equation (6-6)]. Do this, and record the step as in Fig. 6.5. The right column now indicates that the residual is zero at i.

But by changing y_i we also change the residual at j, the change [see Equation (6-6)] being just equal to the change at i. This is recorded at j as shown in Fig. 6.6, in which the value $+1$ is now the residual at j.

Fig. 6.5   Fig. 6.6

This procedure is repeated at all points, the order of operation being immaterial. It will be found that the residual decreases, which, mathematically, means that the procedure converges. The final value of the desired quantity at each point is obtained by adding the left-hand column at each point. Many short cuts are available and become obvious to a person doing work in this field.

To illustrate the application we return to the problem of the simple beam of Fig. 6.2 and perform the relaxation directly, proceeding from left to right in order. We note that since $y_1=y_5=0$, we can choose these values to start with. It is not necessary to carry over changes in residuals to these points. The initially assumed values of the multipliers of PL^3/EI and the initial residuals are

$$y_1 = 0 \qquad\qquad R_1 = 0$$
$$y_2 = 0.002 \qquad\qquad R_2 = -0.0098$$
$$y_3 = 0.002 \qquad\qquad R_3 = -0.0176$$
$$y_4 = 0.002 \qquad\qquad R_4 = -0.0098$$
$$y_5 = 0 \qquad\qquad R_5 = 0$$

In computing the residuals, the value of the moment at each point was used for that point. A more accurate solution would be obtained if averaged or weighted values of M were used. The complete solution follows in Fig. 6.7.

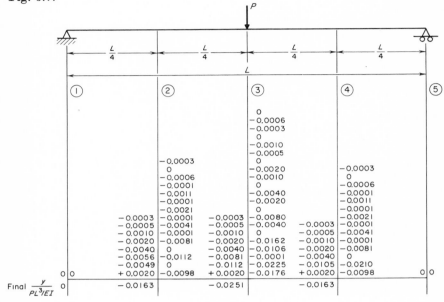

Fig. 6.7

These solutions compare with the exact solutions as follows:

$$y_2 = y_4 = \frac{-PL^3}{61.4EI}\left(\text{vs. } \frac{-PL^3}{69.7EI}, \text{ exact}\right)$$

$$y_3 = \frac{-PL^3}{39.9EI}\left(\text{vs. } \frac{-PL^3}{48EI}, \text{ exact}\right)$$

6-4 A numerical method

The method which will now be described is basically a numerical system for computing shears and moments of beams. However, because beam deflections and slopes are given by moments and shears on a conjugate beam (see Chapter 1), the method will be applicable also to the problem of determining beam slopes and deflections.

Before explaining the method we review some elementary principles. Consider the beam and loading shown in Fig. 6.8.

Recalling that the change in moment between any two points on a beam is equal to the area of the shear diagram between these two points, we see that the shear and moment diagrams can be replaced by

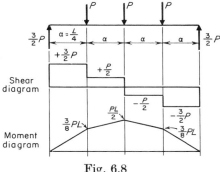

Fig. 6.8

the following numerical arrangement, as shown in Fig. 6.9, in which the shears and moments were obtained by moving from the left end of the beam to the right end, and the usual sign convention was used for shears and moments (see Art. 1-5).

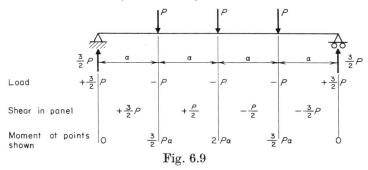

Fig. 6.9

In using the numerical method described herein, it is necessary that beam loadings consist of concentrated loads only. Thus, the actual loading will always be approximated by a system of *equivalent concentrated loads*. There are many ways of obtaining *equivalent loads*. We shall use the simplest type of equivalent load and will assume that all loadings can be approximated by either a uniform or trapezoidal load, each of which in turn can be replaced by the concentrated loadings shown in Fig. 6.10.

Let us now consider the same beam and loading as in Fig. 6.8, with the addition of a moment at the right end as shown in Fig. 6.11.

Note that the previous shear and moment diagrams of Fig. 6.8, are altered very simply in order to obtain the shear and moment diagrams for the given loadings. The shear diagram is simply measured from a new horizontal datum ((M/L) below the previous datum), and the moments are now measured by the vertical ordinate measured

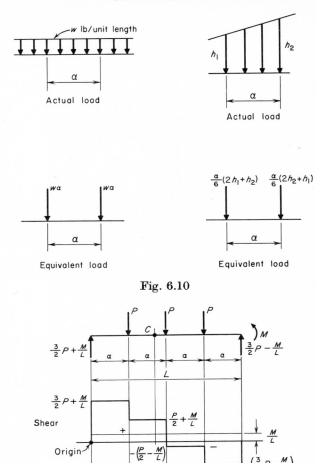

Fig. 6.10

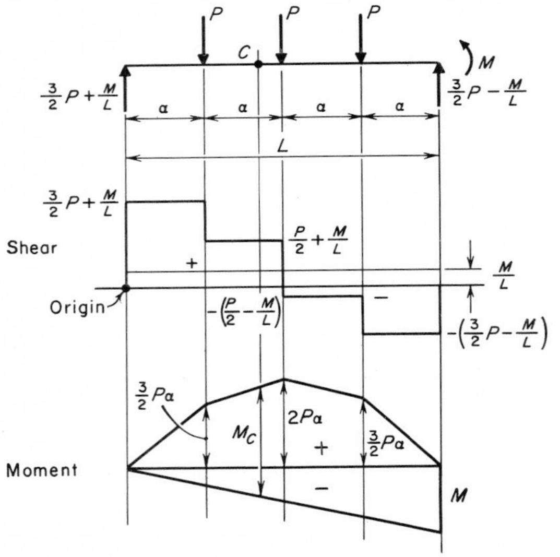

Fig. 6.11

from the slope line as shown for M_C. The numerical solution for this case is shown in Fig. 6.12.

The ideas and relations just presented suggest the following procedure for solving any beam and loading. In order to illustrate the method

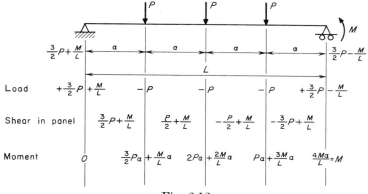

Fig. 6.12

we shall consider the previous beam and loading with particular values, $P = 2$ lb, $M = 20$ ft-lb, $L = 20$ ft, $\alpha = 5$ ft:

(a) Assume any value for the left reaction and show the corresponding load values. For example, let us assume $R_L = 10$ lb (see Fig. 6.13).

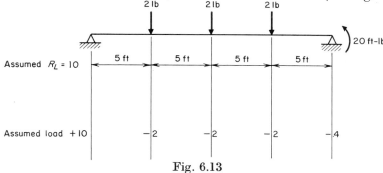

Fig. 6.13

(b) Now show the shear and moments corresponding to the loading of (a) Fig. 6.14.

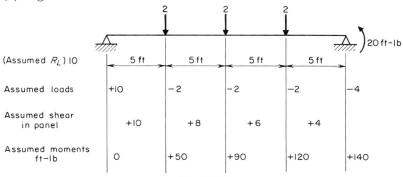

Fig. 6.14

(c) The moment at the right end should be $+20$ ft-lb. However, the assumed left reaction leads to a value of $+140$ ft-lb at this point. The tabular values must therefore be corrected by adding -120 ft-lb at the right end, varying to zero at the left end. This, the resulting corrected shear, the final shear, and final moment are all shown in Fig. 6.15.

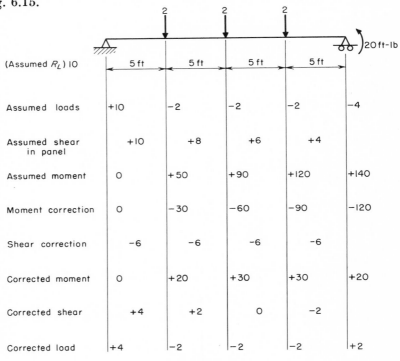

(Assumed R_L) 10		5 ft	5 ft	5 ft	5 ft
Assumed loads	+10	−2	−2	−2	−4
Assumed shear in panel		+10	+8	+6	+4
Assumed moment	0	+50	+90	+120	+140
Moment correction	0	−30	−60	−90	−120
Shear correction		−6	−6	−6	−6
Corrected moment	0	+20	+30	+30	+20
Corrected shear		+4	+2	0	−2
Corrected load	+4	−2	−2	−2	+2

Fig. 6.15

The numerical method described above will now be used to solve for the deflections of the simply supported, centrally loaded beam. The student should verify all figures of the solution which is shown in Fig. 6.16.

It will be noted that for the problem considered in Fig. 6.16 the numerical procedure gives the exact values of the deflections at the load points. This will not, in general, be true for the irregular conjugate beam loadings. However, in all cases, values of deflections (i.e., conjugate beam moments) will be either correct or approximately correct within the limits of the accuracy of the approximations made in replacing the actual conjugate beam loadings by equivalent concentrated loadings.

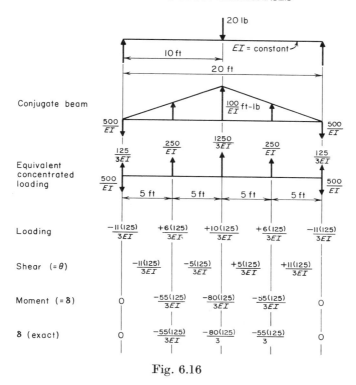

Fig. 6.16

6-5 Approximate trigonometric method for determining beam deflections

The trigonometric method which will now be described is essentially an application of the Principle of Minimum Potential Energy (see Art. 1-25).

Consider a simply supported beam loaded as shown in Fig. 6.17. Also shown is the deflection curve.

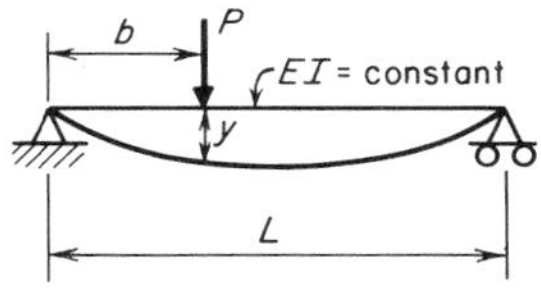

The total energy is given by

$$U = W + V$$

$$U = -Py + \int_0^L \frac{M^2 dx}{2EI} \tag{6-7}$$

Because

$$\frac{M}{EI} = \frac{d^2y}{dx^2}$$

Fig. 6.17

we can also write

$$U = -Py + \frac{EI}{2} \int_0^L \left(\frac{d^2y}{dx^2}\right)^2 dx \qquad (6\text{-}8)$$

and according to the Principle of Minimum Potential Energy, the value of U is stationary at equilibrium or

$$\delta U = 0 = \delta\left[-Py + \frac{EI}{2} \int_0^L \left(\frac{d^2y}{dx^2}\right)^2 dx\right] \qquad (6\text{-}9)$$

so that

$$P(\delta y) = \delta\left[\frac{EI}{2} \int_0^L \left(\frac{d^2y}{dx^2}\right)^2 dx\right] \qquad (6\text{-}10)$$

Equation (6-10) is the basis of the approximate trigonometric procedure introduced by Timoshenko (see references given in footnote 1).

The method assumes that the deflection curve can be given by means of a series of trigonometric terms. For example, the deflection curve of Fig. 6.17 can be represented by

$$y = a_1 \sin\frac{\pi x}{L} + a_2 \sin\frac{2\pi x}{L} + a_3 \sin\frac{3\pi x}{L} + \cdots \qquad (6\text{-}11)$$

By choosing proper values of the a's, it is possible to approximate the curve to any desired degree of accuracy. That this can be done we show as follows:

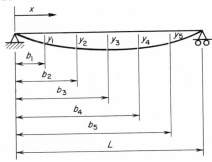

Fig. 6.18

Assume that the correct curve is shown in Fig. 6.18. The true values of $y_1, \cdots y_n$ at the distances $b_1, \cdots b_n$ ($n = 5$ in the figure, but it can have any value) are indicated.

We can determine the coefficients a_1, a_2, a_3, a_4, a_5, such that we obtain the exact values y_1, y_2, y_3, y_4, y_5, at the points b_1, b_2, b_3, b_4, b_5, by utilizing Equation (6-11) successively applied to the five points in question, as follows:

$$y_1 = a_1 \sin \frac{\pi b_1}{L} + a_2 \sin \frac{2\pi b_1}{L} + a_3 \sin \frac{3\pi b_1}{L} + a_4 \sin \frac{4\pi b_1}{L}$$
$$+ a_5 \sin \frac{5\pi b_1}{L}$$

$y_2 = $ similar

$y_3 = $ similar

$y_4 = $ similar

$$(6\text{-}12)$$

$$y_5 = a_1 \sin \frac{\pi b_5}{L} + a_2 \sin \frac{2\pi b_5}{L} \; a_3 \sin \frac{3\pi b_5}{L} + a_4 \sin \frac{4\pi b_5}{L}$$
$$+ a_5 \sin \frac{5\pi b_5}{L}$$

The solution of these five equations will give values for the a's such that Equation (6-13)

$$y = a_1 \sin \frac{\pi x}{L} + a_2 \sin \frac{2\pi x}{L} + a_3 \sin \frac{3\pi x}{L} + a_4 \sin \frac{4\pi x}{L} + a_5 \sin \frac{5\pi x}{L} \quad (6\text{-}13)$$

will satisfy the deflection curve exactly at five points. If desired, we may satisfy the curve exactly at n points. Note: the trigonometric functions chosen automatically satisfy the end boundary conditions,

$$\begin{cases} y = 0 & \text{at} \quad x = 0 \\ y = 0 & \text{at} \quad x = L \end{cases}$$

This must be done in all cases.

Using Equation (6-11) we obtain, from Equation (6-7),

$$U = -P\left[\sum_{n=1}^{n} a_n \sin \frac{n\pi b}{L}\right] + \frac{EI}{2} \int_0^L \left[-\sum_{n=1}^{n} a_n n^2 \left(\frac{\pi}{L}\right)^2 \sin \frac{n\pi x}{L}\right]^2 dx \quad (6\text{-}14)$$

Now, in the above, we have

$$U = U(a_1, a_2, \cdots a_n) \quad (6\text{-}15)$$

so that

$$\delta U = \frac{\partial U}{\partial a_1} da_1 + \frac{\partial U}{\partial a_2} da_2 + \cdots \frac{\partial U}{\partial a_3} da_3 \quad (6\text{-}16)$$

and for $\delta U = 0$, since each of the da_n is independent of the other, it is necessary that

$$\frac{\partial U}{\partial a_1} = \frac{\partial U}{\partial a_2} = \frac{\partial U}{\partial a_3} = \cdots \frac{\partial U}{\partial a_n} = 0 \quad (6\text{-}17a)$$

That is, we shall use the relation,

$$\frac{\partial U}{\partial a_n} = 0 \quad (6\text{-}17)$$

and apply it to Equation (6-14).

If we perform the differentiation, the first term becomes

$$P \sin \left(\frac{n\pi b}{L} \right)$$

and the second term becomes

$$\frac{EI\pi^4}{2L^3} n^4 a_n$$

so that

$$a_n = \frac{2PL^3}{n^4 EI\pi^4} \sin \frac{n\pi b}{L} \tag{6-18}$$

and therefore

$$y = \frac{2PL^3}{EI\pi^4} \sum_{n=1}^{n=k} \frac{1}{n^4} \sin \frac{n\pi b}{L} \sin \frac{n\pi x}{L} \tag{6-19}$$

This equation will give the deflection at any point x on the beam shown in Fig. 6.18. It converges very rapidly and in most cases, only one or two terms of the series are needed to obtain sufficient accuracy.

If a uniform load, w/unit length, is on the beam, Equation (6-19) can still be used, with $P = wdb$, so that

$$dy = \frac{2wL^3}{EI\pi^4} \sum_{n=1}^{n=k} \frac{1}{n^4} \sin \frac{n\pi b}{L} \sin \frac{n\pi x}{L} \, db \tag{6-20}$$

This can then be integrated between required limits without difficulty.

In practically all cases, sufficient accuracy will be obtained by using only one or two terms of the infinite series.

Problems

In the problems which follow obtain the required deflections using

(a) The finite difference method.
(b) The relaxation method.
(c) The numerical procedure.
(d) The approximate trigonometric method.

1. Obtain δ_b, δ_c.

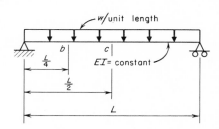

2. Obtain δ_b, δ_c.

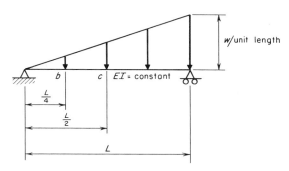

3. Obtain δ_b, δ_c.

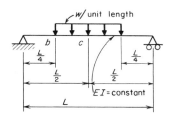

4. Obtain δ_b, δ_c. Hint: For method d, place load P, at a distance e from support A,

$$\text{let } e \to 0, \text{ as } (P)(e) \to M.$$

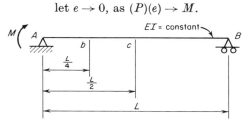

5. Solve problems 1 and 2 above for the given loadings and for the beam as below.

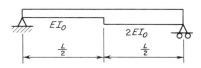

Chapter 7

TORSION OF NONCIRCULAR SECTIONS AND RELATED PROBLEMS

7-1 Introduction

The torsion problem was first solved exactly by St. Venant in 1853, using the methods of the mathematical theory of elasticity. The solution shows that, except for the circular cross section, a plane section before twisting does not remain plane; i.e., warping of the cross section takes place during twist. In this chapter we shall discuss the engineering-type solutions to the torsion problem. This will lead to the subject of shear center and unsymmetrical bending of beams. Following this, we shall describe a method for solving combined bending and torsion problems of floor framing systems using "moment distribution" methods. Finally, a very brief discussion will be given of shear lag.

7-2 The membrane analogy

In 1903 the German engineer, Ludwig Prandtl, published his important *Torsion-Membrane Analogy*. Prandtl noted that the differential equation of the torsion problem is the same as the differential equation for small lateral displacements of the surface of a thin membrane subjected to lateral pressures. If we consider this fact and properly correlate the two sets of boundary conditions, it is possible to draw an analogy between the torsion and the membrane problems. Prandtl's analogy, using a soap film as a membrane, has been successfully used to investigate torsion for different cross sections.[1] It is necessary that the membrane be stretched across a hole having a boundary the same shape as that of the bar under investigation and that it be distorted using a slight lateral pressure.

If this is done, then it can be shown that:

1. The deflection contour lines of the membrane correspond to lines

[1] Early experimental work based upon the analogy was done by A. A. Griffith and G. I. Taylor, in determining the torsional properties of complicated cross sections used in aircraft during the First World War. See *Technical Report, Advisory Committee Aeronautics*, Vol. 3, London, 1917–1918.

of shear stress in the bar, i.e., lines which are parallel to the direction of the shear stresses.

2. The magnitude of the shear stress is proportional to the slope of the membrane normal to the contour.

3. The volume between the deflected membrane and its undeflected (zero displacement) position is proportional to the torsional rigidity, KG, of the section $\left(\text{rigidity} = \dfrac{\text{torque}}{\text{unit rotation}}\right)$.

The above are the membrane analogy relations.

In general, the torsion relation is given by

$$T = KG\theta \qquad (7\text{-}1)$$

where T = internal resisting torque of a section.

G = shearing modulus of elasticity (modulus of rigidity).

θ = unit angle of twist in radians per unit length.

K = a torsion constant, dependent upon the cross section.

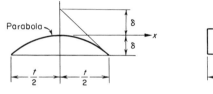

(a) Membrane displacements   (b) Stress contours

Fig. 7.1

7-3 Torsion of rectangular sections

St. Venant found that for rectangular sections of width t and depth h

$$K = \frac{t^3 h}{3} - 2Vt^4 \qquad (7\text{-}2)$$

where V is a factor dependent upon the ratio h/t. For $h/t > 3$, V is practically a constant and equal to 0.105. Equation (7-2) may be verified by use of the membrane analogy. For $h/t > 3$ (thin rectangular sections), the membrane deformations are parabolic except near the ends (Fig. 7.1a). The shear stress contours are indicated in Fig. 7.1b. The maximum stresses occur at the boundary at the center of the long side and become zero at the center line. (Refer to Art. 7-2, statement 2.) The maximum shear stresses are found to have a value,

$$\tau_{max} = \frac{3T}{ht^2} \qquad (7\text{-}3)$$

7-4   Torsion of steel rolled sections

The torsion constant of a rolled section can be evaluated approximately by considering the section to be made up of rectangles. Then

$$K = \sum \left[\frac{t^3 h}{3} - 2Vt^4 \right] \tag{7-4}$$

in which the summation is taken over the flanges and web considered as rectangles. Better values are obtained by considering the fillets and taper of the flanges. Some values of K can be found in a paper by Lyse and Johnston[2] and also in a Bethlehem Steel Company publication.[3]

7-5   Torsion of slotted tubes and complete tubular sections

By the membrane analogy, it is seen that the torsional rigidity of a slotted circular tube is substantially that of a rectangular section with $h = 2\pi R$, and width $= t$. The maximum shear stress is at the long boundaries and is given [see Equation (7-3)] by

$$\tau_{max} = \frac{3T}{2\pi R t^2} \tag{7-5}$$

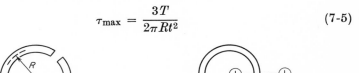

Fig. 7.2   Fig. 7.3

In the development of the membrane analogy as referred to in the preceding sections, it is assumed that the cross section is a singly connected section. By a singly connected section we mean a section which, if cut completely through, would result in two pieces. A tubular or pipe section will remain in one piece if it is cut through at a section 1–1 as illustrated in Fig. 7-3. Hence it is a multiply connected section, and the membrane analogy does not apply in the form previously given.

The membrane analogy can, however, be modified to apply to these sections.[4] For thin single cell* tubular sections it is found that the

[2] I. Lyse and B. G. Johnston, "Structural Beams in Torsion," *Transactions*, ASCE, Vol. 101, 1936, pp. 857–944.

[3] Bethlehem Steel Co., *Torsional Stresses in Structural Beams*, Booklet 5–57, 1950.

[4] S. Timoshenko, *Strength of Materials*, 3rd Ed., Part II, D. Van Nostrand Company, Inc., Princeton, N.J., 1956.

* A single cell cross section is as shown in Fig. 7-3 or 7-5. If a diametral diaphragm were introduced, it would become a double (multiple) cell structure.

shear stress is practically uniform in intensity over any thickness t and acts as shown in Fig. 7.4.

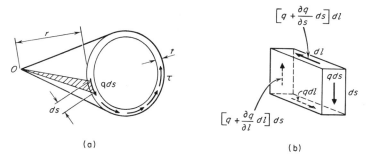

(a)   (b)

Fig. 7.4

For tubular sections of variable thickness t, the quantity $t\tau = a$ constant (see Fig. 7.4b) and is called the unit shearing force, q. That is,

$$q = t\tau \qquad (7\text{-}6)$$

The distribution of q around the perimeter is called the *shear flow*, in force per unit length.

To show that q is constant, consider the equilibrium of the element shown in Fig. 7.4b, assuming q to vary with s and l. Equating forces in two directions, we have

$$\left[q + \frac{\partial q}{\partial s}\right] dl - q\,dl = 0 \quad \text{or} \quad \frac{\partial q}{\partial s} = 0$$

$$\left[q + \frac{\partial q}{\partial l}\,dl\right] ds - q\,ds = 0 \quad \text{or} \quad \frac{\partial q}{\partial l} = 0$$

The conditions $\dfrac{\partial q}{\partial s} = 0 = \dfrac{\partial q}{\partial l}$ can be satisfied only if q is constant.

For an increment of length ds, the total force acting upon this increment is $q\,ds$ and the moment of this force about any point O is $r \cdot q\,ds$. This quantity is seen to be q times twice the shaded area of Fig. 7.4. The total twisting moment T on the section is thus

$$T = \oint rq\,ds = q \cdot 2A \qquad (7\text{-}7a)$$

or

$$q = \frac{T}{2A} \qquad (7\text{-}7b)$$

where A is the area enclosed by the median line of the tubular section.

For a circular tubular section of constant wall thickness,

$$A = 2\pi R$$

where R is the inside radius plus half the wall thickness.

As an illustration of the use of the shear flow relation, consider the rectangular section of Fig. 7.5. For this section $A = (20-1)(12-\frac{1}{2}) = 218.5$ in.^{2} Under a torque of 437,000 in.-lb, the unit shear force

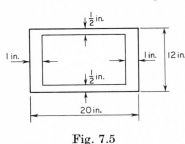

$$q = \frac{T}{2A} = \frac{437,000}{2 \times 218.5} = 1000 \text{ lb/in.}$$

For the vertical members the shear stress is

$$\tau = \frac{q}{t} = \frac{1000}{1} = 1000 \text{ lb/in.}^2$$

for the horizontal members

Fig. 7.5

$$\tau = \frac{1000}{1/2} = 2000 \text{ lb/in.}^2$$

7-6   Deformation of single cell tubular sections

A tubular section subject to pure torque will rotate about some point. Let point O be the center of rotation. A slice of a tubular section of length dl is shown in Fig. 7.6. Let $d\beta$ represent the rotation

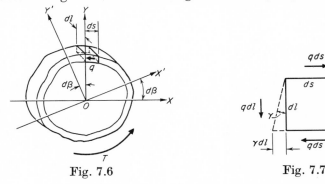

Fig. 7.6   **Fig. 7.7**

of an axis through O due to the shear deformations of the slice of differential length dl. An element of this tubular section is shown in Fig. 7.7. The forces on this element must be in equilibrium and hence are as shown. The deformed element assumes the shape (warping is ignored) indicated by the dotted lines. Now if we refer to Figs. 7.6 and 7.7,

$$\gamma = \text{shear strain} = \frac{q}{tG} \qquad (7\text{-}8)$$

The strain energy of the tubular element of Fig. 7.7 (ignoring warping) is

$$\tfrac{1}{2}(q\,ds)(\gamma\,dl) = dv_i \tag{7-9}$$

The strain energy of the tubular element of Fig. 7.6 is obtained by integrating Equation (7-9) around the circumference, or

$$dV = \oint dv_i = \oint \frac{q\gamma}{2}\,dl\,ds \tag{7-10}$$

substituting $\gamma = q/tG$ from Equation (7-8) in Equation (7-10), we obtain

$$dV = \oint \frac{q^2}{2tG}\,dl\,ds$$

and with $q = T/2A$,

$$dV = \oint \frac{T^2}{8A^2Gt}\,dl\,ds \tag{7-11}$$

The total strain energy of a bar of length l is determined by integrating Equation (7-11) over the length of the bar, in which case we obtain

$$V = \oint \frac{T^2l}{8A^2Gt}\,ds \tag{7-12}$$

By Castigliano's Theorem we obtain the rotation β of the tube of length l

$$\beta = \frac{\partial V}{\partial T} = \oint \frac{Tl}{4A^2Gt}\,ds$$

$$\beta = \oint \frac{ql}{2AGt}\,ds \tag{7-13}$$

The unit angle of twist θ is given by

$$\theta = \frac{\beta}{l} = \oint \frac{q}{2AGt}\,ds \tag{7-14}$$

We can now obtain an expression for the torsion constant of a tubular section.   From Equation (7-1),

$$K = \frac{T}{G\theta} = \frac{T}{G \oint \dfrac{q}{2AGt}\,ds} \tag{7-15}$$

For single cell sections subject to pure torsion, q is constant and may be taken out of the integral in Equation (7-15), in which case

$$K = \frac{T}{G \dfrac{q}{2AG} \oint \dfrac{ds}{t}} = \frac{T}{\dfrac{T}{4A^2} \oint \dfrac{ds}{t}} \tag{7-16}$$

or

$$K = \frac{4A^2}{\oint \dfrac{ds}{t}}$$

For a circular pipe of mean diameter D, the constant becomes

$$K = \frac{4\left(\dfrac{\pi D^2}{4}\right)^2}{\dfrac{1}{t}\cdot \pi D} = \frac{\pi D^3}{4}t \tag{7-16a}$$

For the rectangular section of Fig. 7.5, the torsional constant may be computed as follows

$$A = 218.5 \text{ in.}^2 \text{ (previously obtained)}$$

$$\oint \frac{ds}{t} = (2 \times 11.5/1) + (2 \times 19/\tfrac{1}{2}) = 99.0$$

$$K = \frac{4A^2}{\oint \dfrac{ds}{t}} = \frac{4 \times 218.5 \times 218.5}{99.0} = 1930 \text{ in.}^4$$

The unit twist of this section under a torque of 100,000 in.-lb is (for $G = 12 \times 10^6$ lb/in.^{2})

$$\theta = \frac{T}{GK} = \frac{100,000}{12 \times 10 \times 1930} \frac{\text{radians}}{\text{in.}}$$

$$= 4.32 \times 10^{-6} \frac{\text{radians}}{\text{in.}}$$

For a section 240 in. long, the total rotation β is

$$\beta = \theta \cdot l = 4.32 \times 10^{-6} \times 240 = 1.03 \times 10^{-3} \text{ radians}$$

7-7   Torsion strain energy—general cross section

The strain energy of torsion for the general cross-sectional shape, assuming the cross section is free to warp, may be found as follows.

Differential strain energy = one half the work done by the external loads for an element of length dl or

$$dV = \tfrac{1}{2}Td\beta = \tfrac{1}{2}T \cdot dl \cdot \theta$$

but

$$\theta = \frac{T}{KG}$$

$$dV = \tfrac{1}{2}\frac{T^2 dl}{KG}, \quad V = \int_l \frac{T^2 dl}{2KG} \tag{7-17}$$

[Compare this with Equation (7-12), which gives the strain energy for a tubular section.]

7-8 Combined bending and torsion—definition of the problem

In the previous chapters we have been concerned with bending of bars in a plane of symmetry, i.e., the loads have been applied in the plane of symmetry and the resulting displacements have been in this plane. The planes of symmetry are of necessity also principal planes of inertia. This simplified bending theory together with Navier's hypothesis and the other assumptions enumerated in Chapter 1 lead to the solution for the stress at any point a distance y from the neutral axis, $\sigma = My/I$, where the neutral axis is also an axis of symmetry, i.e., a principal axis. We wish now to consider the more general cases of bending in which

1. The plane of the loads is not a plane of symmetry.
2. The beam cross section is not symmetrical.
3. The loads are applied so that they produce combined bending and twisting of the cross sections.

We begin with a discussion of unsymmetrical bending.

7-9 Unsymmetrical bending—plane of loading passing through the centroid

Let us consider the case of bending of a beam of nonsymmetrical cross section (Fig. 7.8). Let 2-2 be an axis in the loading plane, 1–1

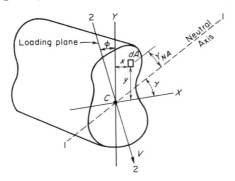

Fig. 7.8

be the neutral axis, not necessarily normal to axis 2–2. It can be shown in the usual way that the neutral axis passes through the centroid of the cross section. Let σ be the normal stress due to bending acting on a differential area dA located by coordinates x and y measured from the principal coordinate axes through the centroid of the cross section.

To satisfy equilibrium,

$$\left.\begin{array}{l} \int_A \sigma dA = 0 \\[2mm] \int_A \sigma_1 y dA = M_x \\[2mm] \int_A \sigma_2 x dA = M_y \end{array}\right\} \qquad (7\text{-}18)$$

where $\sigma = \sigma_1 + \sigma_2$, and $M_x = M \cos \phi$, $M_y = M \sin \phi$ are the components of M along the Y and X axis, respectively, and where M is the resultant moment on the section. The assumption is made, as in the case of symmetrical bending, that the stresses due to bending vary linearly with distance from the principal X–Y axes. Then from Equations (7-18), we can obtain

$$\left.\begin{array}{l} \sigma_1 = \dfrac{M_x y}{\displaystyle\int_A y^2 dA} = \dfrac{M}{I_x} y \cos \phi \\[6mm] \sigma_2 = \dfrac{M_y x}{\displaystyle\int_A x^2 dA} = \dfrac{M}{I_y} x \sin \phi \end{array}\right\} \qquad (7\text{-}18a)$$

and

$$\sigma = M\left[\frac{y \cos \phi}{I_x} + \frac{x \sin \phi}{I_y}\right] \qquad (7\text{-}19)$$

To locate the neutral axis, set $\sigma = 0$ in Equation (7-19) or

$$\frac{y \cos \phi}{I_x} + \frac{x \sin \phi}{I_y} = 0 \qquad (7\text{-}19a)$$

from which

$$\frac{y}{x} = -\frac{I_x}{Iy} \tan \phi \qquad (7\text{-}19b)$$

This expression enables us to find the angle γ locating the neutral axis, since

$$\frac{y}{x} = \tan \gamma = -\frac{I_x}{I_y} \tan \phi \qquad (7\text{-}19c)$$

Then

$$\sigma = \frac{M \cos (\alpha - \phi) Y_{NA}}{I_{NA}} \qquad (7\text{-}20)$$

in which Y_{NA} and I_{NA} are the distance from and the moment of inertia with respect to the neutral axis, 1-1. The moment of inertia of the cross section about the neutral axis can be found by using Mohr's circle of inertia (see Chap. 2).

Consider a differential length of beam, dz. Cut an oblique plane through this differential strip and consider the equilibrium of a free body contained by this plane (Fig. 7.9). The normal stresses acting on the two faces of this element dz apart will not be in balance. Adding up the forces acting on these faces, we obtain an unbalanced force

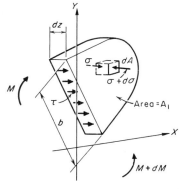

Fig. 7.9

$dF = \int_{A_1} d\sigma dA$. But from Equation (7-19),

$$d\sigma = dM \left(\frac{y \cos \phi}{I_x} + \frac{x \sin \phi}{I_y} \right)$$

so that

$$dF = dM \int_{A_1} \left(\frac{y \cos \phi}{I_x} + \frac{x \sin \phi}{I_y} \right) dA \qquad (7-21)$$

Since $\dfrac{dM}{dz} = V =$ total shear on the section, we obtain

$$dF = Vdz \int_{A_1} \left(\frac{y \cos \phi}{I_x} + \frac{x \sin \phi}{I_y} \right) dA$$

The force dF is kept in equilibrium by shear stresses τ acting on the oblique section. Let τ_{AV} be the average of these shear stresses. Then

$$\tau_{AV} \cdot b \cdot dz = dF = Vdz \int_{A_1} \left(\frac{y \cos \phi}{I_x} + \frac{x \sin \phi}{I_y} \right) dA$$

or

$$\tau_{AV} = \frac{V}{b} \int_{A_1} \left(\frac{y \cos \phi}{I_x} + \frac{x \sin \phi}{I_y} \right) dA \qquad (7-22)$$

7-10 Application to a bar of symmetric cross section

Consider the case of a cantilever beam of rectangular cross section loaded as shown in Fig. 7.10. The maximum moment $(-Pl)$ occurs at the built-in support. The fiber stresses will be found for points $ABCD$. The symmetrical X-Y axes are principal axes. Then,

$$I_x = \frac{bd^3}{12}, \quad I_y = \frac{db^3}{12}, \quad \phi = 30°$$

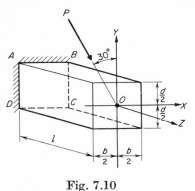

and from Equation (7-19)

$$\sigma_A = Pl\left[+\frac{5.19}{bd^2}+\frac{3}{b^2d}\right]$$

$$\sigma_B = Pl\left[+\frac{5.19}{bd^2}-\frac{3}{b^2d}\right]$$

$$\sigma_C = Pl\left[-\frac{5.19}{bd^2}-\frac{3}{b^2d}\right]$$

$$\sigma_D = Pl\left[-\frac{5.19}{bd^2}+\frac{3}{b^2d}\right]$$

Fig. 7.10

The neutral axis is located by

$$\tan\beta = -\frac{I_x}{I_y}\tan\phi = -\frac{bd^3}{b^3d}\times 0.433 = -0.433\frac{d^2}{b^2}$$

The component deflections of point O can be obtained from the expression for strain energy as follows:

$$V = \int_0^l \left[\frac{M_x{}^2}{2EI_x}+\frac{M_y{}^2}{2EI_y}\right]dz \qquad (7\text{-}23)$$

or

$$V = \int_0^l \frac{P^2(l-z)^2}{2E}\left[\frac{\cos^2\phi}{I_x}+\frac{\sin^2\phi}{I_y}\right]dz$$

The vertical component Δ_y and the horizontal component Δ_x are

$$\Delta_y = \frac{\partial V}{\partial(P\cos\phi)} = \int_0^l \frac{P\cos\phi}{EI_x}(l-z)^2\,dz = \frac{3.46Pl^3}{Ebd^3}$$

$$\Delta_x = \frac{\partial V}{\partial(P\sin\phi)} = \int_0^l \frac{P\sin\phi}{EI_y}(l-z)^2\,dz = \frac{2Pl^3}{Eb^3d}$$

The total deflection $\Delta = \sqrt{\Delta_x{}^2+\Delta_y{}^2}$. Note that the dummy load procedure could have been used here to obtain the same results.

7-11   Application to a bar with one axis of symmetry

A similar application will now be made to a built-in beam of channel section. Let the load be applied through O' as shown in Fig. 7.11. This load exerts a twisting moment about O equal to Pe. At this point we shall assume the load to be so applied that there will be no resultant twist on any section of the beam. As part of our subsequent investigation we shall locate the point O' so that this is so.   The axes

X and Y are principal axes. The component shears and bending moments at any section are V_x, V_y, M_x, M_y, where

$$M_x = P(l-z)\cos\phi \qquad V_x = P\sin\phi$$

$$M_y = P(l-z)\sin\phi \qquad V_y = P\cos\phi$$

The moments are maximum at the support; hence the maximum normal stresses at the support at points A, B, C, D are, from Equation (7-19),

$$\sigma_A = Pl\left[\frac{(h/2)\cos\phi}{I_x} + \frac{c'\sin\phi}{I_y}\right]$$

$$\sigma_B = Pl\left[\frac{(h/2)\cos\phi}{I_x} - \frac{c\sin\phi}{I_y}\right]$$

$$\sigma_C = Pl\left[\frac{-(h/2)\cos\phi}{I_x} - \frac{c\sin\phi}{I_y}\right]$$

$$\sigma_D = Pl\left[\frac{-(h/2)\cos\phi}{I_x} + \frac{c'\sin\phi}{I_y}\right]$$

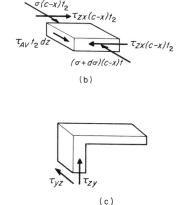

Fig. 7.11

Consider the bending state of stress of any element located a distance z from the support (see Fig. 7.12). If we cut the flange of this element by a plane such as 1-1 (Fig. 7.12a) and isolate the cut-off as a free body, the forces acting upon it are shown in Fig. 7.12b.

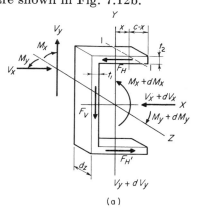

(a)

(b)

(c)

Fig. 7.12

From Equation (7-22) we see that τ_{AV} of Fig. 7.12b is

$$\tau_{AV} = \frac{V}{t_2}\int_x^c \left(\frac{y\cos\phi}{I_x} + \frac{x\sin\phi}{I_y}\right)t_2\,dx$$

or

$$\tau_{AV} = V_y\left(\frac{h-t_2}{2}\right)\frac{(c-x)}{I_x} + V_x\frac{(c^2-x^2)}{2I_y} \tag{7-24}$$

From the equilibrium of the free body (see Fig. 7.12b) we see that

$$\tau_{AV}t_2dz(c-x) = \tau_{zx}(c-x)t_2dz$$

or

$$\tau_{zx} = \tau_{AV} \tag{7-24a}$$

The resultant shear force on the face of one flange

$$F_H = \int_{-(c'-t_1)}^{+c} \tau_{zx}t_2dx$$

$$F_H = \int_{-(c'-t_1)}^{+c}\left[\left(\frac{h-t_2}{2}\right)(c-x)\frac{V_y}{I_x} + \left(\frac{c^2-x^2}{2}\right)\frac{V_x}{I_y}\right]t_2dx \tag{7-25a}$$

Likewise, it can be shown that

$$F_H' = \int_{-(c'-t_1)}^{+c}\left[-\left(\frac{h-t_2}{2}\right)(c-x)\frac{V_y}{I_x} + \left(\frac{c^2-x^2}{2}\right)\frac{V_x}{I_y}\right]t_2dx = -F_H \tag{7-25b}$$

Then, the average shear stress $\tau_{zy} = \tau_{yz}$ (see Fig. 7.12c) is found from Equation (7-22) to be

$$\tau_{zy} = \int_y^{(\frac{1}{2}h-t_2)}\left[y\frac{V_y}{I_x} - \left(c'-\frac{t_1}{2}\right)\frac{V_x}{I_y}\right]dy \tag{7-26}$$

or

$$\tau_{zy} = \left[\frac{(\frac{1}{2}h-t_2)^2-y^2}{2I_x}V_y - \frac{(\frac{1}{2}h-t_2-y)\left(c'-\frac{t_1}{2}\right)}{I_y}V_x\right] \tag{7-26a}$$

By integrating, we obtain

$$F_V = \int_{-(\frac{1}{2}h-t_2)}^{+(\frac{1}{2}h-t_2)} \tau_{zy}t_1dy \tag{7-27}$$

The additional vertical force resulting from the vertical shear stresses in the flanges is neglected in the expression for F_V [Equation (7-27)] and the additional horizontal force resulting from the shear in the web is likewise neglected.

The forces F_V and F_H should now satisfy the equations of equilibrium. If they do not, additional stresses must be present such that the equilibrium equations will be satisfied. The conditions $\sum V = \sum H = \sum M = 0$ lead to the following:

$$V_y + F_V = 0 \tag{7-28a}$$

$$V_x + F_H - F_H' = 0 \tag{7-28b}$$

and if we take moments about point O

$$- V_y e_1 + (F_H + F_H')\left(\frac{h - t_2}{2}\right) + F_V\left(c' - \frac{t_1}{2}\right) = 0 \qquad (7\text{-}28\text{c})$$

Equation (7-28c) locates the point through which V_y (or P) is applied. This point is called the *shear center* and is located on the axis of symmetry. It can be shown by proceeding as above that the shear center always lies on the axis or axes of symmetry of the cross section. In the general case of a bar subjected to transverse loads, torsional stresses are introduced unless the loads are applied through the shear center. Thus, we can define the shear center as follows:

The shear center of a beam is a line made up of points through which the line of action of transverse loads must pass in order that the beam be subjected to bending alone—i.e., bending without torsion.

If P is applied through any point other than the shear center, the resulting torque will develop torsion stress. The torsion stress distribution which results from not applying the load through the shear center usually will not be in accordance with the membrane analogy as described in the first part of this chapter. This is because in the general problem of combined bending and torsion, warping is restrained at prescribed points on the boundary; hence, the membrane analogy does not apply. Approximate solutions of the problem, however, can be found[5] in the literature.

To locate the shear center for the channel section of Fig. 7.12, we write Equation (7-28c) as follows:

$$e_1 = \frac{F_H + F_H'}{V_y}\left(\frac{h - t_2}{2}\right) - \left(c' - \frac{t_1}{2}\right) \qquad (7\text{-}29)$$

from which (see Fig. 7.11)

$$e_2 = \frac{F_H + F_H'}{V_y}\left(\frac{h - t_2}{2}\right) \qquad (7\text{-}29\text{a})$$

This method can be applied to locate the shear center for arbitrary cross-sectional shapes.

The shear center has the following additional property: If a section is subjected to pure torsion, the center of rotation will coincide with

[5] S. Timoshenko, *Strength of Materials*, 3rd Ed., Part II, D. Van Nostrand Company, Inc., Princeton, N.J., 1956, p. 261.

the shear center. This follows from the law of reciprocal deflections which states:[6]

The deflection of a generalized load Q_1, due to another load Q_2, is equal to the deflection of the load Q_2 caused by Q_1.

If Q_1 is a force, Q_2 is a torque, and both are applied at the shear center, the property stated above follows.

7-12 Deflections of unsymmetrical sections

If the loads pass through the shear center, Equation (7-23) may be used to find the strain energy of a beam of unsymmetrical section and Castigliano's Theorem can then be used to find the components of displacement of the center of gravity of any particular cross section. If the loads do not pass through the shear center, the strain energy may be approximated [see Equation (7-17)] by

$$V = \int_l \left[\frac{M_x{}^2}{2EI_x} + \frac{M_y{}^2}{2EI_y} + \frac{T^2}{2KG} \right] dz \qquad (7\text{-}30)$$

In this expression it is assumed that the cross section is free to warp. See Art. 7-20 for the more general expression corresponding to warping restrained.

The component deflections of the center of gravity of any cross section are found as before; the twist of any cross section is also found by applying Castigliano's Theorem.

If preferred, the unit load method can be used in place of Castigliano's Theorem for computing component deflections and twist.

7-13 Shear center of an angle section

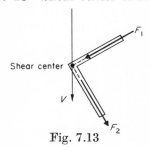

Shear center

V

Fig. 7.13

For an angular cross section the shear stresses due to bending develop resultant shear forces F_1 and F_2 in each leg. The intersection of the lines of action of F_1 and F_2 must be the shear center (see Fig. 7.13). This is so, because the resultant shear V on the section and forces F_1 and F_2 must form a concurrent force system if there is to be no twist on the section.

7-14 Illustrative problem—channel section

Example: A built-up channel section having the cross section shown is loaded as a simple beam with a single concentrated load of 10 kip acting

[6] See Art. 2-11.

through the shear center at the middle of a 14-ft span. Locate the shear center and find the maximum bending and shear stresses.

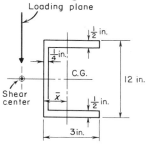

Fig. 7.14

Solution: Ignore the weight of the beam.   The reactions are also applied through the shear center.

Properties of the Section:

$$\bar{x} = \frac{11 \times 0.250 \times 0.125 + 2 \times 3 \times 0.5 \times 1.5}{11 \times 0.25 + 2 \times 3 \times 0.5} = 0.82 \text{ in.}$$

$$I_x = \tfrac{1}{12} \times 0.25 \times (11)^3 + \tfrac{2}{12} \times 3 \times (0.5)^3 + 2 \times 3 \times 0.5 \times (5.75)^2 = 126.8 \text{ in.}^4$$

$$I_y = \frac{2 \times 0.5 \times (3)^3}{12} + \tfrac{11}{12}(0.25)^3 + 11 \times 0.25 \times (0.695)^2 = 3.58 \text{ in.}^4$$

Since the X axis is an axis of symmetry, I_x and I_y are principal moments of inertia and $I_{xy} = 0$

Location of the shear center:

From equilibrium,

$$F_V = 5 \text{ kip} = V_y$$

By Equation (7-25a),

$$F_H = \int_{-(0.82-0.25)}^{+2.18} \left[\left(\frac{12-0.5}{2}\right)(2.18-x)\left(\frac{5}{126.8}\right) \right](0.5)dx = +0.402 \text{ kip}$$

For equilibrium,

$$F_H' = -F_H = -0.402 \text{ kip}, \quad e_2 = \frac{F_H}{V_y}(12-0.5) = 0.930 \text{ in.}$$

Note: Since F_H and F_V contain V_y as a factor, it is seen that the location of the shear center is independent of the load.

Maximum stresses:

The maximum bending and shear stresses are given by Equations (7-19) and (7-22) and are

Bending

$$\sigma_{\max} = \pm \frac{M_x y}{I_x} = \pm \frac{420 \times 6}{126.8} = \pm 19.85 \text{ kip/in.}^2$$

Shear

at the neutral axis

$$\tau_{\max} = \frac{V \int y \, dA}{I_x t} = \frac{5}{126.8 \times 0.25} [3 \times 0.5 \times 5.75 + 5.5 \times 0.25 \times 2.75]$$

$$= 1.955 \text{ kip/in.}^2$$

7-15　Combined bending and torsion of straight bars

Thus far we have assumed no restraint against warping, i.e., elements of the bar are not restrained in any way at the boundary or elsewhere against longitudinal displacements. For these cases of simple torsion it was pointed out that there is a linear relation betweeen torque and unit rotation [Equation (7-1)] and the shear stress relations are given by the membrane analogy. For bars of solid section, such as ellipses or rectangles, restraint against warping has a negligible effect on rotation provided that the cross-sectional dimensions are small when compared with the length of the bar.[7] For structural shapes, however, the effect of warping is appreciable in most cases and cannot be neglected in torsion analysis. A complete mathematical solution of the torsion problem considering warping restraints has not as yet been obtained. Approximate solutions for structural shapes are available,[8] however, and will be outlined in the succeeding articles.

7-16　Torsion of structural shapes subject to restraint against warping

Example: As an example of the general approach that can be used to solve problems of combined bending and torsion, consider the twisting due to an applied torque T, of a symmetrical structural shape whose ends are fixed so that warping of the end section A is prevented (see Fig. 7.15a).

Solution: In the solution to follow it is assumed that

1. The distortion in the plane of the cross section is negligible.
2. All displacements are small enough that secondary effects of displacement can be ignored.
3. The displacements of the flanges are caused primarily by bending of the flanges about the Y axis; shear deformations due to bending are neglected.
4. $\dfrac{I_y}{2}$ is the moment of inertia of one flange about the Y axis.

In Fig. 7.15b, the displacement of any cross section is shown. Since the cross section is symmetric the center of rotation (which we have seen is the

[7] S. Timoshenko, *Strength of Materials*, 3rd Ed., Part II, D. Van Nostrand Company, Inc., Princeton, N.J., 1956, p. 255.

[8] For a list of investigators, *ibid.*, p. 255, and I. Lyse and B. G. Johnston, "Structural Beams in Torsion," *Transactions*, ASCE, Vol. 101, 1936, pp. 857–944.

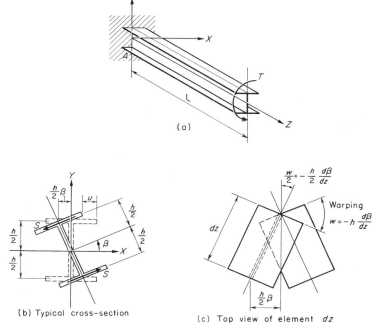

(a)

(b) Typical cross-section

(c) Top view of element dz

Fig. 7.15

shear center and is the center of symmetry) is in this case the center of gravity of the section. Hence, there will be no vertical or lateral displacement of the center of rotation. The flange, however, has been displaced a distance u. An approximate relation between u and the rotation β is

$$u = -\frac{h}{2}\beta \qquad (7\text{-}31)$$

Then by assumption 3 above, using the elementary theory of bending we have

$$M_f = EI_f \frac{d^2u}{dz^2} = -EI_f \frac{h}{2}\frac{d^2\beta}{dz^2} \qquad (7\text{-}32)$$

and the transverse shear in the flange is given by

$$S = \frac{dM_f}{dz} = EI_f \frac{d^3u}{dz^3} = -EI_f \frac{h}{2}\frac{d^3\beta}{dz^3} \qquad (7\text{-}33)$$

In the above, I_f=moment of inertia of flange with respect to the Y axis or $I_f \doteq \frac{I_y}{2}$, and M_f is the bending moment in the flange about the Y axis.

The torque T_1 developed by the pair of transverse shears, S, given by Equation (7-32) is

$$T_1 = Sh = -EI_f \frac{h^2}{2} \frac{d^3\beta}{dz^3}$$

or

$$T_1 = -EI_y \frac{h^2}{4} \frac{d^3\beta}{dz^3} \tag{7-34}$$

Equation (7-34) is an approximate expression for T_1. The torque T_2 developed by the section in pure torsion (no restraints against warping), is given in terms of the torsional rigidity of the section [Equation (7-1)] or,

$$T_2 = KG \frac{d\beta}{dz}$$

The total torsion on any section is $T = T_1 + T_2$ and this is constant over the length L. From the expressions developed above, this becomes

$$T = -EI_y \frac{h^2}{4} \frac{d^3\beta}{dz^3} + KG \frac{d\beta}{dz} \tag{7-35}$$

Since T is constant, $dT/dz = 0$, and Equation (7-35) leads to

$$-EI_y \frac{h^2}{4} \frac{d^4\beta}{dz^4} + KG \frac{d^2\beta}{dz^2} = 0 \tag{7-35a}$$

Equation (7-35) is the (approximate) general differential equation of the problem. Its solution in terms of arbitrary constants A, B, C, D is given by

$$\beta = A \sinh \frac{z}{a} + B \cosh \frac{z}{a} + C + Dz \tag{7-36}$$

where

$$a = \sqrt{\frac{EI_y h^2}{4KG}}$$

7-17 Outline of the solution of a particular problem: simple beam subject to twist T applied at the center of the span

The beam of Fig. 7.16 is simply supported at A and C and is seen to be a combination of two beams of the type shown in Fig. 7.15a. For this problem it follows that

1. There can be no warping at the mid-section of the beam because of symmetry.
2. The section from B to C represents the same set of conditions as occur in the beam of Fig. 7.15a.
3. The section from A to B is the mirror image of the section from B to C; hence its solution is known if the solution for BC is known.
4. Equation (7-36) is the general solution of the beam section between B and C subject to the following boundary conditions:

(a) At $z = L$, $\beta = 0$ and $d^2\beta/dz^2 = 0$.

The condition $\beta = 0$ is prescribed since C is a simple support, and $d^2\beta/dz^2 = 0$ follows since the moment in the flanges must be zero at the supports.

(b) At $z = 0$, there is zero warping; $\therefore w = 0$ (see Fig. 7.15c). This means that at $z = 0$, $w = -h \, d\beta/dz = 0$, or $d\beta/dz = 0$.

(c) At $z = L$, the torque is given by Equation (7-1), since the beam is free to warp at the end sections. This yields the condition

$$\frac{T}{2} = KG \frac{d\beta}{dz}$$

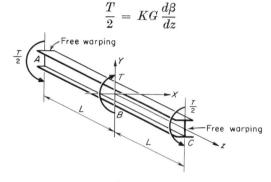

Fig. 7.16

The use of the four boundary conditions expressed in (a), (b), and (c) above will enable one to find the arbitrary constants of Equation (7-36). This will give the solution of the differential equation for the section of the beam from B to C; that from A to B is then known by symmetry.

The complete solution of this and other problems involving I-type beams can be found in a paper by John E. Goldberg.[9] Solutions for various cases are given below for use in the torsion analysis of floor framing systems in Arts. 7-24, 7-25, and 7-26.

Particular I-Type Beam Solutions:

(a) Flanges pinned at each end, warping not restrained, constant torsion, T.

$$\beta = \frac{T}{KG} z \qquad (7\text{-}36\text{a})$$

(b) Arbitrary warping, w_0, at one end, flanges not restrained at other end, constant torsion, T.

$$\beta = a\left(\frac{T}{KG} - \frac{w_0}{h}\right)\left(\tanh \frac{L}{a} \cosh \frac{z}{a} - \sinh \frac{z}{a} - \tanh \frac{L}{a}\right)\left(\frac{\cosh \dfrac{L}{a}}{\cosh \dfrac{L}{a} - 1}\right) + \frac{Tz}{KG}$$

[9] John E. Goldberg, "Torsion of I type and H type Beams," Paper No. 145, *Proceedings*, ASCE, August 1952.

For large values of $\dfrac{L}{a}$, $\left(\dfrac{\cosh \dfrac{L}{a}}{\cosh \dfrac{L}{a} - 1} \right) \doteq 1$ and

$$\beta = a \left(\frac{T}{KG} - \frac{w_0}{h} \right) \left(\tanh \frac{L}{a} \cosh \frac{z}{a} - \sinh \frac{z}{a} - \tanh \frac{L}{a} \right) + \frac{Tz}{KG} \qquad (7\text{-}36b)$$

Note: if one end is built-in set $w_0 = 0$.

(c) Prescribed warping, w_0 and w_L, at both ends, constant torsion, T.

$$\beta = a \left(\frac{w_0}{h} - \frac{T}{KG} \right) \sinh \frac{z}{a}$$

$$+ \frac{a \cosh \dfrac{a}{z}}{\sinh \dfrac{L}{a}} \left[\frac{w_L}{h} - \frac{T}{KG} - \left(\frac{w_0}{h} - \frac{T}{KG} \right) \cosh \frac{L}{a} \right]$$

$$+ \frac{Tz}{KG} - \frac{a}{\sinh \dfrac{L}{a}} \left(\frac{w_L}{h} - \frac{T}{KG} \right) + \frac{a \cosh \dfrac{L}{a}}{\sin \dfrac{L}{a}} \left(\frac{w_0}{h} - \frac{T}{KG} \right) \qquad (7\text{-}36c)$$

(d) Torque T applied L_1 from one end, L_2 from other end; warping w_1 and w_2 prescribed at each end, torque reactions are T_1 and T_2.

This last case is seen to be a composite of two type (c) cases. The additional boundary conditions applicable to each side of T necessary to the complete solution are consistent deformations at the point of juncture, i.e., the point of application of the loading twist, T.

These conditions at the point of application of T are

1. Warping angles must be equal.
2. Angular displacements β_0 must be equal.
3. Longitudinal fiber strains or $d^2\beta/dz^2$ must be equal.
4. $T_1 + T_2 = T$.

Use of these conditions will lead to a series of simultaneous equations that can be solved for w_0 (warping angle at point of application of T), T_1, and T_2. These values can then be used in Equation (7-36c) to define the rotation function β for the portions L_1 and L_2 of the beam. When β is known, the solution is completely defined. If w_1 and w_2 are not defined at the ends of the beam (the beam is free to warp at the boundaries), we find that

$$T_1 = \frac{TL_2}{L_1 + L_2} \qquad (7\text{-}36d)$$

$$T_2 = \frac{TL_1}{L_1 + L_2} \qquad (7\text{-}36e)$$

For $0 \leqslant z \leqslant L_1$, find β_1 using Equation (7-36b) with T_1 in place of T. For $L_1 \leqslant z \leqslant (L_1 + L_2)$, find β_2 using Equation (7-36b) with T_2 in place of T.

7-18 Combined bending and torsion of symmetric structural shapes

In the case of a bending load being applied to a structural shape in addition to a torque, all sections will be subject to lateral and vertical displacements as well as twist. The displacements of the center of gravity of the section are given by coordinates x and y. Three differential equations can be written by considering the problem of twisting without transverse loads and that of bending without twist. For constant torque, if we assume linear superposition of bending and torsion effects is permissible, the general differential equations of the problem of combined bending and twisting become [using Equation (7-35a)]

$$-EI_y \frac{h^2}{4} \frac{d^4\beta}{dz^4} + KG \frac{d^2\beta}{dz^2} = 0$$

$$EI_x \frac{d^4y}{dz^4} = -q_V$$

$$EI_y \frac{d^4x}{dz^4} = -q_H \qquad (7\text{-}37)$$

in which q_V and q_H represent vertical and horizontal load functions, respectively.

7-19 Combined bending and torsion of channel sections

For a channel section subject to twist with warping restraints at the boundaries, the problem differs somewhat from that of the symmetric I-type section. Because the center of rotation is the shear center, the web will be subject to vertical displacements $v \doteq e\beta$, the flanges are horizontally displaced $\mu = \pm \dfrac{h}{2} \beta$. As before, e is the distance between the shear center and the centroid of the web. The differential Equation (7-35) must therefore be modified to allow for the bending of the web. This differential Equation (7-38) is given by[10]

$$T = KG \frac{d\beta}{dz} - EI_y \frac{h^2}{2}\left(1 + \frac{t_1 h^3}{4I_x}\right) \frac{d^3\beta}{dz^3} \qquad (7\text{-}38)$$

where t_1 is the thickness of the web.

[10] S. Timoshenko, *Strength of Materials*, 3rd Ed., Part I, D. Van Nostrand Company, Inc., Princeton, N.J., 1955.

It is seen that Equation (7-38) is of the same type as the equation for the I-beam, Equation (7-35), but that β is measured through the shear center. The general solution of Equation (7-38) is given by Equation (7-36) provided that

$$a = \sqrt{\frac{EI_yh}{2KG}\left(1 + \frac{t_1h^3}{4I_x}\right)}$$

For a channel section subject to torsion only, there will be no displacement of the shear center. For applied torsion plus direct loads applied through the shear center, there will be displacement of the shear center of each cross section. To find these displacements, it is necessary to solve Equation (7-38) together with the equations

$$EI_x\frac{d^4y}{dz^4} = -q_V, \qquad EI_y\frac{d^4x}{dz^4} = -q_H$$

in which the origin of the X, Y axes is taken through the shear center.

7-20 Strain energy of structural I shapes subject to combined bending and twist, warping restrained

An approximate strain energy expression for combined bending and twisting can be developed by combining the strain energy of

1. Bending in the Y plane, $V_1 = \displaystyle\int_L \frac{EI_xy''^2}{2}\,dx$

2. Bending in the X plane, $V_2 = \displaystyle\int_L \frac{EI_yx''^2}{2}\,dx$

3. Bending of the flanges due to twist,

$$V_3 = 2\int_L \frac{M_f^2dz}{EI_y} = \int_L EI_y\frac{h^2}{8}\beta''^2\,dz$$

4. Pure twist of the section, $V_4 = \displaystyle\int_L \frac{T^2dz}{2KG} = \int_L \frac{KG\beta'^2}{2}\,dz$

The total strain energy is then given by

$$V = \frac{1}{2}\int_L \left[EI_xy''^2 + EI_yx''^2 + EI_y\frac{h^2}{4}\beta''^2 + KG\beta'^2\right]dz \qquad (7\text{-}39)$$

In this expression it is assumed that warping is restrained. See Art. 7-12, which considers the less general case in which warping is not restrained.

7-21   Stresses due to combined bending and torsion of I sections

When the general solution for the rotation β has been obtained, the stresses may be found by superposition as follows:

Normal stresses in flanges,

Due to bending in y plane $\sigma_1 = -\dfrac{M_x y}{I_x}$

Due to bending in x plane $\sigma_2 = -\dfrac{M_y x}{I_y}$

Due to bending caused by twist $\sigma_3 = -\dfrac{M_f x}{I_f} = +\dfrac{Ehx}{2}\dfrac{d^2\beta}{dz^2}$

The total normal stress in the flange is therefore given by

$$\sigma_{FL} = \left[-\frac{M_x y}{I_x} - \frac{M_y x}{I_y} + \frac{Ehx}{2}\beta'' \right] \qquad (7\text{-}40a)$$

Normal stresses in the web are given by

$$\sigma_w = -\left[\frac{M_x y}{I_x} + \frac{M_y x}{I_y} \right] \qquad (7\text{-}40b)$$

The second term of Equation (7-40b) will generally be negligible.

Shear stresses can be found by applying balancing forces. In the flanges (see Fig. 7.17)

$$\tau_{zx} t_f dz = \int_x^{b/2} d\sigma_{AV}\cdot t_f dx$$

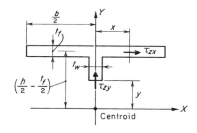

Fig. 7.17

where σ_{AV} is the flange normal stress measured at $y = h/2$. Thus, using Equation (7-40a), we obtain

$$\sigma_{AV} = -\left[\frac{M_x h}{2I_x} + \frac{M_y x}{I_y} - \frac{Ehx}{2}\beta'' \right]$$

$$\frac{d\sigma_{AV}}{dz} = -\left[+\frac{V_y h}{2I_x} + \frac{V_x x}{I_y} - \frac{Ehx}{2}\beta''' \right]$$

$$\tau_{zx} = -\int_x^{b/2} \left[\frac{V_y h}{2I_x} + \frac{V_x x}{I_y} - \frac{Ehx}{2}\beta''' \right] dx \qquad (7\text{-}40c)$$

The shear in the web τ_{zy} is obtained likewise:

$$\tau_{zy}\, t_w\, dz = \int_{-b/2}^{+b/2} (d\sigma_{AV})_{FL}\cdot t_f\, dx + \int_y^{1/2(h-t_f)} d\sigma_w\, t_w\, dy$$

From Equation (7-40b),

$$\frac{d\sigma_w}{dz} = -\frac{V_y y}{I_x}$$

Using this and the expression already obtained for $(d\sigma_{AV})_{FL}$, we have

$$\tau_{zy} t_w \, dz = -\int_{-b/2}^{+b/2} \left[\frac{V_y h}{2I_x} + \frac{V_x x}{I_y} - \frac{Ehx}{2} \beta'''\right] t_f dz \, dx - \int_y^{1/2(h-t_f)} \frac{V_y y}{I_x} t_w \, dz \, dy$$

Simplifying, we obtain

$$\tau_{zy} = -\frac{t_f}{t_w}\left[V_y \frac{h}{2} \frac{b}{I_x}\right] - \frac{V_y}{2I_x}\left[\left(\frac{h-t_f}{2}\right)^2 - y^2\right] \qquad (7\text{-}40\text{d})$$

Similar expressions can be developed for the channel section.

7-22   Combined bending and twist of the general unsymmetric section

The general unsymmetric section may be represented by the cross section of Fig. 7.18.   This is a typical stressed skin and stringer wing cross section. V, H and M are a typical general loading.   The areas of the stringers and skin are usually concentrated at points as shown in the figure and the solution is obtained by satisfying the static requirements of equilibrium and also the requirements of consistent deforma-

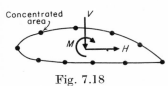

Fig. 7.18

tion.   The methods used are those described in the previous sections of this chapter.   For a more detailed discussion of the problem, the reader is referred to textbooks in airplane structural analysis.[11]

7-23   Floor framing systems subject to combined bending and torsion—solid sections

Beams subjected to vertical load and framing into girders will generally exert torque upon the girders (see Fig. 7.19).   The system shown is subject to combinations of torsion and bending.   Such a system can be analyzed utilizing the theories presented in this chapter. In particular, moment distribution can be extended to cover cases of this kind.[12]   A general method of solution, using moment distribution, will now be described.

[11] Two representative texts are:
A. S. Niles and J. S. Newell, *Airplane Structures*, Vol. 1, 4th Ed., 1951 (and Vol. II, 3rd Ed., 1950) John Wiley and Sons, New York.
E. F. Bruhn, *Analysis and Design of Airplane Structures*, Tri-State Offset Co., Cincinnati, Ohio, 1946.
[12] P. Andersen, "Design of Reinforced Concrete in Torsion," *Transactions*, ASCE, 1938, p. 1503.

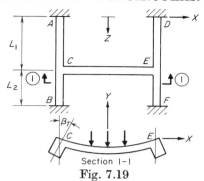

Fig. 7.19

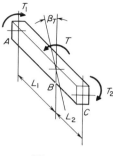

Fig. 7.20

7-24   Floor framing systems—rectangular cross sections

For a concrete floor system with beams of symmetric rectangular section, the effect of warping and restraints can be ignored (see Art. 7-15). In this case, slope-deflection type equations can be developed, from which moment distribution procedures can be set up.

Consider a bar of solid cross section with an external torque T applied somewhere along its length (Fig. 7.20). The bar is supported at the ends in such a way that there can be no rotation and no displacement of the end cross sections. To find the reactions T_1 and T_2, we use the condition that the rotation of sections an infinitesimal distance to either side of T must be the same. Then

$$\beta_T = \frac{T_1 L_1}{KG} = \frac{T_2 L_2}{KG} \tag{7-41a}$$

From equilibrium,

$$T = T_1 + T_2 \tag{7-41b}$$

Solving for T_1 and T_2, we obtain

$$T_1 = \frac{T L_2}{L_1 + L_2}, \qquad T_2 = \frac{T L_1}{L_1 + L_2} \tag{7-41c}$$

In moment distribution terminology, T_1 and T_2 can represent the "fixed-end twists" produced by an applied twist T acting somewhere along the length of the bar.

The distribution factors can be defined in terms of the particular value of $T(=T_0)$ that will make the rotation $\beta_T = 1$ radian.

From Equation (7-41c), this leads to

$$\beta_T = \frac{T_1 L_1}{KG} = \frac{T_0 L_1 L_2}{KG(L_1 + L_2)} = 1 \text{ radian}$$

or

$$T_0 = KG \left(\frac{L_1 + L_2}{L_1 L_2} \right)$$

The portion of T_0 that is distributed to each side of the bar is given by

$$T_{10} = \frac{T_0 L_2}{L_1 + L_2} = \frac{KG}{L_1} \qquad (7\text{-}41\text{d})$$

$$T_{20} = \frac{T_0 L_1}{L_1 + L_2} = \frac{KG}{L_2} \qquad (7\text{-}41\text{e})$$

The torque stiffness factors become, by definition,

$$K_{T_{CA}} = \frac{KG}{L_1}$$

$$K_{T_{CB}} = \frac{KG}{L_2}$$

To avoid unnecessary confusion between K denoting torsion constant and K denoting distribution factors, we substitute the symbol J for the torsion constant, in which case

$$K_{T_{CA}} = \frac{JG}{L_1} \qquad (7\text{-}42\text{a})$$

$$K_{T_{CB}} = \frac{JG}{L_2} \qquad (7\text{-}42\text{b})$$

It will be noted that the torque carry-over factors to ends A and B are both unity provided these ends are constrained against rotation.

Consider the case of a beam CE framing into a girder AB as shown in Fig. 7.19. If we consider joints C and E to be initially constrained against rotation ($\beta_T = 0$), fixed-end moments will be developed in beam CE. If we release joint C in accordance with moment distribution procedure, joint C will rotate until the fixed moment at C is balanced by the change in bending moment on CE and torques T_{BA} and T_{BC} which will develop in the girder AB. The bending moment stiffness factor for CE is given by $\left(\dfrac{4EI}{L}\right)_{CE} = K_{CE}$ Then

$$M_{CE} = \frac{-M_{F_{CE}} \cdot K_{CE}}{K_{T_{CA}} + K_{T_{CB}} + K_{CE}} = -D_{CE} M_{F_{CE}} \qquad (7\text{-}43\text{a})$$

$$T_{CA} = \frac{-M_{F_{CE}} \cdot K_{T_{CA}}}{K_{T_{CA}} + K_{T_{CB}} + K_{CE}} = -D_{T_{CA}} M_{F_{CE}} \qquad (7\text{-}43\text{b})$$

$$T_{CB} = \frac{-M_{F_{CE}} \cdot K_{T_{CB}}}{K_{T_{CA}} + K_{T_{CB}} + K_{CE}} = -D_{T_{CB}} M_{F_{CE}} \qquad (7\text{-}43\text{c})$$

where the D values are the distribution factors. For vertical loads on span CE (Fig. 7.19), the moment distribution procedure applied in accordance with usual practice (see Chapter 4) will finally result in a balance between bending moments in CE and twisting moments in AB and DF. In other words, moments induced by rotations in planes parallel to the XY plane (Fig. 7.19) will be balanced. It will next be necessary to consider rotations in planes parallel to the YZ plane. These will result in bending moments in girders AB and DF. If the loading is not symmetric, twisting moments will also be induced in beam CE. These may or may not be of the same order of magnitude as the torques considered in the original moment distribution. To obtain their values and effects, the moment distribution procedure must be applied in planes parallel to the XY and the YZ planes and the final results obtained by superposition of effects. In addition to this there may be some effects due to differential settlement of supports (see the unsymmetric structure illustrative problem given in Art. 7-26).

Moment Distribution Sign Convention:

In agreement with the sign convention established in Chapter 4, twisting moments will be considered positive if they act counter-clockwise on a positive face of a free body of the joint and if they act clockwise on a negative face. (See Fig. 7.21 for illustration.)

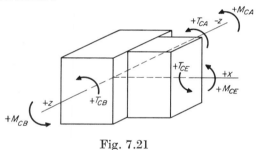

Fig. 7.21

7-25 Illustrative problem—symmetric loads, symmetric structure

Example: A single vertical concentrated load of 40 kip acts on the center of beam CE (Fig. 7.22). Using moment distribution, find the resulting bending moments and torques at A, B, C, E, F, D (use $G=0.4E$.)

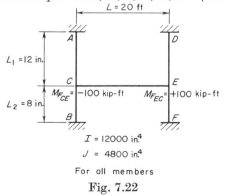

Fig. 7.22

Solution: If we take advantage of symmetry,

$$K_{CE} = \frac{1}{2}\left(\frac{4EI}{L}\right)_{CE} = \frac{1}{2} \times \frac{12,000}{20} \times 4E = 1200E$$

$$K_{T_{CB}} = \frac{JG}{L_2} = \frac{4800 \times 0.4E}{8} = 240E$$

$$K_{T_{CA}} = \frac{JG}{L_1} = \frac{4800 \times 0.4E}{12} = 160E$$

The F.E.M.'s are calculated as $\pm\dfrac{PL}{8} = \pm\dfrac{40 \times 20}{8} = \pm100$ kip-ft and are shown on Fig. 7.22.

Releasing joint C and E simultaneously, we obtain the changes in the moments

$$M_{CE} = +\frac{1200E}{(1200+240+160)E} \times 100 \text{ kip-ft} = +75 \text{ kip-ft}$$

$$T_{CA} = +\frac{240}{1600} \times 100 = +15 \text{ kip-ft}$$

$$T_{CB} = +\frac{160}{1600} \times 100 = +10 \text{ kip-ft}$$

The carry-over factors for torque are $(+1)$; hence

$$T_{AC} = +15 \text{ kip-ft}, \quad T_{BC} = +10 \text{ kip-ft}$$

These values are shown on Fig. 7.23.

Due to the given load the framework will deflect in the YZ plane. By symmetry

$$\Delta_C = \Delta_E \qquad \text{(deflection in } Y \text{ direction)}$$
$$\theta_{CE} = -\theta_{EC} \qquad \text{(rotation in } XZ \text{ plane)}$$
$$\theta_{CB} = \theta_{EF} \qquad \text{(rotation in } YZ \text{ plane)}$$

Hence, it follows that:

1. There is no twist in beam CE.

2. The effect of the symmetric load is distributed equally to both girders.

Each girder then can be analyzed as a beam subject to a load of 20 kip at the 12-ft point. If A and B are simple supports, there will be a moment at $C = \dfrac{8 \times 12}{20} \times 20 = 96$ kip-ft. These moments are not shown on Fig. 7.23. The final answers are tabulated below.

$$M_{CE} = -M_{EC} = -25 \text{ kip-ft}$$

$$T_{AC} = T_{CA} = +15 \text{ kip-ft} = -T_{DE} = -T_{ED}$$

$$T_{CB} = T_{BC} = +10 \text{ kip-ft} = -T_{EF} = -T_{FE}$$

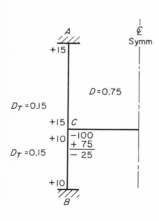

Fig. 7.23

In beam AB, bending moment at C,
$$M_{CA} = +96 \text{ kip-ft} = -M_{CB}$$
In beam DF, bending moment at E,
$$M_{ED} = +96 \text{ kip-ft} = -M_{EF}$$

7-26 Illustrative problems—unsymmetric structure

Example: A single vertical load of 40 kip acts on the center of span CE (Fig. 7.24). Using moment distribution, find the resulting bending moments and torques at A, B, C, E, F, D (use $G = 0.4E$).

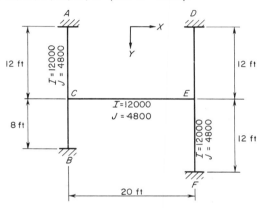

Fig. 7.24

Solution: Stiffness Factors:

$$K_{CE} = \frac{4EI}{L} = 2400E$$

$$K_{T_{CA}} = K_{T_{ED}} = K_{T_{EF}} = \frac{4800 \times 0.4E}{12} = 160E$$

$$K_{T_{CB}} = \frac{4800 \times 0.4E}{8} = 240E$$

The F.E.M.'s are ± 100 kip-ft as before. We will first consider the two-dimensional problem of moments and twists in planes parallel to the XY plane.

Distribution Factors:

Joint C

$$D_{CE} = \frac{2400}{2400 + 160 + 240} = 0.857$$

$$D_{T_{CA}} = \frac{160}{2800} = 0.057$$

$$D_{T_{CB}} = \frac{240}{2800} = 0.086$$

$$\sum = \overline{1.000} \text{ check}$$

Joint E

$$D_{EC} = \frac{2400}{2400+160+160} = 0.882$$

$$D_{T_{EF}} = D_{T_{ED}} = \frac{160}{2720} = 0.059$$

$$\sum = \overline{1.000} \text{ check}$$

Moment Distribution:

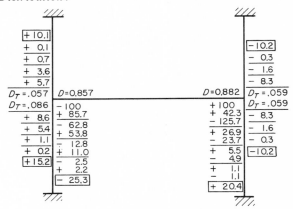

Fig. 7.25

The reaction between beam CE and the girders will now be computed from the equilibrium requirement on CE and their effects upon the girders will be considered. If the beam CE were perfectly flexible in torsion, its two ends would freely rotate through angles β_{CE} and β_{EC}, respectively, so as to be compatible with the slopes of the elastic curves of the girders at their points of juncture with the beam. The beam CE however offers resistance to torsion as expressed by the following equation:

$$T = \left(\frac{JG}{L}\right)_{CE}(\beta_{CE}-\beta_{EC})$$

It is necessary at this point to solve for β_{CE} in terms of the loads applied to girder AB, and to solve for β_{EC} in terms of the loads applied to girder DF. This may be done using the dummy load procedure. If a and b locate the point of application of T at which we measure β, we obtain

$$EI\beta = \frac{1}{3}\frac{Pa^3b+Ta^3}{(a+b)^2} - \frac{1}{3}\frac{Pab^3-Tb^3}{(a+b)^2} \tag{7-44}$$

Then,

$$(EI)_{AB}\beta_{CE} = \frac{1}{3} \times \frac{20.25(12)^3(8)-T(12)^3}{(20)^2} - \frac{1}{3} \times \frac{20.25(12)(8)^3+T(8)^3}{(20)^2}$$

$$\beta_{CE} = \frac{142.7-1.87T}{(EI)_{AB}}$$

$$(EI)_{DF}\beta_{EC} = \frac{1}{3} \times \frac{19.75(12)^4 + T(12)^3}{(24)^2} - \frac{1}{3} \times \frac{19.75(12)^4 - T(12)^3}{(24)^2}$$

$$\beta_{EC} = \frac{2T}{(EI)_{DF}}$$

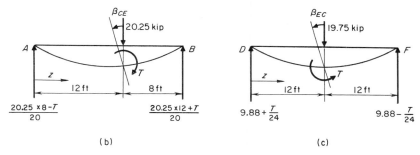

Fig. 7.26

In the present problem

$$(EI)_{AB} = (EI)_{DF} = 12{,}000E$$

Therefore,

$$\beta_{CE} - \beta_{EC} = \frac{142.7 - 3.87T}{12{,}000E}$$

and

$$T = \frac{4800 \times 0.4E}{20} \left(\frac{142.7 - 3.87T}{12{,}000E} \right)$$

Solving this equation, we obtain the torque in beam CE

$$T = 1.105 \text{ kip-ft}$$

The effect of this torque upon the final moments and twists in this case is negligible, and the solution is considered to be obtained by the superposition of moments and twists shown in Fig. 7.25 plus the moments in AB and DF due to the loading shown in Figs. 7.26b and 7.26c.

Although we have found that for the above problem the twists developed in the YZ direction were negligible, one should not draw the conclusion that this is generally the case. For off-center loadings and frameworks that are highly unsymmetric, the twists can be appreciable and must be considered.

In addition to these torque "second-order effects", there are bending moment second-order effects caused by the unsymmetry and introduced by the unequal settlement of supports C and E. These may be of importance and should be considered when necessary. Methods of computing support-deflection effects are given in Chapter 4.

Example: Find the moments and twists induced in the frame of Fig. 7.24 if vertical loads are applied as shown in Fig. 7.27.

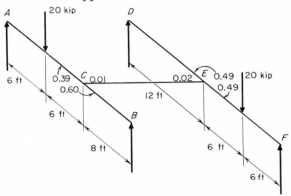

Fig. 7.27

Solution: The solution is made by first assuming vertical supports at C and E. Then these are removed after the primary moment distribution by applying equal but opposite reactions and superposing effects.

Stiffness Factors, assuming supports at C and E:

$$K_{CA} = \frac{3}{4} \times \frac{12,000}{12} \times 4 = 3000$$

$$K_{CB} = \frac{3}{4} \times \frac{12,000}{8} \times 4 = 4500$$

$$K_{EF} = K_{ED} = \frac{3}{4} \times \frac{12,000}{12} \times 4 = 3000$$

$$K_{T_{EC}} = K_{T_{CE}} = \frac{4800 \times 0.4}{20} = 96$$

Distribution Factors:

$$D_{CA} = \frac{3000}{3000 + 4500 + 96} = 0.39$$

$$D_{CB} = \frac{6000}{10,096} = 0.60$$

$$D_{T_{CE}} = \frac{96}{10,096} = 0.01$$

$$D_{ED} = \frac{3000}{3000+3000+96} = 0.49$$

$$D_{EF} = 0.49$$

$$D_{T_{EC}} = \frac{96}{6096} = 0.02$$

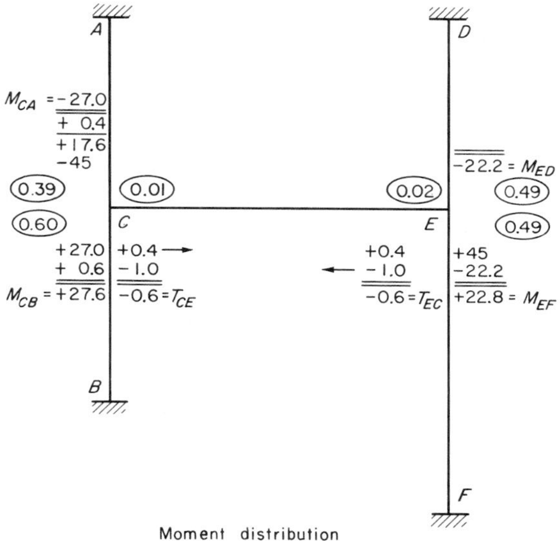

Moment distribution

Fig. 7.28

Moments and reactions on AB and DF due to the primary moment distribution of Fig. 7.28 are shown in Figs. 7.29a and 7.29b. It is necessary now to find moments and twists induced by forces at C and E of $-R_C$ and $-R_E$ as shown in Fig. 7.30.

We find β_{CE} and β_{EC} using Equation (7-44),

$$(EI)_{AB}\beta_{CE} = \frac{1}{3} \times \frac{15.70(12)^3(8) - T'(12)^3}{(20)^2} - \frac{1}{3} \times \frac{15.70(8)^3(12) + T'(8)^3}{(20)^2}$$

$$= 100.5 - 1.87T'$$

$$(EI)_{DF}\beta_{EC} = \frac{1}{3} \times \frac{13.75(12)^3(12) - T'(12)^3}{(24)^2} - \frac{1}{3} \times \frac{13.75(12)^4 - T'(12)^3}{(24)^2}$$

$$= 2T'$$

$$T' = \left(\frac{JG}{L}\right)_{CE}(\beta_{CE} - \beta_{EC})$$

$$T' = \left(\frac{4800 \times 0.4}{20 \times 12,000}\right)(100.5 - 3.87T) = 0.816 \text{ kip-ft}$$

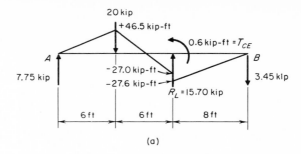

(a)

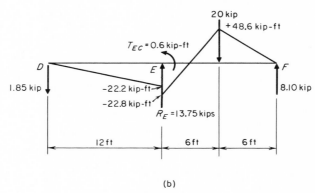

(b)

Fig. 7.29

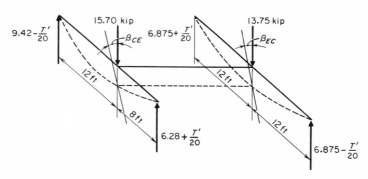

Fig. 7.30

The final solution (ignoring the secondary effects due to $\Delta_{CE} \neq \Delta_{EC}$) is obtained by superposing the results of the primary distribution shown on Figs. 7.29a and 7.29b with the results of the secondary distribution just completed (see Fig. 7.31). The results of this superposition are shown in Fig. 7.32 (the effect of $T' = 0.816$ kip-ft on reactions and moments is omitted as negligible).

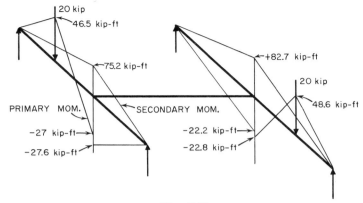

Fig. 7.31

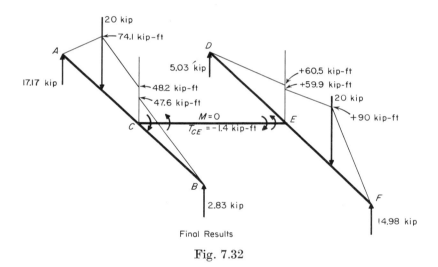

Final Results

Fig. 7.32

7-27   Floor framing systems, combined bending and torsion, I-type sections

Goldberg[13] outlines how a moment distribution procedure can be set up for framing systems composed of I-type sections. In formulating the problem, the support condition of each beam must be evaluated with regard to restraint against warping. The torsional stiffness factors will be dependent upon the assumed warping restraints. For a beam welded directly to a girder, the warping of the end of the beam

---

[13] John E. Goldberg, "Torsion of I Type and H Type Beams," Paper No. 145, *Proceedings*, ASCE, August 1952.

will have to be compatible at the point of juncture with the deformation of the girder.

For beams connected to girders by means of bolted, riveted, or welded web connections (using clip angles), a procedure assuming free warping at the ends can be set up. As indicated by moment rotation experimental data [14] on this type of connection, the moment that is transmitted can be quite small.

It may therefore be necessary to allow for the moment-rotation flexibility of the connection in setting up the stiffness factors to be used in moment distribution. One way in which this can be conveniently accomplished was indicated by Rathbun [14] in 1936.

7-28 Shear lag

It was pointed out in Art. 7-1 that members subjected to shear stresses will, in general, warp so that initially plane cross sections are no longer plane after application of the shear loads. Also, it was pointed out in Art. 1-4 that a basic assumption of the Bernoulli–Euler bending theory (which leads to the simple bending stress relation $\sigma = My/I$) is that plane sections before bending are also plane after bending. Thus, a beam cross section with shear-bending loading is subject to conditions which violate those required for the validity of $\sigma = My/I$.

In the ordinary civil engineering beam-girder type structure, this discrepancy, called *shear lag*, is not a serious one. However, for the structures commonly used in aircraft and ship work—the so-called box-beam type of structure (such as the airplane fuselage, airplane wing, or ship hull cross section)—shear lag may lead to serious errors in the computed values of the bending stresses if these are determined using the simple Bernoulli–Euler equation $\sigma = My/I$ based upon the actual cross section.

The effect is generally greatest in the top or bottom plate sections of the box beams. A typical result is shown in Fig. 7.33. The stresses in the top fibers, as computed using $\sigma = Mc/I$, should be constant. Because of shear lag, however, the actual stresses are lower in the center of the plate and greater near the vertical webs.

The exact solution of shear lag problems is quite complicated. One way to solve these problems is to introduce the concept of *effective areas*. In this procedure, actual areas in the beam cross section are multiplied by an effectiveness coefficient, ϵ (where $0 \leqslant \epsilon \leqslant 1$) before computing section properties, stresses, and similar quantities. In Fig. 7.33, ϵ should be smallest for the area in the center of the top

[14] J. Charles Rathbun, "Elastic Properties of Riveted Connections," *Transactions*, ASCE, Vol. 101, 1936, p. 524.

plate and increase for the areas closer to the vertical webs. The value of ϵ used is based upon experience or test or theory if available.

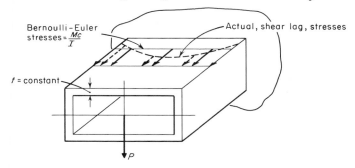

Fig. 7.33

Having determined the values of ϵ, the section properties and stresses ($\sigma = Mc/I_{\text{effective}}$) are obtained in the usual way. This leads to a stress distribution (based upon actual areas) similar to that required for shear lag as shown in Fig. 7.33.[15]

A simplified problem will illustrate a typical shear lag solution.

Example: The box beam shown in Fig. 7.34 is loaded in shear bending. It is assumed that the lumped stringer areas take the bending stress and the skins between the stringers take the shear stress. Determine the bending stresses for the following two cases.

(a) assuming all stringers have $\epsilon = 1$
(b) assuming corner stringers have $\epsilon = 1$ and the intermediate stringers have $\epsilon = 0.5$

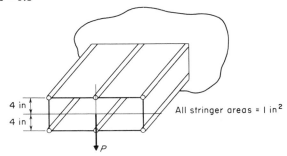

Fig. 7.34

---

[15] For a more complete discussion of shear lag, see Alfred S. Niles and Joseph S. Newell, *Airplane Structures*, Vol. II, 3rd Ed., John Wiley and Sons, Inc., New York, 1950; and John E. Younger, *Mechanics of Aircraft Structures*, 2nd Ed., McGraw-Hill Book Company, Inc., New York, 1942.

Solution:

CASE A

For this case,

$$I = I_{\text{actual}} = I_{\text{effective}} = 6(1)(4^2) = 96 \text{ in.}^4$$

Then

$$\sigma = \frac{Mc}{I} = \frac{M(4)}{96} = \frac{M}{24} \text{ lb/in.}^2 \text{ for all stringers.}$$

CASE B

For this case,

$$I_{\text{eff}} = 4(1)(4^2) + 2(0.5)(1)(4^2) = 80 \text{ in.}^4$$

Then,

$$\sigma_{1_{\text{act}}} = \frac{Mc}{I_{\text{eff}}} = \frac{M}{20} \text{ psi for the corner stringers}$$

also

$$F_{2_{\text{eff}}} = \sigma_{2_{\text{eff}}} A_{2_{\text{eff}}} = \frac{Mc_2}{I_{\text{eff}}} \cdot A_{2_{\text{eff}}}$$

$$= \frac{M}{40} \text{ lb for the inside stringers}$$

Therefore,

$$\sigma_{2_{\text{act}}} = \frac{F_{2_{\text{eff}}}}{A_{2_{\text{act}}}} = \frac{M}{40} \text{ lb/in.}^2 \text{ for the inside stringers}$$

Problems

1. Locate the shear center for the following sections.

(a), (b), (c), and (d).

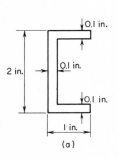

(a)

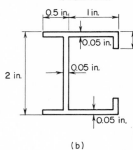

(b)

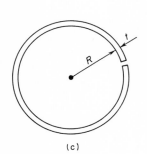

(c)

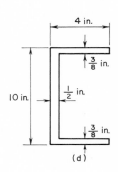

(d)

2. Determine the angle of twist at B and the maximum bending stress at A for a 12 W^r 65 of 10-ft length due to a torque $T = 1800$ ft-lb.

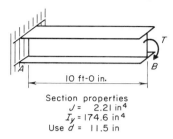

Section properties
$J = 2.21$ in^4
$I_y = 174.6$ in^4
Use $d = 11.5$ in

3. Determine the angle of twist at the center and the maximum bending stress for a 12 W^r 65 of 20-ft length simply supported at the ends and twisted in the center by a torque $T = 2000$ ft-lb.

4. Vertical concentrated loads of 50 kip act in the center of members BE and EH (see figure). Using moment distribution, find the resulting moments and twists in all members. $G = 0.4E$. Neglect warping.

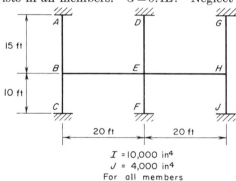

$I = 10,000$ in^4
$J = 4,000$ in^4
For all members

5. For the floor framing system of problem 4, find the moments and twists in all members if the load consists of a uniformly distributed 4000 lb/ft on span BE alone.

Chapter 8

PLASTICITY AND LIMIT DESIGN

8-1 Introduction

Up to this point the theory has been developed upon the assumption that Hooke's Law applies in all cases, i.e., that a linear relation exists between stresses and strains. For an ideal ductile material, i.e., a material which does not work harden, this is true only if the stresses and strains do not exceed the yield point. The stress-strain relation for an ideal ductile material is shown in Fig. 8.1. Note the horizontal line at the yield stress, corresponding to no work hardening.

For this ideal material, the increase in strain without any further increase in stress, such as ϵ', is much larger than the total unit strain (ϵ_y) corresponding to the yield point. The ideal stress-strain curve of Fig. 8.1 is very nearly realized for a mild structural steel, so that we may say that structural steel behaves somewhat like an ideal plastic material.

It should be noted that the actual pattern of stresses and strains in a structural steel member, owing to initial stresses and curvature and other factors, may be far different from those computed using the

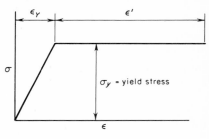

Fig. 8.1

elastic theory. The use of the elastic theory in design is made safe by the introduction of safety factors as required by building codes and specifications. Safety factors can best be determined through experience. It is argued by proponents of the plastic theory of design that if designs are to be accomplished using a minimum of structural materials, use of the elastic theory may prove uneconomical and perhaps even unsafe. This is a matter open to some question and one that we will not attempt to resolve here. A major and desirable advantage stemming from the use of a plastic theory, as we shall see, is the simplicity with which indeterminate structures can be solved.

An early presentation of the theory of plastic design described in this chapter was given by Van den Broek.[1]   This method is essentially an extension of the Bernoulli–Euler Theory of elastic beam analysis to the beam characterized by the idealized stress-strain curve of Fig. 8.1 and is frequently called the *theory of limit design* or *ultimate design*.[2]

The limit design analysis of trusses, which requires consideration of the load carrying capacity of compressive members and consequently involves questions of limit design elastic stability, will not be considered.   Limit design of beams only will be discussed.

8-2   Stresses in beams in the plastic range

It is assumed, in developing the basic relations between bending stresses in a beam cross section and the internal bending moment within this section, that a plane section before bending remains plane after bending even though the yield stress has been reached within the cross section.   The stress distribution in a beam of symmetric cross section loaded in the plane of symmetry is shown in Fig. 8.2.

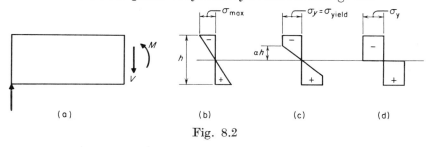

Fig. 8.2

Fig. 8.2b shows the elastic stress distribution corresponding to a load of given intensity.   Suppose that the load is increased in intensity

[1] J. A. Van den Broek, *Theory of Limit Design*, John Wiley and Sons, Inc., New York, 1948.

[2] The problem of *ultimate design* has received some attention also in connection with the design of reinforced concrete structures.   It is quite complicated in these cases and different results are obtained depending upon the original assumptions.   See Reports of ASCE–ACI Joint Committee on Ultimate Strength Design, Paper No. 809, *Proceedings*, ASCE, October 1955, and the extensive bibliography included in this paper.

Some fundamental principles and theorems dealing with the failure (or ultimate design) of beams and frames are given in the papers by H. J. Greenberg and W. Prager, "Limit Design of Beams and Frames," *Proceedings*, ASCE, February 1951, and D. C. Drucker, W. Prager, and H. J. Greenberg, "Extended Limit Design Theorems for Continuous Media," *Quarterly of Applied Mathematics*, Vol. 9, 1952.   British procedure in limit design is summarized in the bulletin, *The Collapse Method of Design*, Publication No. 5, British Constructional Steel Work Association, 1952.   See also C. S. Gray, L. E. Kent, W. A. Mitchell, and G. B. Godfrey, *Steel Designers' Manual*, Frederick Ungar Publishing Company, New York, 1955; and J. Foulkes, "The Minimum Weight Design of Structural Frames," *Proc. of the Royal Society*, Vol. A 223, 1954.   A recent fairly complete treatment of the engineering phases of limit design is B. G. Neal, *The Plastic Methods of Structural Analysis*, John Wiley and Sons, Inc., New York, 1956.

until $\sigma_{max} = \sigma_{yield}$. The corresponding stress distribution will still be elastic but the value of σ_{max} will have approached its limit. A further increase in load will produce the stress distribution of Fig. 8.2c. In the limit the final stress distribution will become that of Fig. 8.2d.

For a beam of rectangular section of width b and depth h, the bending moment corresponding to elastic stress distribution of Fig. 8.2b is

$$M_E = \sigma_{max} \frac{bh^2}{6} \tag{8-1}$$

The moment corresponding to the stress distribution of Fig. 8.2c is

$$M_y = \sigma_y \frac{bh}{2} \cdot \frac{h}{2} - \sigma_y b \left[\frac{\alpha h}{2} \cdot \frac{2}{3} \alpha h \right]$$

or

$$M_y = \sigma_y \frac{bh^2}{4} \left[1 - \frac{4}{3} \alpha^2 \right] \tag{8-2}$$

The maximum moment a rectangular section can develop without exceeding the yield stress is the limit of M_y as α approaches zero and is called the *ultimate moment*. It is given by

$$M_{ult} = \sigma_y \frac{bh^2}{4} \tag{8-3}$$

The ratio of M_{ult} to $M_{E_{max}}$ is obtained when $\sigma_{max} = \sigma_y$ in Equation (8-1). This ratio is 1.5 Thus the limit design theory shows the ultimate bending strength of a rectangular beam section to be 50% greater than the maximum value obtained from the elastic theory.

The ratio of the limit design strength of an I-type beam to its maximum elastic theory strength is not so great as for a rectangular

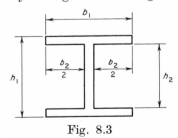

Fig. 8.3

section. For these members the limit design strength averages between 10% and 20% greater than the strength by the elastic theory. Thus, for the I-shaped beam of Fig. 8.3,

$$I = \frac{b_1 h_1^3}{12} - \frac{b_2 h_2^3}{12}$$

$$M_{E_{\max}} = \frac{\sigma_{\max}}{6h_1}(b_1h_1{}^3 - b_2h_2{}^3)$$

$$M_{E_{\max}} = \sigma_{\max}\frac{b_1h_1{}^2}{6}\left(1 - \frac{b_2h_2{}^3}{b_1h_1{}^3}\right) \tag{8-4}$$

Also,

$$M_{\text{ult}} = \sigma_y\left[\frac{b_1h_1{}^2}{4} - \frac{b_2h_2{}^2}{4}\right] = \sigma_y\frac{b_1h_1{}^2}{4}\left(1 - \frac{b_2h_2{}^2}{b_1h_1{}^2}\right) \tag{8-5}$$

The moment when $\sigma_{\max}$ is just equal to the yield stress, σ_y is obtained from Equation (8-4). The ratio of the ultimate strength to the maximum elastic strength is

$$\frac{M_{\text{ult}}}{M_y} = \frac{3}{2}\cdot\frac{1 - \dfrac{b_2h_2{}^2}{b_1h_1{}^2}}{1 - \dfrac{b_2h_2{}^3}{b_1h_1{}^3}} \tag{8-6}$$

From Equation (8-6), we see that M_{ult}/M_y must always be less than 1.5 for an I-beam.

8-3 Plastic deformation of beams

By the elastic theory the radius of curvature of a point on the elastic curve is related to M/EI by

$$\frac{d^2y}{dx^2} = \frac{1}{\rho} = \frac{M_{E_{\max}}}{EI} = \frac{2\sigma_{\max}}{Eh} \tag{8-7}$$

As the loads are gradually increased, $1/\rho$ increases linearly with $M_{E_{\max}}$ up to the point where the stress on the extreme fiber becomes the yield stress.

For stresses corresponding to the pattern of Fig. 8.2c, it is clear that the relation between curvature and stress becomes

$$\sigma_y = \frac{E\alpha h}{\rho}$$

or

$$\frac{d^2y}{dx^2} = \frac{1}{\rho} = \frac{\sigma_y}{\alpha Eh} \tag{8-8}$$

As the moment on the section approaches the ultimate, α approaches zero (see Fig. 8.2d). The radius of curvature for this case must approach zero. This means that the beam would rotate freely about this section or that the section is behaving as a hinge. This is called a plastic hinge, and we may say that a section subject to its ultimate moment becomes a plastic hinge.

By neglecting shear deformations, Equation (8-8) can be solved to find the equation of the deflection curve in the plastic region. For a beam of rectangular cross section, from Equation (8-2),

$$\alpha = \sqrt{\frac{3}{4}\left[1 - \frac{4M_y}{\sigma_y bh^2}\right]} \qquad (8-9)$$

Substituting this value in Equation (8-8), we have

$$\frac{d^2y}{dx^2} = \frac{1}{\rho} = \frac{\sigma_y}{Eh}\frac{1}{\sqrt{\frac{3}{4}\left[1 - \frac{4M_y}{\sigma_y bh^2}\right]}} \qquad (8-10)$$

Solution of Equation (8-10) will give the deflection curve for a rectangular beam in the region of plastic deformation. A similar equation can be developed for the I-beam.[3]

8-4   Ultimate strength of determinate beams

The ultimate strength of a simple beam of rectangular section with a concentrated load at the center (Fig. 8.4) will occur when the moment at the center is equal to the ultimate moment. From Equation (8-3),

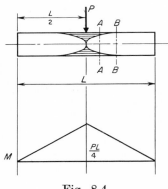

Fig. 8.4

$$M_{\text{ult}} = \sigma_y\frac{bh^2}{4} = \frac{PL}{4} \qquad (8-11)$$

The corresponding ultimate load that the beam can carry is computed from Equation (8-11) and is

$$P_{\text{ult}} = \frac{\sigma_y bh^2}{L}$$

The stress distribution under the load is shown in Fig. 8.4. At section A-A the stress distribution is that of Fig. 8.2c and at section B-B it is that of Fig. 8.2b. At section B-B the maximum stress at the extreme fiber will just equal the yield stress. All points within the shaded area are stressed to the yield point. All other points are stressed in accordance with the elastic theory.

Study of Fig. 8.4 reveals that the development of one plastic hinge in a determinate beam results in effective destruction of the beam.

---

[3] Another method for determining the deflections of beams and frames subject to the plastic stress distributions assumed in this chapter is described by G. C. Ernst, G. R. Swihart, and A. R. Riveland, "The Mechanics of Ultimate Loads, Slopes and Deflections for Continuous Beams and Rigid Frames," *Bulletin No. 1*, November 1954, University of Nebraska Engineering Experiment Station.

Rotation of the section under the load would become so large that the beam would be prevented from performing its function.   Evidently a determinate beam cannot be designed to carry its ultimate load. Factors of safety must be introduced to prevent the development of a plastic hinge.

8-5   Ultimate strength of indeterminate beams

The moment diagrams corresponding to three values of uniform loads are shown for the fixed-end beam of Fig. 8.5.   For $w = w_1$, it

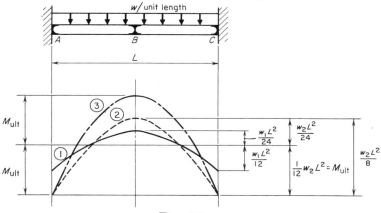

Fig. 8.5

is assumed that the stresses throughout the beam are elastic.   When w is increased to the value w_2, the stresses on the cross section at the supports have become equal to the yield stress and no further increase in support moments is possible.   If w is increased further, the sections adjacent to the supports behave as plastic hinges, rotate, and the moments at the supports remain constant at M_{ult}.   For equilibrium, it is necessary that the moments at interior sections increase.   Upon further increase of load w, the point is reached where the moment at the center of the beam becomes equal to the ultimate moment.   We now have three plastic hinges and further increase in load is not possible without excessive rotations at the plastic hinges. The ultimate load w_{ult} can be computed from the moment diagram 3 as

$$\frac{w_{\text{ult}} L^2}{8} = 2 M_{\text{ult}}$$

or

$$w_{\text{ult}} = \frac{16 M_{\text{ult}}}{L^2} \tag{8-12}$$

For a rectangular section, using Equation (8-3),

$$w_{\text{ult}} = 4\sigma_y \frac{bh^2}{L^2} \tag{8-13}$$

Let us compare this value with the maximum load computed from elastic theory with $\sigma_{\max} = \sigma_y$. We have, for the elastic theory,

$$w_{E_{\max}} = \frac{12}{L^2} \cdot \frac{\sigma_y bh^2}{6} = 2\sigma_y b \frac{h^2}{L^2} \tag{8-14}$$

so that, from Equations (8-13) and (8-14),

$$w_{\text{ult}} = 2w_{E_{\max}}$$

This result would seem to indicate that, for beams of rectangular section, design of fixed-end beams by elastic theory is too conservative. Since the true fixed-end beam can rarely be approached in practice, this result is not too important practically.

Of far more significance is the fact that a beam, which is statically indeterminate in elastic theory, has been easily solved by statics when its design is based upon ultimate load theory. It is not necessary to solve simultaneous equations with the above method. The necessary conditional equations are obtained by the introduction of plastic hinges at the points of maximum moments. At these points the moments are known, thereby permitting us to solve for the unknown redundants.

8-6 Ultimate strength of continuous beams

Continuous beams are readily solved by limit design. The elastic moments for a two-span continuous beam are shown in Fig. 8.6a, and the limit design ultimate moment diagram is shown in Fig. 8.6b.

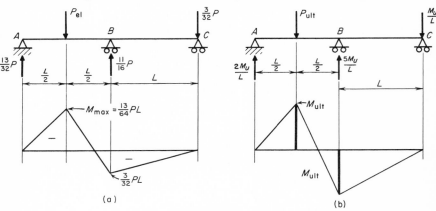

Fig. 8.6

If the maximum stress under the load, assuming elastic theory stress distribution, is just equal to the yield stress, then for a rectangular section (see Fig. 8.6a)

$$P_{E_{max}} = \frac{64}{13}\frac{M_{max}}{L} = \frac{64}{13L}\sigma_y\frac{bh^2}{6} = \frac{32}{39}\sigma_y\frac{bh^2}{L} \qquad (8\text{-}15a)$$

The limit or ultimate load is obtained by adding the vertical forces of Fig. 8.6b. This gives

$$P_{ult} = \frac{6M_{ult}}{L} = 6\sigma_y\frac{bh^2}{4L} = \frac{3}{2}\sigma_y\frac{bh^2}{L} \qquad (8\text{-}15b)$$

so that

$$\frac{P_{ult}}{P_{E_{max}}} = \frac{3}{2}\cdot\frac{39}{32} = 1.83 \qquad (8\text{-}15c)$$

The limit capacity of this continuous beam is seen to be 1.83 times its elastic capacity.

For the same continuous beam symmetrically loaded (Fig. 8.7a and b), the ultimate load is that load which produces plastic hinges at D, B, and E. As before

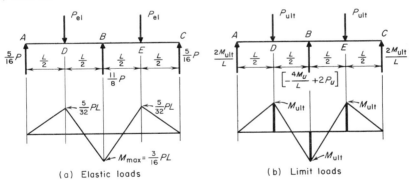

Fig. 8.7

(a) Elastic loads   (b) Limit loads

$$P_{E_{max}} = \frac{16}{3}\frac{M_{max}}{L} = \frac{16}{3}\sigma_y\frac{bh^2}{6L} = \frac{8}{9}\sigma_y\frac{bh^2}{L} \qquad (8\text{-}16a)$$

From the equilibrium of the free body of span AB, we have

$$P_{ult} = \frac{6M_{ult}}{L} = 6\sigma_y\frac{bh^2}{4L} = \frac{3}{2}\sigma_y\frac{bh^2}{L} \qquad (8\text{-}16b)$$

$$\frac{P_{ult}}{P_{E_{max}}} = \frac{3}{2}\cdot\frac{9}{8} = 1.685 \qquad (8\text{-}16c)$$

The limit capacity of this beam is 1.685 times its elastic capacity. Comparison with the last problem shows that changes in loading conditions affect the limit capacity of a given beam.

8-7   Residual stresses, reactions, and moments

An ideal plastic material is characterized by the fact that, if the material is stressed to a point beyond the elastic limit and is then unstressed, there will be a residual strain. Thus, if a material is stressed to point B on the stress-strain curve (Fig. 8.8) and then unstressed, the stress-strain curve while unloading is the line BC. The line BC is parallel to the original loading line OB. The unloading curves are therefore elastic.

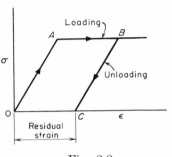

Fig. 8.8

Suppose that a rectangular section has been subjected to its ultimate moment:

$$M_{\text{ult}} = \sigma_y \frac{bh^2}{4}$$

The corresponding stress distribution is shown in Fig. 8.9a. Now, if all of the loads producing the moment are removed, the change in

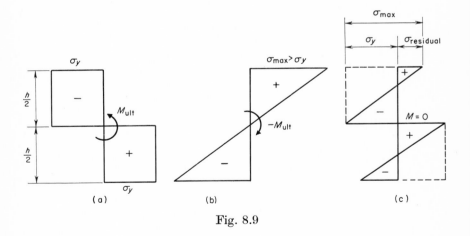

Fig. 8.9

stress will have an elastic distribution (Fig. 8.9b). The sum of the two stress patterns (Figs. 8.9a and b) gives the final stress distribution of Fig. 8.9c. The residual stresses hold themselves in equilibrium

and there will be no residual moment or thrust on the section.   For a
rectangular section, we have for the top fiber residual stress

$$-\sigma_y + \sigma_{\text{max}} = \sigma_{\text{res}}$$

$$-\sigma_y + \frac{6M_{\text{ult}}}{bh^2} = \sigma_{\text{res}}$$

But $M_{\text{ult}} = \sigma_y \dfrac{bh^2}{4}$.   Then

$$\sigma_y \left(\frac{6 \dfrac{bh^2}{4}}{bh^2} - 1 \right) = \sigma_{\text{res}} = +\frac{\sigma_y}{2} \text{ (tensile)} \qquad (8\text{-}17)$$

In the case of a continuous beam, removal of the applied load alone
does not result in the above residual stresses.   These stresses are only
possible if the reaction restraints are also removed.   For example,

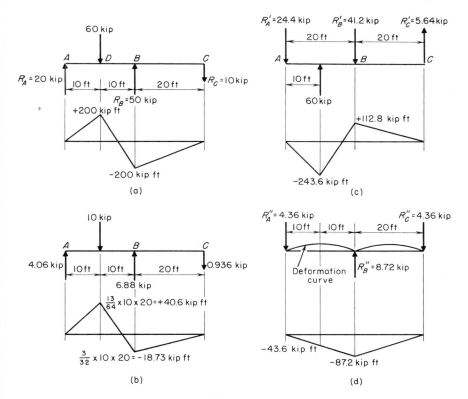

Fig. 8.10

consider the beam of Figs. 8.6 and 8.10. Suppose that the ultimate load is 60 kip and that the span L is 20 ft. From Equation (8-15b),

$$M_{\text{ult}} = \frac{P_{\text{ult}} \cdot L}{6} = \frac{60 \times 20}{6} = 200 \text{ kip-ft}$$

The moment diagram for this case is shown on Fig. 8.10a.

If we now remove the 60-kip load, the changes in stress and strain will be elastic. Fig. 8.10b shows the elastic theory moment diagrams for a load of 10 kip. The elastic theory moment diagram for a load of 60 kip must then be six times as great. These are shown in Fig. 8.10c. The sum of the moments of Figs. 8.10a and 8.10c leave residual moments as shown in Fig. 8.10d. The corresponding residual reactions are also shown. Residual deformations result in the deformation curve of Fig. 8.10d. It will be noted that the slope of the deformation curve is no longer continuous at B. This results from the permanent deformation of the plastic hinge.

Suppose that this beam (in the state of residual stress of Fig. 8.10d) is now loaded once again with $P = 10$ kip. The moment diagram for this case is obtained by superposition of the moments of Figs. 8.10b and 8.10d. These are shown in Fig. 8.11. The maximum moment at B

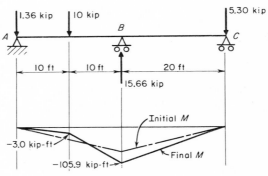

Fig. 8.11

is now about five times as great as it would have been if the 10-kip load were applied to an initially unstressed beam.

If the 10-kip load were applied in an upward direction, the moments would be those of Fig. 8.12. A reversed load of 38.5 kip will produce a plastic hinge under the load (Fig. 8.13). The ultimate load will be reached when the moment diagram is that of Fig. 8.14. The reactions are obtained by superposition of initial residual reactions with those produced by P.

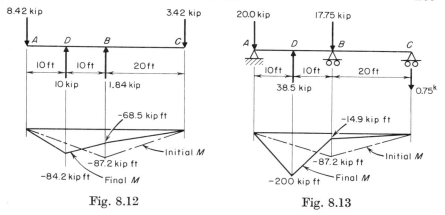

Fig. 8.12   Fig. 8.13

Due to plastic deformation, failure of the beam would be produced after a few reversals, each reversal causing an additional permanent

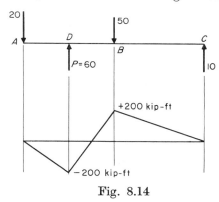

Fig. 8.14

set.   Hence reversal of loading requires the use of safety factors larger than those necessary for loads in one direction.

8-8   Limit design procedures

Practical use of limit design demands a careful appraisal of loading conditions and safety factors.   In the absence of specific codes governing the safety factors to be applied to ultimate loads, the designer should carefully consider possible reversal of loads and their effects. If the beam of the preceding article were subjected to repeated reversals of loads, it would be found that the ultimate load becomes smaller with each reversal.   Obviously, then, in practical design, ultimate reversible repeating loads should never be applied to a structure.

Problems

1. Referring to the beam of Fig. 8.6, determine the location X, and value of P_{ult} such that this has its minimum value.

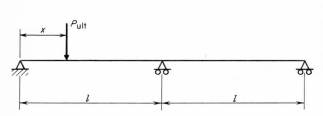

2. Determine $\dfrac{P_{ult}}{P_{E_{max}}}\left(\text{or }\dfrac{w_{ult}}{w_{E_{max}}}\right)$ for each of the structures and loadings shown. Consider all sections rectangular.

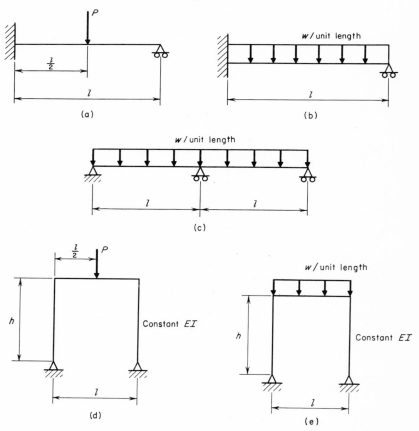

(a)

(b)

(c)

(d)

(e)

3. A four-span continuous beam of constant section carries a dead load of 500 lb/ft and a live load of 800 lb/ft. Determine the design moments by (a) elastic theory, (b) limit design theory.

Hint: Determine elastic moments first using influence lines for placing live loads for maximum effects. Then for limit design, set up a prestress line on the moment diagram to equalize the maximum moments.

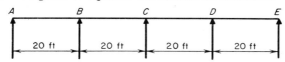

4. Solve problem 3 for a concentrated live load of 10,000 lb.

Chapter 9

SLAB AND SHELL STRUCTURES

9-1 Introduction

The general topic of "slabs and shells" separates naturally into two parts:

1. The analysis and design of flat plates (or slabs).
2. The analysis and design of curved plates or shells.

Of the two topics, the theoretical treatment of the first is simplest. Therefore, quite naturally, more progress has been made in the study of flat plates. The first part of this chapter will be devoted to a relatively brief discussion of this subject from the standpoint of the structural engineer. Solutions of the differential equations involved in flat plate theory will be obtained by numerical (relaxation) means for a limited number of special cases which are typical of those encountered in engineering practice.

Following this, the subject of shell analysis will be discussed in some detail. After a brief historical summary of the methods of shell analysis, some articles are devoted to a detailed presentation of four different methods of shell analysis:

1. An approximate method based upon the assumption of simple beam action.

2. An approximate method assuming pure membrane action.

3. A method which has been developed in the United States and will probably become the standard for American design methods.[1]

4. One of the methods used in Great Britain[2] which is probably typical of European design practice in shell analysis.

A typical problem will be solved by some of these methods to

---

[1] "Design of Cylindrical Shell Roofs," ASCE, *Manual of Engineering Practice No. 31*, 1952. We shall refer to this as the *ASCE Manual* or simply as the *Manual*.

[2] J. E. Gibson and D. W. Cooper, *The Design of Cylindrical Shell Roofs*, D. Van Nostrand Company, Princeton, N.J., 1955. We shall refer to this as "Gibson and Cooper." The fundamental equation used in this book was derived originally by L. H. Donnell in his NACA Technical Note, *Stability of Thin Walled Tubes under Torsion*, TN 479, 1933, and in the paper "A New Theory for the Buckling of Thin Cylinders under Axial Compression and Bending," *Transactions*, ASME, 1934.

illustrate the procedure and also to give some indication of the relative values obtained in the different methods.[3]

9-2 Slab structures

A slab is essentially a flat plate and as such is a basic structural element of modern engineering structures. It may be thought of as the two-dimensional equivalent of the beam (which is really a one-dimensional element). The flat plate, in general, resists loads applied either transversely or axially, and it resists these by means of direct stresses, shear stresses, bending stresses, and torsional stresses.

The starting point in all flat plate discussions must be the development of the differential equations governing plate action. These will be given in the next article. Following this, some simple solutions will be presented.

9-3 Differential equation of bending—simple plate theory

The following assumptions are made in deriving the differential equation for the laterally loaded thin plate.

1. The material is homogeneous, isotropic, and elastic.

2. The least lateral dimension of the plate is at least ten times the thickness.

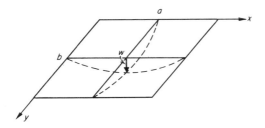

Deflection of simply
supported plate

Fig. 9.1

[3] The classical treatment of plates and shells is given in A. E. H. Love, *A Treatise on the Mathematical Theory of Elasticity*, Cambridge University Press, 4th Ed., 1927. A more recent discussion is given in S. Timoshenko, *Theory of Plates and Shells*, Engineering Societies Monographs, McGraw-Hill Book Company, New York, 1940. This is perhaps the standard American reference on this subject. A very complete bibliography of shell papers (up to about 1954) is contained in *Proceedings of a Symposium on Concrete Shell Roof Construction* published and printed by the Cement and Concrete Association, 52 Grosvenor Gardens, London, S.W.1, 1954, which also contains papers describing modern British practice in shell analysis and construction. A similar American report is contained in *Proceedings of a Conference on Thin Concrete Shells*, M.I.T., June 1954.

3. A vertical element of the plate before bending remains perpendicular to the middle surface of the plate after bending.

4. Strains are small: deflections are less than the order of one hundredth of the span length; the strain of the middle surface is zero or negligible.

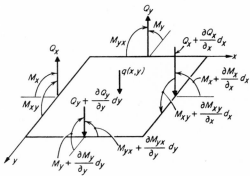

Element of plate with applied
loads and moments

Fig. 9.2

The deflected simply supported rectangular plate is shown in Fig. 9.1. Positive shears, twists, and moments acting upon any differential element of the plate are shown in Fig. 9.2. Applying Hooke's Law and the equations of equilibrium to the free body of the differential element leads to the following equations, [4]

$$\frac{\partial M_x}{\partial_x} + \frac{\partial M_{yx}}{\partial y} = Q_x \tag{9-1a}$$

$$\frac{\partial M_y}{\partial y} - \frac{\partial M_{xy}}{\partial x} = Q_y \tag{9-1b}$$

$$\frac{\partial Q_x}{\partial x} + \frac{\partial Q_y}{\partial y} = -q \tag{9-1c}$$

$$M_{xy} = -M_{yx} = D(1-\nu)\frac{\partial^2 w}{\partial x\,\partial y} \tag{9-1d}$$

$$M_x = -D\left(\frac{\partial^2 w}{\partial x^2} + \nu\,\frac{\partial^2 w}{\partial y^2}\right) \tag{9-1e}$$

$$M_y = -D\left(\frac{\partial^2 w}{\partial y^2} + \nu\,\frac{\partial^2 w}{\partial x^2}\right) \tag{9-1f}$$

[4] S. Timoshenko, *Theory of Plates and Shells*, Engineering Societies Monographs, McGraw-Hill Book Company, New York, 1940.

where q is the lateral load function in x and y, w is the vertical deflection of any point in the plate, D is the plate stiffness $= \dfrac{Eh^3}{12(1-\nu^2)}$, h is the thickness of the plate, ν is Poisson's ratio.

Equations 9.1 lead to the general differential equation of simple rectangular plate theory,

$$\frac{\partial^4 w}{\partial x^4} + 2\frac{\partial^4 w}{\partial x^2 \partial y^2} + \frac{\partial^4 w}{\partial y^4} = \frac{q}{D} \tag{9-2}$$

In terms of the operator $\nabla^2 = \dfrac{\partial^2}{\partial x^2} + \dfrac{\partial^2}{\partial y^2}$, Equation (9-2) becomes

$$\nabla^2 . \nabla^2 w = \nabla^4 w = \left(\frac{\partial^2}{\partial x^2} + \frac{\partial^2}{\partial y^2}\right)\left(\frac{\partial^2 w}{\partial x^2} + \frac{\partial^2 w}{\partial y^2}\right)$$

or

$$\nabla^4 w = \frac{q}{D} \tag{9-2a}$$

It is interesting to note the similarity between the form of Equation (9-2a) and the fourth-order differential equation of simple beam theory, $\dfrac{d^4 w}{dx^4} = \dfrac{q}{EI}$.

The solution of a specific problem of bending of a simple rectangular plate requires finding a function w which satisfies Equation (9-2) and also the boundary conditions of the specific problem. When w is known, moments, twists, and shears can be calculated using the given equations. Stresses can be found as follows:

$$\sigma_x = -\frac{Ez}{1-\nu^2}\left(\frac{\partial^2 w}{\partial x^2} + \nu\frac{\partial^2 w}{\partial y^2}\right) \tag{9-3a}$$

$$\sigma_y = -\frac{Ez}{1-\nu^2}\left(\frac{\partial^2 w}{\partial y^2} + \nu\frac{\partial^2 w}{\partial x^2}\right) \tag{9-3b}$$

$$\tau_{xy} = \frac{Ez}{1+\nu}\frac{\partial^2 w}{\partial x \partial y} \tag{9-3c}$$

in which z is the distance of the point in question from the middle surface (positive z measured down from middle surface).

9-4   Boundary conditions for various plate end supports [5]

The boundary conditions for a plate simply supported at an edge $x = a$ (see Fig. 9.1) are

$$w(a, y) = 0 \tag{9-4a}$$

and

$$\left[\frac{\partial^2 w}{\partial x^2} + \nu\frac{\partial^2 w}{\partial y^2}\right]_{x=a} = 0 \tag{9-4b}$$

[5] *Ibid.*, p. 89.

Equation (9-4b) arises from the following:

$$M_x(a, y) = -D\left(\frac{\partial^2 w}{\partial x^2} + \nu \frac{\partial^2 w}{\partial y^2}\right)\Bigg|_{x=a} = 0$$

Since $\dfrac{\partial^2 w}{\partial x^2} = 0$ for a simple support, Equation (9-4b) can be written

$$\nabla^2 w\big|_{x=a} = 0$$

For a plate built in at an edge $x = a$, the boundary conditions are

$$w(a, y) = 0 \qquad\qquad (9\text{-}4c)$$

and

$$\frac{\partial w}{\partial x}(a, y) = 0 \qquad\qquad (9\text{-}4d)$$

At a free boundary $x = a$, we have boundary conditions (arising from the fact that moments and shears are zero on the free boundary)

$$\left[\frac{\partial^3 w}{\partial x^3} + (2-\nu)\frac{\partial^3 w}{\partial x\,\partial y^2}\right]_{x=a} = 0 \qquad\qquad (9\text{-}4e)$$

and

$$\left(\frac{\partial^2 w}{\partial x^2} + \nu \frac{\partial^2 w}{\partial y^2}\right)_{x=a} = 0 \qquad\qquad (9\text{-}4f)$$

9-5 Strain energy of simple plates

The strain energy expression for a simple rectangular plate will be given without proof,[6]

$$V = \frac{1}{2}D\!\int\!\!\int_{\text{area}}\left\{\left(\frac{\partial^2 w}{\partial x^2} + \frac{\partial^2 w}{\partial y^2}\right)^2 - 2(1-\nu)\left[\frac{\partial^2 w}{\partial x^2}\frac{\partial^2 w}{\partial y^2} - \left(\frac{\partial^2 w}{\partial x\,\partial y}\right)^2\right]\right\}dx\,dy \quad (9\text{-}5)$$

The term inside the brackets is known as the Gaussian curvature,

$$\text{G.C.} = \left[\frac{\partial^2 w}{\partial x^2}\frac{\partial^2 w}{\partial y^2} - \left(\frac{\partial^2 w}{\partial x\,\partial y}\right)^2\right] \qquad\qquad (9\text{-}5a)$$

If the function $w(x, y) = f(x) \cdot \phi(y)$ (product of a function of x only and a function of y only) and $w = 0$ at the boundary, then the integral of the Gaussian curvature over the entire plate equals zero. Under these conditions

$$V = \tfrac{1}{2}D\!\int\!\!\int_{\text{area}} (\nabla^2 w)^2 dx\,dy \qquad\qquad (9\text{-}5b)$$

Thus, for a rectangular plate simply supported or with built-in edges along all four boundaries, the strain energy can be found by Equation (9-5b), providing $w(x, y) = f(x) \cdot \phi(y)$.

[6] *Ibid.*

9-6 Solution of the differential equation for the laterally loaded plate

Equation (9-2) can be solved by the following methods:

1. Exact methods in which a function w is known which satisfies the equation and the boundary conditions.

2. Expansion of w and q into Fourier Series and obtaining a series form of solution.

3. Application of the principle of minimum potential energy using assumed functions of w which satisfy the boundary conditions.

4. Finite differences or other numerical methods.

These methods are applied in the solutions of various problems by Timoshenko.[7] They are considered beyond the scope of a single volume on structural analysis. However, it is felt that it is desirable to give at least one method of obtaining a solution of the plate problem. Since the designer and analyst are interested in numerical values of deflections, stresses, etc., the solution presented here will be by finite differences (see Chapter 6 for the application of the method to beams).

9-7 The numerical solution of simple plate problems by finite differences

Applications of the finite differences method to plate problems will be developed by first defining basic quantities and then introducing these in the differential equation $\nabla^4 w = q/D$. The result will be a series of linear equations which can be solved simultaneously to give the required solution. The rectangular plate is divided into strips, and the load intensity at the corner of each strip is calculated (Fig. 9.3).

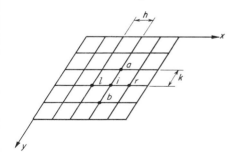

Fig. 9.3

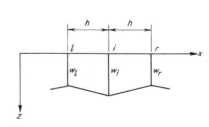

Fig. 9.4

In accordance with finite difference procedure[8] (see Chapter 6), the first and second partial derivatives of w become (see Fig. 9.4), for the point i,

$$\frac{\partial w}{\partial x}\bigg]_{i,r} = \frac{w_r - w_i}{h} \tag{9-6a}$$

[7] *Ibid.*   [8] First-order differences only are considered.

where $\dfrac{\partial w}{\partial x}\bigg]_{i,\,r}$ means that it is the first partial derivative of w with respect to x taken at point i and written in terms of w_r and w_i.

The average value of $\partial w/\partial x$ is

$$\frac{\partial w_i}{\partial x} = \frac{1}{2}\left[\frac{w_r - w_i}{h} + \frac{w_i - w_l}{h}\right] = \frac{w_r - w_l}{2h} \tag{9-6b}$$

For $\partial w/\partial x$ in terms of w_i and w_l (see Fig. 9.4), we have

$$\frac{\partial w}{\partial x}\bigg]_{i,\,l} = \frac{w_i - w_l}{h}$$

Then

$$\frac{\partial^2 w}{\partial x^2}\bigg]_i = \frac{\dfrac{\partial w}{\partial x}\bigg]_{i,\,r} - \dfrac{\partial w}{\partial x}\bigg]_{i,\,l}}{h} = \frac{\dfrac{w_r - w_i}{h} - \dfrac{w_i - w_l}{h}}{h}$$

or

$$\frac{\partial^2 w}{\partial x^2}\bigg]_i = \frac{w_r - 2w_i + w_l}{h^2} \tag{9-6c}$$

Likewise we obtain

$$\frac{\partial^2 w}{\partial y^2}\bigg]_i = \frac{w_a - 2w_i + w_b}{k^2} \tag{9-6d}$$

Then

$$\nabla^2 w_i = \frac{\partial^2 w}{\partial x^2}\bigg]_i + \frac{\partial^2 w}{\partial y^2}\bigg]_i \tag{9-6e}$$

If the spans between strips in the x and y direction are equal ($h = k$), then

$$\nabla^2 w_i = \frac{1}{h^2}[w_a + w_b + w_r + w_l - 4w_i]. \tag{9-6f}$$

The deflection of a square simply supported plate will now be found using finite differences. Equation (9-6f) will be applied in stages as follows:

The differential equation of our problem is Equation (9-2a)

$$\nabla^2 \cdot \nabla^2 w = \frac{q}{D}$$

Introduce the function ϕ where

$$\phi = (\nabla^2 w)D \tag{9-7a}$$

Substituting this in Equation (9-2a), we obtain

$$\nabla^2 \phi = q \tag{9-7b}$$

If values of ϕ can be found for various points on the plate, then w can be found by solving Equation (9-7a), $\nabla^2 w = \phi/D$.

Let us arbitrarily divide our plate into four equal squares (Fig. 9.5). Then $h = a/2$ as shown. The values of the function are desired at

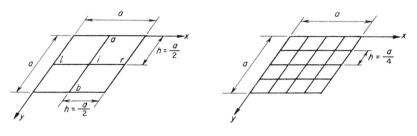

Fig. 9.5   Fig. 9.6

points a, b, l, r, i. From the boundary conditions it follows that $w_a = w_b = w_l = w_r = 0$ and that $\nabla^2 w_a = \nabla^2 w_b = \nabla^2 w_l = \nabla^2 w_r = 0$. But if $\nabla^2 w = 0$, on the boundary then [Equation (9-7a)], $\phi_a = \phi_b = \phi_l = \phi_r = 0$.

Applying the finite difference equation to Equation (9-7b), we obtain

$$\nabla^2 \phi = (\phi_a + \phi_b + \phi_l + \phi_r - 4\phi_i)\frac{1}{h^2} = q \qquad (9\text{-}8\text{a})$$

But $\phi_a = \phi_b = \phi_l = \phi_r = 0$; hence from Equation (9.8a),

$$\phi_i = -\frac{qh^2}{4} = -\frac{qa^2}{16} \qquad (9\text{-}8\text{b})$$

From Equation (9-7a), $\nabla^2 w_i = \phi_i/D$. In finite difference terms this becomes

$$(w_a + w_b + w_l + w_r - 4w_i)\frac{1}{h^2} = \frac{\phi_i}{D} = -\frac{qa^2}{16D} \qquad (9\text{-}8\text{c})$$

But $w_a = w_b = w_l = w_r = 0$ from the boundary conditions, thus

$$w_i = -\frac{h^2}{4}\left(-\frac{qa^2}{16D}\right) = \frac{qa^4}{256D} \qquad (9\text{-}8\text{d})$$

Comparison with the exact solution of w_i obtained from Timoshenko [9] shows the solution obtained in Equation (9-8d) for w_i to be in error by 3.5%.

A more accurate solution can be obtained by dividing the square plate into more segments (Fig. 9.6). The general method of solution

[9] *Ibid.*

will be shown for a square plate of side length a, loaded with a transverse load expressed by $q(x, y) = q \dfrac{x}{a}$ (Fig. 9.7).

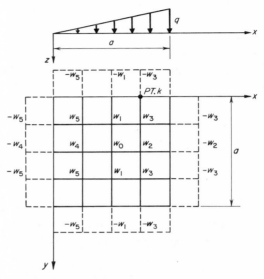

Fig. 9.7

The square plate is divided into 16 equal parts with $h = a/4$. The deflections w_0, w_1, w_2, w_3, w_4, w_5, considering symmetry, are shown for the corners of each segment. The value of w is zero at the boundary; also $\nabla^2 w = 0$ at the boundary. Values of the load for the points 0 and 1 are: $q_0 = \dfrac{q}{2} = q_1$

at points 2 and 3 $q_2 = \tfrac{3}{4} q = q_3$
at points 4 and 5 $q_4 = \tfrac{1}{4} q = q_5$

From Equation (9-7), we have for any point i

$$\nabla^2 \phi_i = (\phi_a + \phi_b + \phi_l + \phi_r - 4\phi_i) \frac{1}{h^2} = q_i \qquad (9\text{-}9a)$$

We must determine values of ϕ_k, with the points k on the boundary. We have from Equation (9-7a) $\phi_k = (\nabla^2 w_k) D$. For points on the boundary $\nabla^2 w_k = 0$; thus $\phi_k = 0$ at these points.

For a point on the boundary such as k (Fig. 9.7), it is necessary to consider the plate extending fictitiously beyond the edge such that its deflection will be at the intersections of the dotted lines, as shown in Fig. 9.7. This is necessary in order that $\nabla^2 w_k = 0$ for points on the boundary. Equation (9-9a) will now be written for various points.

$$\text{at point 0} \qquad (\phi_1 + \phi_1 + \phi_4 + \phi_2 - 4\phi_0) = \left(\frac{q}{2}\right)\left(\frac{a}{4}\right)^2 = \frac{qa^2}{32} \qquad\qquad \text{(9-9b)}$$

$$\text{at point 1} \qquad (\phi_0 + 0 + \phi_5 + \phi_3 - 4\phi_1) = \left(\frac{q}{2}\right)\left(\frac{a}{4}\right)^2 = \frac{qa^2}{32} \qquad\qquad \text{(9-9c)}$$

$$\text{at point 2} \qquad (\phi_3 + \phi_3 + \phi_0 + 0 - 4\phi_2) = \left(\frac{3}{4}q\right)\left(\frac{a}{4}\right)^2 = \frac{3qa^2}{64} \qquad\qquad \text{(9-9d)}$$

$$\text{at point 3} \qquad (0 + \phi_2 + \phi_1 + 0 - 4\phi_3) = \left(\frac{3}{4}q\right)\left(\frac{a}{4}\right)^2 = \frac{3qa^2}{64} \qquad\qquad \text{(9-9e)}$$

$$\text{at point 4} \qquad (\phi_5 + \phi_5 + 0 + \phi_0 - 4\phi_4) = \left(\frac{1}{4}q\right)\left(\frac{a}{4}\right)^2 = \frac{qa^2}{64} \qquad\qquad \text{(9-9f)}$$

$$\text{at point 5} \qquad (0 + \phi_4 + 0 + \phi_1 - 4\phi_5) = \left(\frac{1}{4}q\right)\left(\frac{a}{4}\right)^2 = \frac{qa^2}{64} \qquad\qquad \text{(9-9g)}$$

We have at this point of the solution, six simultaneous equations in six unknowns.

Solution by the Gauss–Seidel method gives the following values:

$$\phi_0 = -2.250\,\frac{qa^2}{64}$$

$$\phi_1 = -1.750\,\frac{qa^2}{64}$$

$$\phi_2 = -2.178\,\frac{qa^2}{64}$$

$$\phi_3 = -1.732\,\frac{qa^2}{64}$$

$$\phi_4 = -1.322\,\frac{qa^2}{64}$$

$$\phi_5 = -1.019\,\frac{qa^2}{64}$$

From values of ϕ_i, values of w_i can be obtained by solving Equation (9-7a), $\nabla^2 w_i = \phi_i/D$. If we write the six equations for $\nabla^2 w_i$, we will then have six equations whose left-hand terms will be the same as those given in Equations (9-9b) through (9-9g).   These are

$$2w_1 + w_4 + w_2 - 4w_0 = \frac{\phi_0}{D}\,h^2 = -2.250\,\frac{qa^2}{64D}\left(\frac{a}{4}\right)^2 = -2.250\,\frac{qa^4}{1024D}$$

$$w_0 + w_5 + w_3 - 4w_1 = -1.750\,\frac{qa^4}{1024D}$$

$$w_0 + 2w_3 - 4w_2 = -2.178\,\frac{qa^4}{1024D}$$

$$w_1 + w_2 - 4w_3 = -1.732\,\frac{qa^4}{1024D}$$

$$w_5 + w_0 - 4w_4 = -1.322\,\frac{qa^4}{1024D}$$

$$w_4 + w_1 - 4w_5 = -1.019\,\frac{qa^4}{1024D}$$

The solutions of the above equations are best obtained by the Gauss–Seidel method and are

$$w_0 = 0.002015\,\frac{qa^4}{D}$$

$$w_1 = 0.00147\,\frac{qa^4}{D}$$

$$w_2 = 0.00163\,\frac{qa^4}{D}$$

$$w_3 = 0.00120\,\frac{qa^4}{D}$$

$$w_4 = 0.00130\,\frac{qa^4}{D}$$

$$w_5 = 0.000935\,\frac{qa^4}{D}$$

The answer given for w_0 by Timoshenko[10] using an analytical method of solution is

$$w_0 = 0.00203\,\frac{qa^4}{D}$$

Thus the answer obtained numerically differs by 0.75% from the value obtained analytically.

[10] *Ibid.*

Moments, stresses, etc., can be found by using Equations (9-1). For example, M_x at point 0 is

$$M_{x_0} = -D\left(\frac{\partial^2 w_0}{\partial x^2} + \nu \frac{\partial^2 w_0}{\partial y^2}\right)$$

$$\frac{\partial^2 w_0}{\partial x^2} = \frac{w_2 - 2w_0 + w_4}{h^2} = \frac{0.00163 - 2(0.002015) + 0.00130}{(a/4)^2}\frac{qa^4}{D}$$

$$= -0.01748\frac{qa^2}{D}$$

$$\frac{\partial^2 w_0}{\partial y^2} = \frac{w_1 - 2w_0 + w_1}{h^2} = \frac{2(0.00147 - 0.002015)}{(a/4)^2}\frac{qa^4}{D}$$

$$= -0.01760\frac{qa^2}{D}$$

therefore

$$M_{x_0} = (0.0175 + 0.0176\nu)qa^2$$

Similarly

$$M_{y_0} = (0.0176 + 0.0175\nu)qa^2$$

$$M_{x_0 y_0} = 0$$

$$\sigma_{x_0} = -(0.0175 + 0.0176\nu)\frac{Eqa^2 z}{(1 - \nu^2)D}$$

$$\sigma_{y_0} = (0.0176 + 0.0175\nu)\frac{Eqa^2 z}{(1 - \nu^2)D}$$

$$M_{x_0 y_0} = \tau_{x_0 y_0} = 0$$

9-8   Finite differences solution—∇^4 operator

Example: The boundary conditions for a built-in plate are zero deflection and zero slope. The two stage solution using the auxiliary function ϕ cannot be used in this case because ϕ is not zero on the boundary. It is therefore necessary to set up a finite difference expression for $\nabla^4 w$ in order to solve this type of problem.

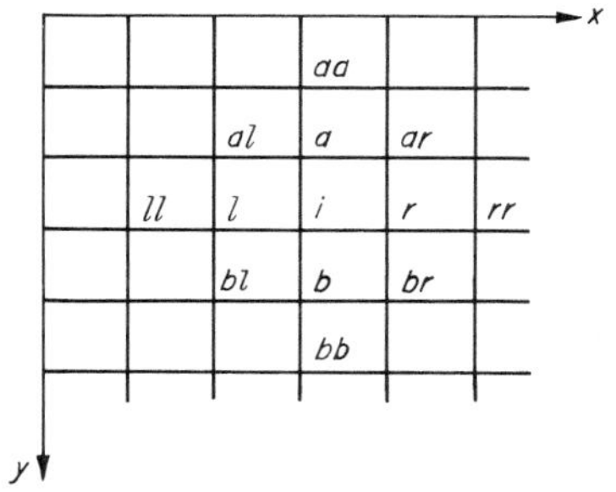

Fig. 9.8

Solution: A portion of a grid is shown in Fig. 9.8. We wish to express $\nabla^4 w$ in terms of the displacements of adjacent points. We had

$$\frac{\partial^2 w_b}{\partial y^2} = \frac{w_{bb} + w_i - 2w_b}{h^2}$$

$$\frac{\partial^2 w_a}{\partial y^2} = \frac{w_{aa} + w_i - 2w_a}{h^2}$$

$$\frac{\partial^2 w_i}{\partial y^2} = \frac{w_a + w_b - 2w_i}{h^2}$$

Then, since $\dfrac{\partial^4 w_i}{\partial y^4} = \dfrac{\partial^2}{\partial y^2}\left(\dfrac{\partial^2 w_i}{\partial y^2}\right)$, we have

$$\frac{\partial^4 w_i}{\partial y^4} = \left(\frac{\partial^2 w_a}{\partial y^2} + \frac{\partial^2 w_b}{\partial y^2} - 2\frac{\partial^2 w_i}{\partial y^2}\right)\frac{1}{h^2} = \frac{1}{h^4}\left(w_{aa} - 4w_a + 6w_i - 4w_b + w_{bb}\right) \quad \text{(9-10a)}$$

Likewise it can be shown that

$$\frac{\partial^4 w_i}{\partial x^4} = \frac{1}{h^4}\left(w_{ll} - 4w_l + 6w_i - 4w_r + w_{rr}\right) \quad \text{(9-10b)}$$

and

$$\frac{\partial^4 w_i}{\partial x^2 \partial y^2} = \frac{\partial^2}{\partial y^2}\left(\frac{\partial^2 w_i}{\partial x^2}\right) = \left(\frac{\partial^2 w_a}{\partial x^2} + \frac{\partial^2 w_b}{\partial x^2} - 2\frac{\partial^2 w_i}{\partial x^2}\right)\frac{1}{h^2}$$

or

$$\frac{\partial^4 w_i}{\partial x^2 \partial y^2} = \left(w_{ar} + w_{al} - 2w_a + w_{br} + w_{bl} - 2w_b - 2w_r - 2w_l + 4w_i\right)\frac{1}{h^4} \quad \text{(9-10c)}$$

By combining Equations (9-10a, b, c) we obtain an expression for $\nabla^4 w_i$,

$$\nabla^4 w_i = \frac{1}{h^4}\left[(w_{aa} + w_{bb} + w_{ll} + w_{rr}) + 2(w_{ar} + w_{al} + w_{br} + w_{bl})\right.$$
$$\left. - 8(w_a + w_b + w_l + w_r) + 20w_i\right] \quad \text{(9-10d)}$$

Equation (9-10d) represents the first-order finite difference operation for $\nabla^4 w_i$. To facilitate its use, the operator can be shown in diagrammatic form (Fig. 9.9).[11]

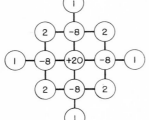

The problem of a square plate, of side length a loaded with a constant distributed load and built-in on all edges, is solved using four increments (Fig. 9.10).

At points 1, 2, 3, 4, the boundary condition may be written

$$\frac{\partial w_1}{\partial x} = \frac{\partial w_2}{\partial y} = \frac{\partial w_3}{\partial x} = \frac{\partial w_4}{\partial y} = \frac{1}{2}\left[\frac{w_0}{h} - \frac{w_0}{h}\right] = 0$$

Fig. 9.9   In order to satisfy this boundary condition, the

[11] M. Salvadori, "Numerical Computation of Buckling Loads by Finite Differences," *Proceedings*, ASCE, December 1949, p. 1441.

plate is considered extended beyond its boundaries so that we have deflections w_0 as shown at the intersection of the dotted lines of Fig. 9.10.

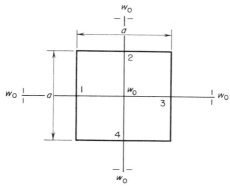

Fig. 9.10

For this case, applying Equation (9-10d) to point 0 gives

$$\nabla^4 w_0 = 24 w_0/h^4 = q/D$$

or

$$w_0 = \frac{1}{24}\left(\frac{a}{2}\right)^4 \frac{q}{D} = 0.0026\,\frac{qa^4}{D}$$

The error in the above answer is 118%. The discrepancy is so large because of the impossibility of satisfactorily approximating the boundary conditions with the very rough grid chosen. If instead of 4 sections, the network is made to consist of 16 sections, the resulting solution will be in error by 42%. Correspondingly better values will be attained with finer networks.

9-9 Plates with intermediate supports

The finite difference solution can also be applied to plates continuous over several supports. For a simply supported plate with an intermediate support (Fig. 9.11), the boundary conditions are

$$w(0, y) = w(a, y) = w(2a, y) = w(x, 0) = w(x, b) = 0$$

$$\nabla^2 w(0, y) = \nabla^2 w(2a, y) = \nabla^2 w(x, 0) = \nabla^2 w(x, b) = 0$$

The additional conditions arise from the continuity of the plate at the middle support; in particular, continuity of slope. To illustrate the method of solution, the following problem is solved.

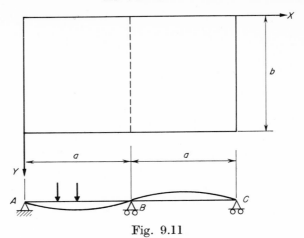

Fig. 9.11

Example: A continuous plate of length $2a$ and breadth a is simply supported on all sides and also in the middle. One half the plate is uniformly loaded. Find displacements by finite differences. Divide the plate into 18 equal segments. To satisfy the boundary conditions, consider the plate extended beyond the supports with deflections as shown.

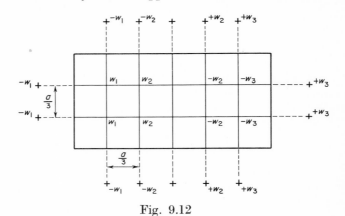

Fig. 9.12

Solution: Set up difference equations for points 1, 2, 3 using the operator of Fig. 9.9.

1. $\quad -2w_1 + 2w_2 - 8w_2 - 8w_1 + 20w_1 = \dfrac{q}{D}\dfrac{a^4}{81}$

2. $\quad -2w_2 + 2w_1 - 8w_2 - 8w_1 + 20w_2 = \dfrac{q}{D}\dfrac{a^4}{81}$

3. $\quad 2w_3 - 2w_2 + 8w_2 + 8w_3 - 20w_3 = 0$

Solve these equations simultaneously and obtain solutions for w_1, w_2, w_3 as follows,

$$w_1 = 1.50 \frac{qa^4}{81D}$$

$$w_2 = 0.25 \frac{qa^4}{81D}$$

$$w_3 = 0.150 \frac{qa^4}{81D}$$

These represent the approximate solution to the problem.

9-10 Thin shell structures

The exact relations governing the action of shells must be based upon the equations of the mathematical theory of elasticity. Some of the developments along these lines are described by Love.[12] However, these exact equations of elasticity lead to expressions and equations which are so complicated that it is impossible to obtain solutions for the shell problems of practical interest. In an attempt to obtain solutions to at least some of these problems, the exact equations have been approximated in various ways by different investigators, leading to different final forms of a differential equation, generally in terms of the displacement, w. These equations are almost invariably of the eighth order—but there the similarity ends. Depending upon the assumptions made in the derivations, the equations take quite different forms. They are occasionally called the exact differential equations of the shell problem. We shall call them "exact," in quotation marks, in order to distinguish them from other, admittedly, approximate methods and equations which we shall also discuss.

It must be clearly understood, however, that these "exact" solutions are in no sense of the word exact—and, in fact, we have no real assurance that any particular solution obtained by an "exact" method is more accurate than one obtained by an approximate method for the ordinary engineering-type shell structure.

Another point which must be kept in mind is that the various "exact" methods do not always give solutions that agree with each other. An excellent study along these lines was made by McNamee.[13] He showed that for the various simplified conditions which he considered, the apparent agreement between the different methods could be good or poor—and this study was admittedly an incomplete

[12] A. E. H. Love, *A Treatise on the Mathematical Theory of Elasticity*, Cambridge University Press, 4th Ed., 1927.

[13] J. J. McNamee, *Existing Methods for the Analysis of Concrete Shell Roofs*, Proceedings of a Symposium on Concrete Shell Roof Construction, Cement and Concrete Association, London, 1954.

one.   Any thorough analysis along these lines would of necessity have to determine the fundamental properties of eighth-order differential equations, including a determination of the effect on the solutions (and also on the derivatives of the solutions, which are the stresses, etc.) due to the inclusion or the omission of various physical parameters, various differential terms, etc.   This has not been done and until steps have been taken in this direction, a real fundamental knowledge of the similarities or divergences of the solutions obtained by the different methods will not be known.

In addition to the above, we should note the following complications which are introduced in the practical problem of shell design:

1. The shells generally have a discontinuous type of action due to the necessity for having edge beams along the bottom of the shell and arches or bulkheads at the ends of the shell.

2. The structure is occasionally of a multiple (continuous) shell design.

3. Many shells are built of reinforced concrete, which is a non-homogeneous material for which the equations of elasticity take a particularly complicated form.

Hence, for all practical engineering purposes, a truly exact shell analysis is impossible.

In the following articles, two approximate methods and two "exact" methods will be discussed.   The first "exact" method is a procedure based upon a formal solution of the derived differential equation and assumed boundary conditions.[14]   The second method is one which has been presented in a publication of the American Society of Civil Engineers.[15]   These two methods probably do not give identical results, which is understandable since they differ both in the differential equations and in the procedures used in solving the differential equations.

One approximate method which will be described is a beam type of shell analysis.   The results obtained by this method will be compared with those obtained by the ASCE Manual methods.

Because the ASCE Manual method uses what is essentially a perturbation to a basic membrane solution (which can in itself be taken as an approximate solution to the shell problem), we shall also discuss in some detail the membrane theory for cylindrical shells (Art. 9-21) and the membrane theory for general shells of revolution (Art. 9-32).

---

[14] J. E. Gibson and D. W. Cooper, *The Design of Cylindrical Shell Roofs*, D. Van Nostrand Company, Princeton, N.J., 1955.

[15] ASCE Manual.

9-11 Fundamentals of thin shell behavior

The shell is a three-dimensional structure whose basic resistance to load is through tension and compression. To illustrate, let us draw the following analogies. A beam resists transverse loads by development of bending and shear stress: a cable can resist the same load through tension alone. A plate is likened to a two-dimensional beam and resists transverse loads by two dimensional bending and shear: a membrane is the two-dimensional equivalent of the cable and resists loads through tensile stresses. Imagine a membrane with large deflections (Fig. 9.13a). Reverse the load and the membrane and

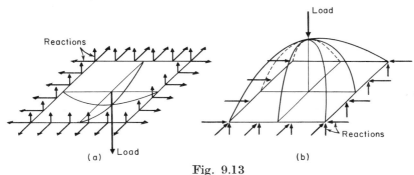

Fig. 9.13

we have the structural shell (Fig. 9.13b), provided that the shell is stable for the type of load shown. The membrane resists the load through tensile stresses but the ideal thin shell must be capable of developing both tension and compression.

However, the similarity between the behavior of a shell and a membrane is not complete because of the so-called boundary disturbances which arise in the shell. These boundary disturbances give rise to bending moments and shears, usually localized in the region immediately adjacent to the boundary. Frequently these are of sufficient magnitude to control the design. Determination of the boundary disturbances is usually a difficult mathematical and numerical procedure. Here, publications such as the ASCE Manual become extremely useful.

9-12 Types of shells

Structural shells can be divided into three general classes:

1. Cylindrical shells and segments thereof.

2. Shells of revolution (for instance, the shell generated by a circle revolving about a diameter is a sphere (Fig. 9.14a), that formed by revolving a line is a cone, etc.).

3. Shells formed by the sliding of one curve along another curve (saddle shells).

The ASCE Manual deals only with shells of the first type.

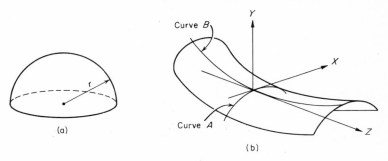

Fig. 9.14

9-13   Methods of shell analysis

For our purposes we may say that there are three general methods that can be used in the analysis of structural shells.   These are:

1. "Exact" solutions of the differential equation for given boundary conditions.

2. Application of the strength of materials beam theory (approximate).

3. Membrane theory (approximate).

The second and third methods are limited in application to certain special cases, see Art. 9-16.   An extension of the third method, in which corrections are introduced to account for the boundary disturbances (which are bending rather than membrane effects) is the basis of the ASCE Manual method of solution, which is considered an "exact" solution.

9-14   Circular cylindrical shells—"exact" elastic theory

A cylindrical shell of radius r and span length L is shown in Fig. 9.15.   A differential element $rd\phi dx$ is (for the general case) subject to forces, shears, and moments shown in Fig. 9.16.   The units of these are force per unit length and moment per unit length.   The displacements of a point on the surface are given by u in the x or longitudinal direction, v in the tangential direction, w in the radial direction.   The three components of the surface forces are shown as X in the x direction, Y in the tangential direction, Z in the radial direction.   Positive directions for all coordinates, displacements, forces,

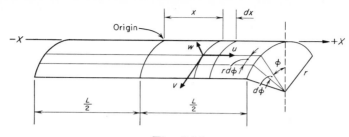

Fig. 9.15

shear, and moments, are shown in Figs. 9.15 and 9.16. For a shell thickness h, the middle surface is defined as that surface which bisects the thickness. For a longitudinal section, this middle surface passes through the centroid of the section, but for a transverse section the middle surface does not pass through the centroid. The neutral axis for all sections is assumed to be that axis containing the centroid.

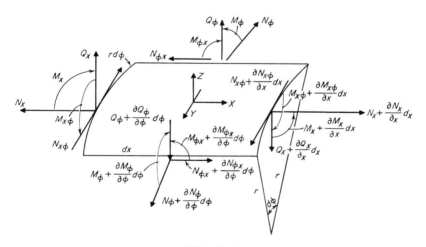

Fig. 9.16

If we apply the equilibrium conditions to the forces and moments acting on the element (Fig. 9.16), we obtain the following six equilibrium equations.[16]

$$\frac{\partial N_x}{\partial x} + \frac{\partial N_{\phi x}}{r \partial \phi} + X = 0 \qquad (9\text{-}11)$$

$$\frac{\partial N_{x\phi}}{\partial x} + \frac{\partial N_\phi}{r \partial \phi} - \frac{Q_\phi}{r} + Y = 0 \qquad (9\text{-}12)$$

[16] Gibson and Cooper, *op. cit.*

$$\frac{\partial Q_x}{\partial x} + \frac{\partial Q_\phi}{r\,\partial\phi} + \frac{N_\phi}{r} - Z = 0 \qquad (9\text{-}13)$$

$$\frac{\partial M_x}{\partial x} + \frac{\partial M_{\phi x}}{r\,\partial\phi} - Q_x = 0 \qquad (9\text{-}14)$$

$$\frac{\partial M_\phi}{r\,\partial\phi} + \frac{\partial M_{x\phi}}{\partial x} - Q_\phi = 0 \qquad (9\text{-}15)$$

$$N_{x\phi} - N_{\phi x} = 0 \qquad (9\text{-}16)$$

The equations for strains will be given without proof.[17]

$$\epsilon_x = \frac{\partial u}{\partial x} - z\,\frac{\partial^2 w}{\partial x^2} \qquad (9\text{-}17)$$

$$2\gamma_{x\phi} = \frac{1}{r+z}\,\frac{\partial u}{\partial\phi} + \frac{r+z}{r}\,\frac{\partial v}{\partial x} - \left(\frac{z}{r+z} + \frac{z}{r}\right)\frac{\partial^2 w}{\partial x\,\partial\phi} \qquad (9\text{-}18)$$

$$\epsilon_\phi = \frac{1}{r}\,\frac{\partial v}{\partial\phi} - \frac{z}{r(r+z)}\,\frac{\partial^2 w}{\partial\phi^2} + \frac{w}{r+z} \qquad (9\text{-}19)$$

where z is the coordinate distance locating an element from the middle surface, ϵ_x and ϵ_ϕ are unit strains in the x and ϕ directions, and $\gamma_{x\phi}$ is the shear strain. Applying Hooke's Law we can obtain the normal and shear stresses by multiplying the unit strains by the proper moduli. By integration of stresses we can obtain expressions for the unit forces of Fig. 9.16 in terms of the displacement. These are (derivations omitted, see reference 17), if Poisson's ratio is assumed zero:

$$M_x = \frac{Eh^3}{12}\,\frac{\partial^2 w}{\partial x^2} = D\,\frac{\partial^2 w}{\partial x^2} \qquad (9\text{-}20)$$

$$M_\phi = \frac{D}{r^2}\,\frac{\partial^2 w}{\partial\phi^2} \qquad (9\text{-}21)$$

$$M_{x\phi} = M_{\phi x} = \frac{D}{r}\,\frac{\partial^2 w}{\partial x\,\partial\phi} \qquad (9\text{-}22)$$

$$Q_x = D\left[\frac{\partial^3 w}{\partial x^3} + \frac{1}{r^2}\,\frac{\partial^3 w}{\partial x\,\partial\phi^2}\right] \qquad (9\text{-}23)$$

$$Q_\phi = D\left[\frac{1}{r^3}\,\frac{\partial^3 w}{\partial\phi^3} + \frac{1}{r}\,\frac{\partial^3 w}{\partial x^2\,\partial\phi}\right] \qquad (9\text{-}24)$$

$$N_\phi = -Dr\left[\frac{\partial^4 w}{\partial x^4} + \frac{2}{r^2}\,\frac{\partial^4 w}{\partial x^2\,\partial\phi^2} + \frac{\partial^4 w}{r^4\partial\phi^4}\right] + Zr \qquad (9\text{-}25)$$

[17] *Ibid.*, p. 9.

$$\frac{\partial N_{x\phi}}{\partial x} = \frac{\partial N_{\phi x}}{\partial x} = Dr\left[\frac{\partial^5 w}{r\partial\phi\ \partial x^4} + \frac{2\partial^5 w}{r^3\partial\phi^3\ \partial x^2} + \frac{\partial^5 w}{r^5\partial\phi^5}\right] - \frac{\partial Z}{\partial\phi} - Y \quad (9\text{-}26)$$

$$\frac{\partial^2 N_x}{\partial x^2} = -D\left[\frac{\partial^6 w}{r\partial\phi^2\ \partial x^4} + \frac{2}{r^3}\frac{\partial^6 w}{\partial\phi^4\ \partial x^2} + \frac{\partial^6 w}{r^5\partial\phi^6}\right] + \frac{1}{r}\left[\frac{\partial^2 Z}{\partial\phi^2} + \frac{\partial Y}{\partial\phi}\right] - \frac{\partial X}{\partial x} \quad (9\text{-}27)$$

$$N_x = Eh\frac{\partial u}{\partial x} \quad (9\text{-}28)$$

$$N_\phi = Eh\left[\frac{1}{r}\frac{\partial v}{\partial\phi} + \frac{w}{r}\right] \quad (9\text{-}29)$$

$$N_{x\phi} = N_{\phi x} = \frac{Eh}{2}\left[\frac{1}{r}\frac{\partial u}{\partial\phi} + \frac{\partial v}{\partial x}\right] \quad (9\text{-}30)$$

The above eleven equations contain eleven unknowns. By elimination of the unknowns we can obtain the following equation, which is the basic differential equation of the problem.[18]

$$r^8\left[\frac{\partial^2}{r^2\partial\phi^2} + \frac{\partial^2}{\partial x^2}\right]^4 w + \frac{Ehr^6}{D}\frac{\partial^4 w}{\partial x^4}$$

$$= \frac{r^6}{D}\left[r^2\left(\frac{\partial^2}{r^2\ \partial\phi^2} + \frac{\partial^2}{\partial x^2}\right)^2 Z + r\frac{\partial^2}{r^2\partial\phi^2}\left(\frac{\partial Y}{r\partial\phi} - \frac{\partial X}{\partial x}\right) + 2r\frac{\partial^3 Y}{r\partial\phi\ \partial x^2}\right] \quad (9\text{-}31)$$

Equation (9-31) is an eighth-order partial differential equation. A solution of this equation will be the solution of a particular problem if it also satisfies the boundary conditions.

The solution of the homogeneous part of Equation (9-31) is conveniently expressed by Gibson and Cooper as

$$w = (A_1 e^{M_1\phi} + A_2 e^{M_2\phi} + \cdots A_8 e^{M_8\phi})\cos nkx \quad (9\text{-}32)$$

where $A_1, A_2, \cdots A_8$ are eight arbitrary constants, to be determined from the boundary conditions, and $k = \pi/L$. For simply supported shells (origin for x at the center of the shell), $w = 0$ at $x = \pm L/2$. For this case n is taken equal to unity in Equation (9-32). This value of n will be used in what follows and therefore we limit ourselves to a discussion of shells with zero deflection at $x = \pm L/2$. The eight values of M are given by Gibson and Cooper as

$$M = \pm(m_1 + in_1)\frac{C}{\sqrt[4]{2}} \text{ and } M = \pm(m_2 \pm in_2)\frac{C}{\sqrt[4]{2}} \quad (9\text{-}33a)$$

where $i = \sqrt{-1}$ and

$$C^8 = \frac{Ehr^6\pi^4}{L^4 D} = \frac{12r^6}{h^2}\cdot\frac{\pi^4}{L^4} \quad (9\text{-}33b)$$

[18] For some of the other shell differential equations, see J. J. McNamee, *Existing Methods for the Analysis of Concrete Shell Roofs*, Proceedings of a Symposium on Concrete Shell Roof Construction, Cement and Concrete Assn., London, 1954.

and

$$m_1 = \sqrt{\frac{\sqrt{(1+\gamma)^2+1}+(1+\gamma)}{2}} \tag{9-33c}$$

$$n_1 = \sqrt{\frac{\sqrt{(1+\gamma)^2+1}-(1+\gamma)}{2}} \tag{9-33d}$$

$$m_2 = \sqrt{\frac{\sqrt{(1-\gamma)^2+1}-(1-\gamma)}{2}} \tag{9-33e}$$

$$n_2 = \sqrt{\frac{\sqrt{(1-\gamma)^2+1}+(1-\gamma)}{2}} \tag{9-33f}$$

$$\gamma = \frac{\sqrt{rh}}{\sqrt[4]{3}}\cdot\frac{\pi}{L} \tag{9-33g}$$

For given shell dimensions, γ and C can be calculated first, then m_1, n_1, m_2, n_2, and from these, values of M are computed. At this point, w will be defined in terms of eight arbitrary constants. Using the known boundary conditions, the constants can be determined and the solution of the homogeneous equation will be known.

9-15   The particular solution of the differential equation

The particular solution of the differential equation is conveniently obtained by expanding the load function into a Fourier series and using only the first term of the series to represent the load. This will lead to approximate final answers, but it is assumed that the errors are of acceptable magnitudes. For a uniformly distributed load q lb/ft^2, the series expansion is

$$p = \frac{4q}{\pi}\sum_{n=1}^{\infty}\frac{1}{n}\cos nkx \sin n\frac{\pi}{2}, \quad \text{where } k = \frac{\pi}{L}.$$

Using only the first term of the series, the load function becomes

$$p = \frac{4q}{\pi}\cos kx \tag{9-34}$$

The longitudinal, transverse, and radial components of p are

$$X = 0$$

$$Y = \frac{4q}{\pi}\cos kx \sin \phi$$

$$Z = -\frac{4q}{\pi}\cos kx \cos \phi$$

The particular solution is then obtained from Equation (9-31) as

$$w = F \frac{4q}{\pi} \cos \phi \cos kx \qquad (9\text{-}35)$$

where the constant F is

$$F = -\frac{r^4}{D} \left\{ \frac{(kr)^4 + 4(kr)^2 + 2}{[1 + (kr)^2]^4 + \dfrac{E(kr)^4 \cdot r^2 h}{D}} \right\} \qquad (9\text{-}35a)$$

The complete solution of the differential Equation (9-31) is then the homogeneous solution plus the particular solution. Thus for uniform load and a simply supported shell ($w = 0$ at $x = \pm L/2$), we have the complete solution

$$w = (A_1 e^{M_1 \phi} + A_2 e^{M_2 \phi} + \cdots A_8 e^{M_8 \phi}) \cos kx + F \frac{4q}{\pi} \cos \phi \cos kx \qquad (9\text{-}36)$$

9-16 Some general remarks on the theory of cylindrical shells

A complete presentation of the "exact" theory and "exact" solutions of cylindrical shells is beyond the scope of a text on structural analysis. Gibson and Cooper have performed an excellent task in arranging coefficients used in their form of "exact" computational analysis of cylindrical shells. They give complete solutions for several problems using this "exact" theory. Gibson and Cooper also use the elementary beam theory of strength of materials and the membrane theory (see Art. 9-21) in obtaining approximate solutions for cylindrical shells. They classify shells as long, intermediate, and short, as follows:

$$\frac{L}{r} > 2.5 \qquad \text{is long}$$

$$0.5 < \frac{L}{r} < 2.5 \qquad \text{is intermediate}$$

$$\frac{L}{r} < 0.5 \qquad \text{is short}$$

and on the basis of their solutions, draw the following conclusions:

1. For long shells, the elementary beam theory for a cylindrical shell (with or without edge beams) gives good results for preliminary design. Values of maximum and minimum stresses differ by about 20% or 30% from the values obtained by using the "exact" theory. In using this approximate theory, the simple flexure formula $\sigma = My/I$ is applied to the circular segment cross section of the shell.

2. The membrane theory gives a good check on short shells except near the boundaries of the shell.

3. For intermediate shells, neither the elementary beam theory nor the membrane theory give satisfactory results.

9-17 Boundary conditions for a simply supported shell

For a simply supported shell (see Fig. 9.17), the eighth-order differential equation leads to a solution containing eight arbitrary constants. For symmetry of shape and loading, the eight constants

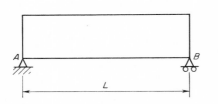

Fig. 9.17

reduce to four. It is necessary therefore to use four boundary conditions to evaluate the arbitrary constants. These are, for the free edge AB

$$M_\phi = 0; \quad N_\phi = 0; \quad N_{\phi x} = 0;$$

$$Q'_\phi = Q_\phi + \frac{\partial M_{\phi x}}{\partial x} = 0$$

It is necessary to use these boundary conditions in order to obtain a solution for the simply supported shell.

9-18 The approximate (beam) design of a simply supported long shell

To illustrate a method of design and analysis for cylindrical shells, some problems will now be solved using, first, approximate methods, and later "exact" methods based upon the ASCE Manual. The preliminary design of a reinforced concrete simply supported long shell can be made using elementary beam theory (see Art. 9-16). This approximate method is illustrated by the following example.

Example: Given

Length of shell $L = 130$ ft
Radius of shell $r = 50$ ft
                  $\phi_K = 35°$
Shell thickness $h = 3$ in.
Dead load $= 36$ lb/ft²
Live load $= 20$ lb/ft²
_____
Total load $= 56$ lb/ft² of horizontal projection

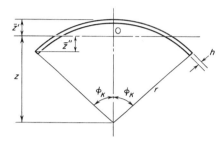

Fig. 9.18

Solution: *Properties of the Section:*[19]

Length of arc

$$= 2r\phi_K$$

Location of center of gravity

$$= \bar{z} = \frac{r \sin \phi_k}{\phi_k} = \frac{50 \times 0.57358}{0.610865} = 46.947$$

$$\bar{z}' = r - z = r\left(1 - \frac{\sin \phi_k}{\phi_k}\right) = 3.053$$

$$\bar{z}'' = r(1 - \cos \phi_k) - \bar{z}' = 50(1 - 0.81915) - 3.053 = 5.989$$

The neutral axis is taken as the horizontal line through O (Fig. 9.18).
Moment of inertia I_O of the arc segment about the neutral axis

$$I_O = 2hr^3\left(\frac{\phi_k}{2} + \frac{\sin 2\phi_k}{4} - \frac{\sin^2 \phi_k}{\phi_k}\right) = 111.25 \text{ ft}^4$$

Loads and Stresses:

The load/lineal ft is $56 \times 2r \sin \phi_k$

or $p = 56 \times 2 \times 50 \times 0.5736 = 3212$ lb/ft

[19] See Gibson and Cooper.

The maximum moment (shell simply supported) is

$$M_{\max} = \frac{pL^2}{8} = \frac{3212(130)^2}{8} = 6,780,000 \text{ lb-ft}$$

Maximum unit stress on top fiber,

$$\sigma_x = -\frac{M_{\max} \bar{z}'}{I_O} = -186,000 \text{ lb/ft}^2 = -1290 \text{ lb/in.}^2$$

Maximum unit stress on bottom fiber,

$$\sigma_x = +\frac{M_{\max} \bar{z}''}{I_O} = +359,000 \text{ lb/ft}^2 = +2490 \text{ lb/in.}^2$$

$$N_x \text{ (top fiber)} = h\sigma_y = -46,400 \text{ lb/ft}$$

$$N_x \text{ (bottom fiber)} = +89,800 \text{ lb/ft}$$

The above values may contain differences of up to 50% when compared with the results of an "exact" analysis (see Art. 9-29).

From the values of σ_x computed, it is clear that the shell will be overstressed in tension. It is therefore necessary to change the cross section. This is done by introducing edge beams which are continuous with the shell and run the full length of the shell (see Fig. 9.19).

9-19   Cylindrical shells with edge beams—approximate (beam) analysis

Example: Consider the simply supported cylindrical shell with edge beams of Fig. 9.19. This shell will be analyzed by the elementary beam theory to get an approximate idea of the effect upon the maximum stresses of adding the edge beams.

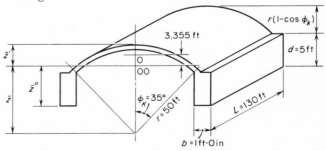

Fig. 9.19

Given: $L=130$ ft, $r=50$ ft, $\phi_k=35°$, $h=3$ in. Total uniform total $=56$ lb/ft^2 of horizontal projection. Edge beam dimensions are 1 ft wide by 5 ft deep.

Properties of the section:

$$\bar{z} = \frac{\left[hr^2 \sin \phi_k + \left(r \cos \phi_k - \dfrac{d}{2}\right)bd\right]}{rh\phi_k + bd} \tag{9-37}$$

$$\bar{z} = 43.5924 \text{ ft}$$

$$\bar{z}' = 50 - \bar{z} = 6.4076 \text{ ft}$$

$$\bar{z}'' = r(1 - \cos \phi_k) - \bar{z}' + 5' = 7.6349 \text{ ft}$$

Solution: The distance between the center of gravity (point O) of the shell and the center of gravity (point OO) of the shell plus edge beams is (see Art. 9-18) $6.4076 - 3.053 = 3.355$ ft. The distance between the c.g. of the edge beam and point OO is $r(1 - \cos \phi_k) + 2.500 - \bar{z}' = 5.1249$ ft. The moment of inertia of the composite section, I_{OO} is now determined.

$$I_{OO} = I_O + 2rh\phi_k(3.355)^2 + 2\frac{bd^3}{12} + 2bd(5.1249)^2 = 568.9 \text{ ft}^4$$

Load per lineal foot, allowing for the weight of the edge beam (assume concrete weighs 144 lb/cu ft), is

$$p = (3212 + 2 \times 12 \times 60) \text{ lb/ft}$$

$$p = 4652 \text{ lb/ft}$$

Then

$$M_{\max} = \frac{pL^2}{8} = \frac{4652(130)^2}{8} = 9,830,000 \text{ lb-ft}$$

At top of shell,

$$\text{Maximum } \sigma_x = -\frac{9,830,000 \times 6.4076}{568.9} = -110,700 \text{ lb/ft}^2 = -770 \text{ lb/in.}^2$$

At bottom of shell and at top of edge beam,

$$\text{Maximum } \sigma_x = \frac{+9,830,000 \times 2.6349}{568.9} = +45,600 \text{ lb/ft}^2 = +316 \text{ lb/in.}^2$$

At bottom of edge beam,

$$\text{Maximum } \sigma_x = \frac{+9,830,000 \times 7.6349}{568.9} = +132,300 \text{ lb/ft}^2 = +918 \text{ lb/in.}^2$$

The tensile stresses will be carried by steel reinforcement in reinforced concrete construction.

The unit forces corresponding to the stresses listed above are

$$N_x = -770 \times 3 \times 12 = -27,700 \text{ lb/ft for the top of the shell}$$

$$N_x = +316 \times 3 \times 12 = +11,370 \text{ lb/ft for the bottom edge of the shell}$$

Comparison of the above solution with that for the same shell without edge beams, although both are approximations, indicates clearly the large reduction in stress that takes place at the lower edge of the shell upon addition of the edge beams. (For "exact" values of N, see Art. 9-29.)

9-20   Simply supported cylindrical shell—"exact" solution procedure

The simply supported shell of the preceding articles can be analyzed with or without edge beams using the methods illustrated by Gibson and Cooper. As has been stated previously, it is beyond the scope of this text to go through a typical solution of this kind. However, it is also possible to obtain an "exact" solution of the problem using the ASCE Manual. It will be assumed that the reader has access to this Manual and references will be made in this text to tables in the Manual. The ASCE procedure follows:

I. For simply supported cylindrical shells without edge beams

   (a) Find the membrane stresses.
   (b) Correct the membrane stresses for effects produced by so-called line loads acting along the free edge.
   (c) The sum of the corrections and the membrane stresses is the final solution to the problem.

II. For simply supported cylindrical shells with edge beams

   (a) Find the solution for the shell without edge beams as outlined under I above.
   (b) Add corrective line loads to the edge of the shell such that at the point of contact between the shell and the edge beam

      1. The longitudinal stress in the shell is equal to the longitudinal (fiber) stress of the edge beam.
      2. The vertical deflection of the shell is the same as the vertical deflection of the edge beam.
      3. Other boundary conditions, that theoretically should be considered in the solution, such as the twist of the shell and edge beam and the horizontal force between the shell and beam, are usually ignored.

   (c) The sum of the simply supported shell solution and the corrections due to edge beam interaction is the final solution of the problem.

To introduce this method of analysis, it is necessary first to present the membrane theory of cylindrical shells.

9-21   Symmetrically loaded cylindrical shells—membrane theory

A thin cylindrical shell is shown in Fig. 9.20a. Assuming that there are no internal bending moments, the membrane forces per unit length acting upon a differential element are shown in Fig. 9.20b. Z, X, Y are the normal, longitudinal, and tangential components of

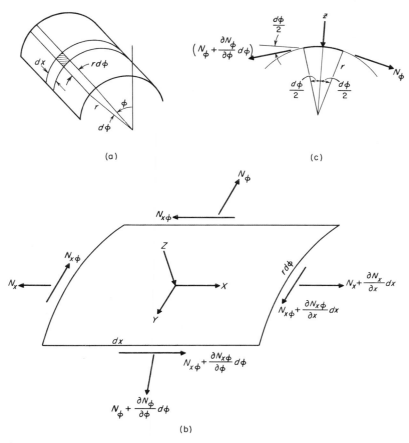

Figs. 9.20

the external load per unit area acting upon the element. The equilibrium equations of the element are:

In the X direction:

$$-N_x r d\phi + \left(N_x + \frac{\partial N_x}{\partial x} dx\right) r d\phi - N_{x\phi} dx$$

$$+ \left(N_{x\phi} + \frac{\partial N_{x\phi}}{\partial \phi} d\phi\right) dx + X r d\phi \, dx = 0$$

or $\qquad \dfrac{\partial N_x}{\partial x} r d\phi \, dx + \dfrac{\partial N_{x\phi}}{\partial \phi} d\phi \, dx + X r d\phi \, dx = 0$

or $\qquad \dfrac{\partial N_x}{\partial x} + \dfrac{1}{r} \dfrac{\partial N_{x\phi}}{\partial \phi} + X = 0$ $\qquad\qquad$ (9-38a)

In the tangential direction:

$$-N_\phi\, dx + \left(N_\phi + \frac{\partial N_\phi}{\partial \phi}\, d\phi\right) dx - N_{x\phi}\, rd\phi + \left(N_{x\phi} + \frac{\partial N_{x\phi}}{\partial x}\, dx\right) rd\phi$$
$$+ Yrd\phi\, dx = 0$$

or

$$\frac{\partial N_\phi}{\partial \phi}\, d\phi\, dx + \frac{\partial N_{x\phi}}{\partial x}\, rd\phi\, dx + Yrd\phi\, dx = 0$$

or

$$\frac{1}{r}\frac{\partial N_\phi}{\partial \phi} + \frac{\partial N_{x\phi}}{\partial x} + Y = 0 \qquad (9\text{-}38b)$$

In the normal direction (see Fig. 9.20c):

Taking normal components of the tangential unit forces and remembering that $\sin\dfrac{d\phi}{2} \doteq \dfrac{d\phi}{2}$ (note that the tangential shears cancel out around the curve), we obtain

$$\left(N_\phi + N_\phi + \frac{\partial N_\phi}{\partial \phi}\, d\phi\right) dx\, \frac{d\phi}{2} + Zrd\phi\, dx = 0$$

Ignoring the differential term $\dfrac{1}{2}\dfrac{\partial N_\phi}{\partial \phi}\, d\phi$, we obtain after canceling $dx\, d\phi$

$$N_\phi = -Zr \qquad (9\text{-}38c)$$

The three simultaneous equations of equilibrium derived above can be solved as follows if we know the load functions X, Y, and Z:

1. Find N_ϕ from Equation (9-38c).
2. Using $\partial N_\phi/\partial \phi$, integrate Equation (9-38b) for $N_{x\phi}$.
3. Using $\partial N_{x\phi}/\partial \phi$, integrate Equation (9-38a) for N_x.

9-22 Simply supported cylindrical shell—dead load membrane stresses

Consider a simply supported cylindrical shell subject to constant dead load p in pounds per square foot. By simply supported, we mean that the shell supports at A and B offer no flexural resistance. The origin of the X axis is taken at midspan. The dead load on any element of area is divided into normal and transverse components

$$Z = p \cos \phi$$
$$Y = p \sin \phi$$

The longitudinal component X is zero. From Equation (9-38c), the tangential force per unit length is

$$N_\phi = -Zr = -pr \cos \phi \qquad (9\text{-}39)$$

and

$$\frac{1}{r} \frac{\partial N_\phi}{\partial \phi} = p \sin \phi$$

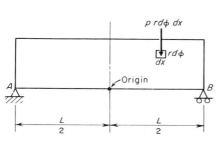
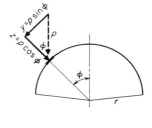

Fig. 9.21

From Equation (9-38b),

$$\frac{1}{r} \frac{\partial N_\phi}{\partial \phi} + \frac{\partial N_{x\phi}}{\partial x} + Y = 0$$

or

$$\frac{\partial N_{x\phi}}{\partial x} = -2p \sin \phi$$

If we integrate with respect to X,

$$N_{x\phi} = -2px \sin \phi + f_1(\phi)$$

where $f_1(\phi)$ is an undefined function of ϕ. We can obtain $f_1(\phi)$ by noting that because of symmetry $N_{x\phi} = 0$ along a section through the origin; hence $f_1(\phi) = 0$. Therefore

$$N_{x\phi} = -2px \sin \phi \qquad (9\text{-}40)$$

We can now obtain the unit force in the X direction at any point from Equation (9-38a).

$$\frac{\partial N_x}{\partial x} = \frac{1}{r} (2px \cos \phi)$$

Integrating with respect to X, we find that

$$N_x = \frac{px^2}{r} \cos \phi + f_2(\phi)$$

where $f_2(\phi)$ is a second undefined function of ϕ. The function $f_2(\phi)$

can be found as follows. At the ends of the simply supported shell $(x = \pm L/2)$, since there is no flexural rigidity, $N_x = 0$

or

$$N_x|_{x=L/2} = \frac{pL^2}{4r} \cos \phi + f_2(\phi) = 0$$

from which

$$f_2(\phi) = -\frac{pL^2}{4r} \cos \phi \quad \text{and}$$

$$N_x = \left(\frac{px^2}{r} - \frac{pL^2}{4r}\right) \cos \phi = \frac{pL^2}{r}\left(\frac{x^2}{L^2} - \frac{1}{4}\right) \cos \phi \tag{9-41}$$

The question arises at this point regarding theory and practice. How is it possible to simulate in practice the conditions assumed in the above analysis? In particular, how is it possible to support a shell so

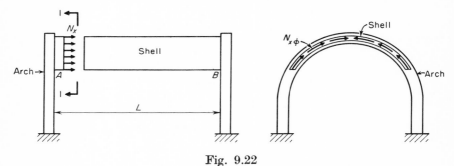

Fig. 9.22

that it offers zero flexural rigidity ($N_x = 0$) at the ends? One such practical example is shown in Fig. 9.22. We have a cylindrical shell supported over a span length L by two stiffener arches. These arches are relatively flexible in the x direction, but relatively rigid in resisting loads in the plane of the arch. As an approximation we can say that the arch offers no flexural resistance to the shell ($N_x = 0$ at the junction of arch and shell). From Equation (9-40) we see that at $x = \pm L/2$, $N_{x\phi} = \pm pl \sin \phi$. This means that the stiffener arch is subject to shear forces as expressed by the equation and as shown in view 1–1 of Fig. 9.22. Next consider the edge AB of the shell. Along this edge N_ϕ must be zero, but from Equation (9-39), we see that this is possible only if $\phi_k = 90°$; i.e., if the shell section is a semicircle. If ϕ_k is not $90°$, we will have to introduce a stiffening member (Fig. 9.23) capable of resisting the unit forces N_ϕ. Furthermore, regardless of the value of ϕ_k, $N_{x\phi} = -2px \sin \phi_k$ at this edge and is never zero. Thus the stiffening beam is required if we are to *approach* a membrane state of

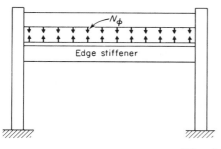
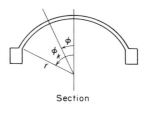

Section

Fig. 9.23

stress. It will be seen that even with a stiffening beam, because of the interaction between the stiffener and the shell, we do not have a membrane state of stress, but under some conditions ($L/r < 0.5$) we will have very nearly a state of membrane stress.

9-23 Uniformly loaded, simply supported cylindrical shells—membrane stresses

The simply supported cylindrical shell subject to uniform load p in pounds per square foot of horizontal projection can be analyzed in a similar manner. Assuming no internal bending moments, i.e., that a

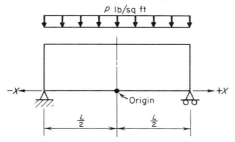
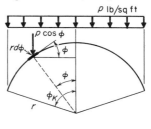

Fig. 9.24

membrane state of stress exists, the membrane unit forces can be found by successive use of Equations (9-38).

The load acting upon an element of area $rd\phi\, dx$ is $pr \cos \phi \cdot d\phi \cdot dx$. Thus, the intensity of loading is seen to be $p \cos \phi$. The normal, tangential, and longitudinal components are

$$Z = p \cos^2 \phi$$

$$Y = p \cos \phi \sin \phi$$

$$X = 0$$

From Equation (9-38c), the tangential unit force N_ϕ is

$$N_\phi = -Zr = -pr \cos^2\phi \qquad (9\text{-}42)$$

and

$$\frac{1}{r}\frac{\partial N_\phi}{\partial \phi} = +2p \cos\phi \sin\phi$$

Using this in Equation (9-38b), we obtain

$$\frac{\partial N_{x\phi}}{\partial x} = -3p \cos\phi \sin\phi = -\frac{3}{2}p \sin 2\phi$$

$$N_{x\phi} = -\tfrac{3}{2}px \sin 2\phi + f_1(\phi)$$

But by symmetry at $x = 0$ (the center of the shell), the shear force $N_{x\phi}$ in a vertical section must be zero, thus $f_1(\phi) = 0$. Therefore,

$$N_{x\phi} = -\tfrac{3}{2}px \sin 2\phi \qquad (9\text{-}43)$$

and

$$-\frac{1}{r}\frac{\partial N_{x\phi}}{\partial \phi} = +3\frac{px}{r} \cos 2\phi$$

Using these values in Equation (9-38a), we obtain

$$\frac{\partial N_x}{\partial x} = 3\frac{px}{r} \cos 2\phi$$

and integrating,

$$N_x = \frac{3}{2}\frac{px^2}{r} \cos 2\phi + f_2(\phi)$$

For simple supports, $N_x = 0$ at $x = \pm L/2$; then

$$f_2(\phi) = -\frac{3}{2}\frac{pL^2}{4r} \cos 2\phi$$

so that

$$N_x = \frac{3}{2}\frac{pL^2}{r} \cos 2\phi \left[\frac{x^2}{L^2} - \frac{1}{4}\right] \qquad (9\text{-}44)$$

As we have done for dead load, let us investigate the shell boundaries to see whether or not the assumed membrane state of stress is possible.
Along the longitudinal edge of the shell

$$N_\phi = -pr \cos^2\phi_k$$

This term cannot be zero unless $\phi_k = 90°$; therefore, in general, we will need to develop a tangential stress along this boundary. Along this same edge, the unit shears are

$$N_{x\phi} = -\tfrac{3}{2}px \sin 2\phi_k$$

These shears exist for all values of ϕ_k except $\phi_k = 90°$; therefore, in general, some means of developing these edge shears must be provided. This is done by using an edge beam (see Fig. 9.25). For a half cylindrical shell ($\phi_k = 90°$), the edge beam is not necessary to maintain a membrane state of stress for uniform load. But we have seen that even for $\phi_k = 90°$, the membrane state of stress cannot be approached under dead load [see Equations (9-39) and (9-40)] except with the edge beam; therefore the edge beam must be provided for all values of ϕ_k if we are to approach a membrane state of stress.

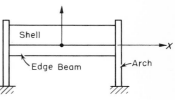

Fig. 9.25

At the junction with the supporting arch, $N_{x\phi} = \pm \dfrac{3}{2} \dfrac{pL}{2} \sin 2\phi$; the interaction between the arch and the shell must be such as to develop these shears if we are to approach a membrane state of stress.

We now will analyze conditions at the junction of the shell and supporting end arch.

9-24 Cylindrical shells—interaction between shell and supporting arches

Even for the simply supported arches discussed in the last two articles, aside from the edge beam disturbances, a pure membrane state of stress is not possible. To show this, consider the membrane tangential unit forces, N_ϕ, in the region of junction of the shell and supporting arch. These forces produce unit stresses

$$\sigma_\phi = \frac{N_\phi}{h} \tag{9-45}$$

where h is the shell thickness.

The corresponding tangential membrane strain is given approximately (Poisson's ratio neglected) by

$$\epsilon_\phi = \frac{\sigma_\phi}{E} = \frac{N_\phi}{Eh} \tag{9-46}$$

These strains correspond to a shortening of the circumferential length of the shell. But at the point of juncture with the arch, ϵ_ϕ is very nearly zero for compatibility with arch strains. Therefore the shell will not be subject to strains corresponding to a membrane state of stress in the vicinity of the arch. The deformations are approximately as shown in Fig. 9.26 with corresponding bending stresses in the shell itself. A similar effect can be produced by unequal temperature and shrinkage expansions between the arch and the shell. These

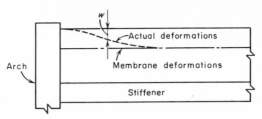

Fig. 9.26

effects must be taken into account in proportioning the shell and require an increase in shell thickness for sections close to the arch. This will be discussed in more detail in the succeeding articles.

9-25   Corrections for interaction between arch and shell

The interaction between arch and shell causes a boundary disturbance which is quite difficult to evaluate by exact analysis.

An approximate method of analysis is to consider the shell to behave in the same way as a full cylindrical shell of infinite length subject to boundary shears Q_0 and moments M_0 per unit length as shown in Fig. 9.27.   This is the procedure followed in the ASCE Manual.   The

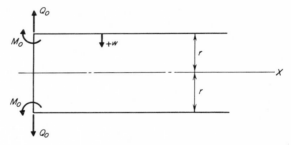

Fig. 9.27

problem of the infinite cylinder is discussed and solved in Timoshenko *Plates and Shells*, page 392.   The differential equation in terms of radial displacements w is shown to be

$$\frac{d^4w}{dx^4} + \frac{Ehw}{r^2D} = 0 \qquad (9\text{-}47)$$

where h is the shell thickness and $D = \dfrac{Eh^3}{12(1-\nu^2)}.$

This equation is of the same form as that of a beam on an elastic foundation.

The solution of Equation (9-47) is

$$w = \frac{\rho^{-\beta x}}{2\beta^3 D}[\beta M_0(\sin \beta x - \cos \beta x) - Q_0 \cos \beta x] \qquad (9\text{-}48)$$

where

$$\beta = \frac{\sqrt[4]{3(1-\nu^2)}}{\sqrt{rh}} = \frac{1.3}{\sqrt{rh}} \quad \text{for } \nu = 0.3 \qquad (9\text{-}49)$$

For large values of β, we can see that the radial deformations w will be small provided x is not small. Since β is dependent upon $\sqrt{rh}$, we see that a large β results from a small $\sqrt{rh}$. For a shell radius of 60 ft with a 3-in. thickness, with $\nu = 0.3$

$$\sqrt{rh} = \sqrt{60 \times \tfrac{3}{12}} = 3.87$$

$$\beta = \frac{1.3}{3.87} = 0.336, \quad D = \frac{Eh^3}{12(1-\nu^2)} = 2.25E$$

$$w = \frac{e^{-0.336x}}{171.5E}[0.336M_0(\sin 0.336x - \cos 0.336x) - Q_0 \cos 0.336x]$$

Values of $e^{-0.336x}$ are shown in Table 9.1 for $x = 0, 1, 2$, etc. It is seen

TABLE 9.1

x, ft.	0	1	2	3	4	5	6	7	10
$e^{-0.336x}$	1	0.715	0.511	0.352	0.260	0.186	0.133	0.095	0.0348

that these practically vanish 10 ft from the origin. We can conclude that boundary forces applied to a thin cylindrical shell will generally have little effect on the greatest part of the interior portion of the shell. This is true except for very small values of β.

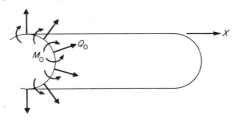

Fig. 9.28

We will assume that for a segment of a cylinder such as we have been considering in the membrane analysis of a simply supported cylindrical shell, the conclusions reached above can be applied to obtain approximate numerical solutions for the boundary disturbances arising through interaction between the shell and the arch. An estimate of the amount of error inherent in such an approximation can be made by comparison with an "exact" solution.

9-26   Cylindrical shells—interaction between arch and shell—deformations of the shell

Let u, v, and w represent the longitudinal (x), transverse (y), and radial (z), displacements of a point (1) on the middle surface of the shell as it is displaced to $1'$ (Fig. 9.29). The corresponding unit strains in the x, y, and z directions are

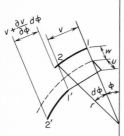

Fig. 9.29

$$\epsilon_x = \frac{\partial u}{\partial x} \tag{9-50a}$$

$$\epsilon_\phi = \frac{\left(v + \dfrac{\partial v}{\partial \phi}\, d\phi\right) - v + r\,d\phi - (r + w)\,d\phi}{r\,d\phi}$$

or

$$\epsilon_\phi = \frac{1}{r}\frac{\partial v}{\partial \phi} - \frac{w}{r} \tag{9-50b}$$

The shear strain in the tangential direction is

$$\gamma_{x\phi} = \frac{1}{r}\frac{\partial u}{\partial \phi} + \frac{\partial v}{\partial x} \tag{9-50c}$$

Assuming that the strains given by Equations (9-50) are caused by membrane stresses and applying Hooke's Law, we obtain

$$\epsilon_x = \frac{\partial u}{\partial x} = \frac{1}{Eh}(N_x - \nu N_\phi) \doteq \frac{N_x}{Eh} \tag{9-51a}$$

$$\epsilon_\phi = \frac{1}{r}\frac{\partial v}{\partial \phi} - \frac{w}{r} = \frac{1}{Eh}(N_\phi - \nu N_x) \doteq \frac{N_\phi}{Eh} \tag{9-51b}$$

$$\gamma_{x\phi} = \frac{\partial u}{r\,\partial \phi} + \frac{\partial v}{\partial x} = \frac{2(1+\nu)}{Eh}N_{x\phi} \doteq \frac{2}{Eh}N_{x\phi} \tag{9-51c}$$

The approximations are made by assuming Poisson's ratio is zero.

The deformations u, v, and w can be found by solving Equations (9-51) provided that N_x, N_ϕ, and $N_{x\phi}$ are known functions. The procedure will be illustrated for the cylindrical shell subject to dead load of Art. 9-22. We had

$$N_x = \frac{pL^2}{r}\left(\frac{x^2}{L^2} - \frac{1}{4}\right)\cos\phi$$

$$N_\phi = -pr\cos\phi$$

$$N_{x\phi} = -2px\sin\phi$$

Solving for u from Equation (9-51a), we have

$$\frac{\partial u}{\partial x} = \frac{pL^2}{Ehr}\left(\frac{x^2}{L^2} - \frac{1}{4}\right)\cos\phi$$

and integrating,

$$u = \frac{pL^2}{Ehr}\left(\frac{x^3}{3L^2} - \frac{x}{4}\right)\cos\phi + f_1(\phi)$$

But at the center line, $x = 0$, the longitudinal displacement u must be zero by symmetry; thus $f_1(\phi) = 0$ and

$$u = \frac{pL^2x}{Ehr}\left(\frac{x^2}{3L^2} - \frac{1}{4}\right)\cos\phi$$

or

$$u = -\frac{pr}{Eh}\left[\left(\frac{L}{2r}\right)^2 x - \frac{x^3}{3r^2}\right]\cos\phi \qquad (9\text{-}52a)$$

and

$$\frac{1}{r}\frac{\partial u}{\partial\phi} = +\frac{p}{Eh}\left[\left(\frac{L}{2r}\right)^2 x - \frac{x^3}{3r^2}\right]\sin\phi$$

From Equation (9-51c),

$$\frac{\partial v}{\partial x} = \left[-\frac{4px}{Eh} - \frac{p}{Eh}\left(\frac{L}{2r}\right)^2 x + \frac{p}{Eh}\frac{x^3}{3r^2}\right]\sin\phi$$

$$= \frac{p}{Eh}\left\{\frac{x^3}{3r^2} - \left[4 + \left(\frac{L}{2r}\right)^2\right]x\right\}\sin\phi$$

and integrating,

$$v = \frac{pr}{Eh}\left\{\frac{x^4}{12r^3} - \left[4 + \left(\frac{L}{2r}\right)^2\right]\frac{x^2}{2r}\right\}\sin\phi + f_2(\phi)$$

At $x = \pm L/2$, we may consider the transverse displacement of the shell and of the arch to be zero, from which we obtain

$$f_2(\phi) = -\frac{pr^2}{Eh}\left\{\frac{1}{12}\left(\frac{L}{2r}\right)^4 - \left[4 + \left(\frac{L}{2r}\right)^2\right]\frac{1}{2}\left(\frac{L}{2r}\right)^2\right\}\sin\phi$$

and

$$v = -\frac{pr^2}{Eh}\left\{\frac{1}{12}\left[\left(\frac{L}{2r}\right)^4 - \left(\frac{x}{r}\right)^4\right] + \right.$$

$$\left.\left[2 + \frac{1}{2}\left(\frac{L}{2r}\right)^2\right]\left[\left(\frac{x}{r}\right)^2 - \left(\frac{L}{2r}\right)^2\right]\right\}\sin\phi \qquad (9\text{-}52b)$$

$$\frac{\partial v}{\partial\phi} = -\frac{pr^2}{Eh}\left\{\frac{1}{12}\left[\left(\frac{L}{2r}\right)^4 - \left(\frac{x}{r}\right)^4\right] + \left[2 + \frac{1}{2}\left(\frac{L}{2r}\right)^2\right]\left[\left(\frac{x}{r}\right)^2 - \left(\frac{L}{2r}\right)^2\right]\right\}\cos\phi$$

From Equation (9-51b) we obtain the radial displacements for the shell subject to membrane stresses,

$$w = \frac{\partial v}{\partial \phi} - \frac{rN_\phi}{Eh}$$

or

$$w = \frac{pr^2}{Eh} \cos \phi \left\{ 1 - \frac{1}{12} \left[\left(\frac{L}{2r}\right)^4 - \left(\frac{x}{r}\right)^4 \right] - \right.$$
$$\left. \left[2 + \frac{1}{2}\left(\frac{L}{2r}\right)^2 \right] \left[\left(\frac{x}{r}\right)^2 - \left(\frac{L}{2r}\right)^2 \right] \right\} \quad \text{(9-52c)}$$

At the boundary,

$$x = \pm\frac{L}{2}$$

$$w_b = +\frac{pr^2}{Eh} \cos \phi \quad \text{(9-52d)}$$

For a particular value of x, the radial displacements are seen to be a factor times $\cos \phi$. If we restrict ourselves to shells subtending an angle of not more than 90°, then $\phi_k \leqslant 45°$, and $\cos \phi$ varies between values 0.707 and 1. For these shells, we may consider w constant with ϕ without introducing too much error. We can then treat the displacements of the cylindrical segment as identical with the displacements of a complete cylinder, Equation (9-48). We had for the complete cylinder:

$$w = \frac{e^{-\beta x}}{2\beta^3 D} \left[\beta M_0(\sin \beta x - \cos \beta x) - Q_0 \cos \beta x \right] \quad \text{(9-48)}$$

Differentiating, we obtain the slope

$$\frac{dw}{dx} = \frac{e^{-\beta x}}{2\beta^2 D} \left[2\beta M_0 \cos \beta x + Q_0(\cos \beta x + \sin \beta x) \right] \quad \text{(9-52e)}$$

At $x = 0$,

$$w_0 = -\frac{1}{2\beta^3 D} \left[\beta M_0 + Q_0 \right] \quad \text{(9-52f)}$$

$$\frac{dw_0}{dx} = \frac{1}{2\beta^2 D} \left[2\beta M_0 + Q_0 \right] \quad \text{(9-52g)}$$

We now consider two extreme assumed connection conditions between the shell and the arch.

    I. The shell is assumed built-in to an infinitely stiff arch.

    II. The connection between the arch and the shell is assumed to be a pin connection.

CASE I. If we assume the shell connected to an infinitely stiff arch, then

$$\frac{dw_0}{dx} = 0 = \frac{1}{2\beta^2 D}[2\beta M_0 + Q_0]$$

or

$$Q_0 = -2\beta M_0$$

The shell deflection at $x = \pm L/2$ is taken as zero (arch deflections are ignored). By superposition of Equations (9-52d) and (9-52f), we obtain

$$w\big|_{x=0} = -\frac{pr^2}{Eh}\cos\phi + \frac{1}{2\beta^3 D}[\beta M_0 + Q_0] = 0$$

or, since $Q_0 = -2\beta M_0$,

$$-\frac{pr^2}{Eh}\cos\phi + \frac{1}{2\beta^3 D}[-\beta M_0] = 0$$

we find

$$M_0 = -2\beta^2 D\frac{pr^2}{Eh}\cos\phi$$

We had

$$\beta = \frac{\sqrt[4]{3(1-\nu^2)}}{\sqrt{rh}} \doteq \frac{\sqrt[4]{3}}{\sqrt{rh}}\quad\text{(neglecting }\nu\text{)}$$

from which

$$M_0 \doteq -\frac{2\sqrt{3}}{rh}\cdot\frac{Eh^3}{12(1-\nu^2)}\cdot\frac{pr^2}{Eh}\cos\phi \doteq -\frac{1}{2\sqrt{3}}prh\cos\phi \quad (9\text{-}53)$$

$$Q_0 = \frac{2\sqrt[4]{3}}{\sqrt{rh}}\cdot\frac{1}{2\sqrt{3}}prh\cos\phi$$

or

$$Q_0 = \frac{1}{\sqrt[4]{3}}p\sqrt{rh}\cos\phi = 0.76\,p\sqrt{rh}\cos\phi \quad (9\text{-}54)$$

Equations (9-53) and (9-54) give the approximate values of the boundary moments and shears which must be introduced to make boundary displacements of the shell compatible with those of the arch, subject to the assumption that the connection between the shell and arch is completely rigid.

The corresponding moment penetration is expressed as follows:

$$M_x = -D\frac{d^2w}{dx^2} = \frac{e^{-\beta x}}{\beta}[\beta M_0(\sin\beta x + \cos\beta x) + Q_0(\sin\beta x)] \quad (9\text{-}55)$$

The corresponding bending stresses N_{xM} are

$$N_{xM} = \frac{M_x h}{2D} \tag{9-56}$$

The shears as a function of x are

$$Q_x = -D \frac{d^3 w}{dx^3} = -e^{-\beta x}[2\beta M_0 \sin \beta x - Q_0(\cos \beta x - \sin \beta x)] \tag{9-57}$$

Referring to Fig. 9.26, we see that for an interior transverse section of the shell, the transverse unit force N_ϕ is determined from the membrane state of stress. This is not so for sections adjacent to the supporting arch where N_ϕ is given approximately as follows,

$$N_\phi = \frac{w}{r} \cdot Eh \tag{9-58}$$

in which the ratio w/r is the average transverse unit strain of the shell. At the support, N_ϕ as determined from Equation (9-58) will be zero if we neglect radial deflections of the arch.

SUMMARY CASE I: (Built-in connection between arches and shell, or arch with infinite torsional rigidity.) For cylindrical shells with edge beams and supported by end arches, the arch connections being rigid enough that the ends of the shell can be considered built-in, the shell stresses produced will in the first approximation be the sum of the membrane stresses, the stress due to interaction of shell and edge beam, and the stresses produced by the corrective end moments, M_0, and end shears Q_0. This is so, provided the shell is long enough that the effects of the corrective end shears and end moments applied at one end do not affect the opposite end of the shell. We have yet to obtain the stresses due to interaction of the shell and the edge stiffener beam.

CASE II: If we assume a pin connection between the end arch and the shell (or arch with zero torsional rigidity), then dw/dx is not zero at the junction of the arch and shell, but $M_0 = 0$. From Equation (9-48), the deflection of the infinite cylinder becomes

$$w = \frac{-e^{-\beta x}}{2\beta^3 D} Q_0 \cos \beta x \tag{9-59}$$

At $x = 0$,

$$w_0 = \frac{-Q_0}{2\beta^3 D} \tag{9-59a}$$

By superposition of Equations (9-59a) and (9-52d), we obtain

$$-\frac{Q_0}{3\beta^3 D} - \frac{pr^2}{Eh}\cos\phi = 0$$

or

$$Q_0 = -0.38\sqrt{rh}\, p\cos\phi \qquad (9\text{-}60)$$

Internal moments and shears are given by Equation (9-55) and (9-57) (with $M_0=0$). The maximum M_x is found to occur at $x=0.60\sqrt{rh}$ for which $\beta x = \dfrac{\sqrt[4]{3}}{\sqrt{rh}}\,(0.60)\sqrt{rh}=0.933$, and maximum

$$M_x = -\frac{0.394}{1.552}(\sqrt{rh})(0.38)(\sqrt{rh})(0.803)\,p\cos\phi = -0.077rh.$$

SUMMARY CASE II: As for Case I, we can say that in the first approximation for cylindrical shells with edge beams, the shell stresses will be the sum of the membrane stresses, the stresses due to interaction of shell with edge beam, and the stresses produced by the corrective end shear Q_0, provided again that the shell is long enough that the effects of shears applied at one end will not affect the other end of the shell. Also, the effects of the interaction between the edge beams and the shell have yet to be computed.

9-27   Effective area of shell interaction with arch—arch rib and connection infinitely stiff

It is desired at this point to investigate the stiffening effect of the shell upon the arch, i.e., what portion of the shell, of length b_e, can be considered to act as part of the arch cross section in resisting load. We may define several different values of this so-called "effective width" of the shell. One such definition is obtained as follows.

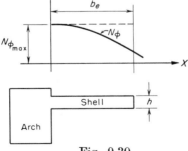

Fig. 9.30

In the transverse direction, the membrane unit force N_ϕ for dead load was seen to be $N_\phi = -pr\cos\phi$ when the radial deformations are given by Equation (9-52c). For compatibility of deformations between arch and shell, the radial displacements were changed by an additional amount expressed by Equation (9-48). At $x = 0$, the change in radial displacement was given as

$$w_0 = -\frac{1}{2\beta^3 D}(\beta M_0 + Q_0) \qquad (9\text{-}52\text{e})$$

If we equate this value to the change in radius of an equivalent ring of effective area $b_e h$, subject to internal pressures Q_0, we obtain

$$\frac{1}{2\beta^3 D}(\beta M_0 + Q_0) = \frac{Q_0 r^2}{Eb_e h} \qquad (9\text{-}61\text{a})$$

For a built-in arch and shell connection with infinite torsional rigidity, we have $\beta M_0 = -Q_0/2$. Substituting this value in Equation (9-61a), we obtain

$$\frac{1}{2\beta^3 D}\frac{Q_0}{2} = \frac{Q_0 r^2}{Eb_e h}$$

Solving for b_e gives

$$b_e = \frac{r^2}{Eh} \cdot 4\beta^3 D = \frac{4r^2}{Eh}\left(\frac{\sqrt[4]{3}}{rh}\right)^3 D$$

or

$$b_e = \frac{\sqrt{rh}}{\sqrt[4]{3}} = 0.76\sqrt{rh} \qquad (9\text{-}61\text{b})$$

Likewise it can be shown that, if the arch rib has zero or negligible torsional rigidity, the effective width of penetration, using the same definition of effectiveness as before, is

$$b_e = 0.38\sqrt{rh} \qquad (9\text{-}62)$$

9-28   Cylindrical shells—interaction between shell and edge beams

Thus far in the investigation of our problem, we have developed the necessary equations for the membrane stresses and through approximations are able to correct for the interaction between the shell and the supporting arches. We have also seen that for a membrane state of stress to exist, tangential and shearing forces must be applied along the free longitudinal edges of the shell. Without edge beams these boundary forces cannot exist, and hence a membrane state of stress is not possible. With edge beams, these stresses will not have the necessary magnitudes and distributions so that a membrane state of stress will exist; so again a membrane state of stress is not possible. The solution of the problem of a simply supported shell with or without edge beams therefore cannot be obtained by membrane analysis alone. As indicated in earlier sections of this chapter, aside from the exact solution of the boundary value problem, an "exact" solution of the shell without edge beam problem may be obtained by the summation of the membrane stresses and the stresses due to line forces acting along the longitudinal edge, these line forces being made equal and opposite to those boundary forces found necessary for a state of membrane stress to exist within the shell. A solution of the shell with edge beam problem may then be obtained by adding additional line forces to the solution previously obtained for the shell without edge beam. These line forces are selected so that the stresses and deformations of the longitudinal edge of the shell will be compatible with the stresses and deformations of the edge beam.

To obtain the effect of the line forces upon the internal stresses and deformations of the shell, it is necessary to resort to an "exact" solution of the problem. Tabulated results of these solutions for various combinations of spans, radii, and thicknesses of concrete are available in the ASCE Manual previously referred to. To illustrate the use of the Manual, the cylindrical shell of Art. 9-18 will be analyzed.

9-29 Simply supported long cylindrical shell—"exact" solution using the manual

Example: Given

| Span | $l = 130$ ft | Shell thickness | $h = 3$ in. |

Radius $r = 50$ ft

$$\frac{l}{r} = \frac{130}{50} = 2.6$$

$$\phi_k = 35°$$

p_D = dead load = 36 lb/ft² (measured along curve)

p_u = live load = 20 lb/ft² of horizontal projection

Solution: STEP 1: Find the membrane stresses. Tabular coefficients in the work to follow are marked by a solid line over the number and are taken from Table 1B of the Manual. Note that the origin of the longitudinal coordinate, x, is taken as the left support. Formulas are taken freely from the Manual Table 1B.

Membrane Stresses along the Longitudinal Edge (Line Loads)

$$N_\phi = T_\phi \text{ (in Manual notation)} = p_u r \cdot (\text{coeff}) \cdot \sin \frac{\pi}{l} x$$

$$+ p_D r \cdot (\text{coeff}) \cdot \sin \frac{\pi}{l} x \quad (9\text{-}63)$$

The load functions are expanded into a Fourier series, Equation (9-64). This is done so that the line loads will be trigonometric functions of the same kind as the general solution of the eighth-order differential equation.

$$p = \frac{4p}{\pi}\left[\sin\frac{\pi x}{l}+\frac{1}{3}\sin\frac{3\pi x}{l}+\frac{1}{5}\sin\frac{5\pi x}{l}+\cdots\right] \qquad (9\text{-}64)$$

To simplify the computations which follow, only the first term of the above series will be used to represent the load functions. This is permissible, at least for preliminary design, as it is the dominant term. The magnitude of the resultant error, however, is uncertain. The effects of the neglected terms can be included after the preliminary design has been established.

Using tabulated values and the first term of the series for the load function, we obtain

$$N_\phi = \left[\frac{4}{\pi}\times20\times50(-\overline{0.6710})+\frac{4}{\pi}\times36\times50\times(-\overline{0.8191})\right]\sin\frac{\pi x}{l}$$

$$N_\phi = -2731.5\sin\frac{\pi x}{l}\ \text{lb/ft}$$

For comparison, the value obtained from Equations (9-39) and (9-42) are

$$N_\phi = -p_D r\cos\phi_k - p_u r\cos\phi_k = -2189\ \text{lb/ft}$$

Likewise

$$N_{x\phi} = S\ \text{(in Manual notation)}$$

$$= p_u r\left[\frac{l}{r}\times\text{coeff}\right]\cos\frac{\pi x}{l}+p_D r\left[\frac{l}{r}\times\text{coeff}\right]\cos\frac{\pi x}{l} \qquad (9\text{-}65)$$

$$= \left[\frac{4}{\pi}\times20\times50\times2.6\times(-\overline{0.4487})+\frac{4}{\pi}\times36\times50\times2.6\times(-\overline{0.3652})\right]\cos\frac{\pi x}{l}$$

$$N_{x\phi} = -3661.4\cos\frac{\pi x}{l}\ \text{lb/ft}$$

Using Equation (9-43), we obtain a comparison with the "exact" $N_{x\phi}$

$$N_{x\phi} = -2p_D\frac{l}{2}\sin\phi_k-\frac{3}{2}p_u\frac{l}{2}\sin2\phi_k = -4515\ \text{lb/ft} \qquad (9\text{-}66a)$$

$$N_x = T_x\ \text{(in Manual notation)}$$

$$N_x = p_u r\left[\left(\frac{l}{r}\right)^2(\text{coeff})\right]\sin\frac{\pi x}{l}+p_D r\left[\left(\frac{l}{r}\right)(\text{coeff})\right]\sin\frac{\pi x}{l}$$

$$= \left[\frac{4}{\pi}\times20\times50\times(2.6)^2(-\overline{0.1040})+\frac{4}{\pi}\times36\times50\times(2.6)^2(-\overline{0.1660})\right]\sin\frac{\pi x}{l}$$

$$= \left(\frac{l}{r}\right)^2[-512.84]\sin\frac{\pi x}{l}$$

$$= -3466.8\sin\frac{\pi x}{l}\ \text{lb/ft} \qquad (9\text{-}66b)$$

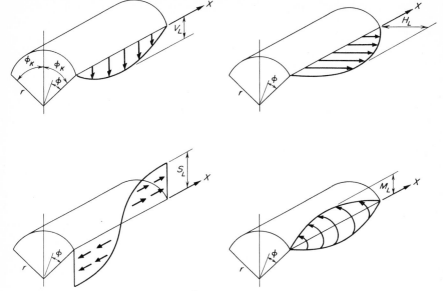

Fig. 9.31

The line loads acting on the longitudinal edge are shown in Fig. 9.31. These are

$$\text{Vertical force} = +N_\phi \sin \phi_k = -2731.5 \sin \frac{\pi x}{l} \sin \phi_k \quad \text{(9-67a)}$$

$$\text{Horizontal force} = +N_\phi \cos \phi_k = -2731.5 \sin \frac{\pi x}{l} \cos \phi_k \quad \text{(9-67b)}$$

$$\text{Shear force} = +N_{x\phi} = -3661.4 \cos \frac{\pi x}{l} \quad \text{(9-67c)}$$

$$\text{Moment} = 0 \text{ (in this case)} \quad \text{(9-67d)}$$

Thus, a membrane state of stress exists within the simply supported shell provided the above line loads are applied at the boundary.

The vertical deflection (positive downward) of the longitudinal edge is next found using formulas and coefficients, again from Manual Table 1B.

$$\text{Membrane } \Delta_V = \frac{l^4}{r^3 hE} \left\{ p_u r \left[1 + \frac{1}{2}\left(\frac{\pi r}{l}\right)^2 + \frac{1}{12}\left(\frac{\pi r}{l}\right)^4 \right] \text{(coeff)} \right.$$

$$\left. + p_D r \left[\left(\frac{2r}{\pi l}\right)^2 + \frac{2}{\pi^4} + \left(\frac{r}{l}\right)^4 \text{(coeff)} \right] \right\} \sin \frac{\pi x}{l} \quad \text{(9-68)}$$

$$\Delta_V = \frac{l^4}{r^3 hE} \left\{ 20 \times 50 \left[1 + \frac{1}{2}(0.385\pi)^2 + \frac{1}{12}(0.385\pi)^4 \right] (+\overline{0.06771}) \right.$$

$$\left. + 36 \times 50 \left[\left(\frac{2 \times 0.385}{\pi}\right)^2 + \frac{2}{\pi^4} + (0.385)^4(+\overline{0.6710}) \right] \right\} \sin \frac{\pi x}{l}$$

$$\Delta_V = \frac{l^4}{r^3 hE} (300.53) \sin \frac{\pi x}{l}$$

STEP 2: Find the effects of equal and opposite line loads applied at longitudinal edge (see Fig. 9.31).

$$V_L = -N_\phi \sin \phi_k = 2731.5 \times 0.5736 = +1566.8$$

$$H_L = -N_\phi \cos \phi_k = 2731.5 \times 0.8192 = +2237.6$$

$$S_L = -N_{x\phi} = +3661.4$$

From Manual tables we can find the effects of the above line loads as follows:

Enter table with $r/l = 50/130 = 0.385$ (necessitates interpolation)

$$\frac{r}{t} = \frac{50 \times 12}{3} = 200$$

$$\phi_k = 35°$$

Then N_x at the longitudinal edge ($\phi = 0$) due to the line loads is obtained as follows:

$$N_x = \left(\frac{l}{r}\right)^2 [V_L(\text{coeff}) + H_L(\text{coeff}) + S_L(\text{coeff})] \sin \frac{\pi x}{l} \qquad (9\text{-}69)$$

where the coefficients are given in Manual Table 2A.

$$N_x = \left(\frac{l}{r}\right)^2 [+1566.8(+\overline{31.74}) + 2237.6(-\overline{12.22}) + 3661.4(+\overline{1.552})] \sin \frac{\pi x}{l}$$

$$= \left(\frac{l}{r}\right)^2 [+28{,}069.2] \sin \frac{\pi x}{l}$$

The vertical deflection of the edge due to the line loads is

$$\Delta_V = \frac{l^4}{r^3 h E} [V_L(\text{coeff}) + H_L(\text{coeff}) + S_L(\text{coeff})] \sin \frac{\pi x}{l} \qquad (9\text{-}70)$$

The coefficients are obtained from Manual Table 2B.

$$\Delta_V = \frac{l^4}{r^3 h E} [+1566.8(\overline{259.6}) + 2237.6(-\overline{127.7}) + 3661.4(\overline{3.968})] \sin \frac{\pi x}{l}$$

$$= \frac{l^4}{r^3 h E} (+135{,}864) \sin \frac{\pi x}{l}$$

STEP 3: Find N_x and Δ_V for the simply supported shell by adding the results of Steps 1 and 2:

$$N_x = \left(\frac{l}{r}\right)^2 [-512.84 + 28{,}069.2] \sin \frac{\pi x}{l} = +27{,}556.4 \left(\frac{l}{r}\right)^2 \sin \frac{\pi x}{l}$$

$$\Delta_V = \frac{l^4}{r^3 h E} (+300.5 + 135{,}864) \sin \frac{\pi x}{l} = +136{,}164 \frac{l^4}{r^3 h E} \sin \frac{\pi x}{l}$$

At $x = \dfrac{l}{2}$, $N_x = +27{,}556.4(2.6)^2 = +186{,}281$ lb/ft

This compares with the value of $+89,800$ lb/ft obtained previously by the elementary beam theory analysis. The agreement is not good in this case.

At this point we have the solution of the simply supported shell with free edges. It is possible to find the stress component at any point of the shell by using tabular coefficients from the Manual as we have done for N_x at $l/2$. The complete stresses will not be worked out for this case.

STEP 4: Having solved the problem of the simply supported shell we now find the effects due to interaction of the shell with the edge beam.

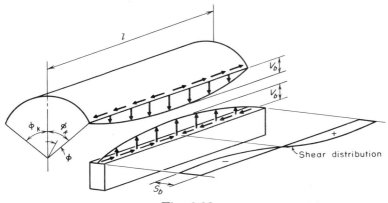

Fig. 9.32

As in the case of the dead and live loads, it is assumed that the interactive forces are very nearly expressed by the first term of a Fourier series expansion. The possible interaction forces are vertical, horizontal, longitudinal shears, transverse shears, transverse moments, and twisting moments. If we assume the edge beam to have zero torsional rigidity and zero lateral resistance to load and ignore other factors, the interaction forces are reduced to two principal forces; namely, a vertical force $V_b \sin \pi x/l$ and a shear force $S_b \cos \pi x/l$. These are shown in Fig. 9.32. This is the method followed in the ASCE Manual and is used in the following computations.

Due to the interaction forces, there will be produced in the shell a longitudinal stress and a vertical deflection along the edge [see Equations (9-69) and (9-70)].

$$N_x = \left(\frac{l}{r}\right)^2 [V_b(+\overline{31.74}) + S_b(+\overline{1.552})] \sin \frac{\pi x}{l}$$

$$\Delta_V = \frac{l^4}{r^3 hE} [V_b(+\overline{259}) + S_b(+\overline{3.96})] \sin \frac{\pi x}{l}$$

where the coefficients are the same as those used in Step 2.

It is necessary at this point to derive equations expressing the fiber stresses and the vertical deflection of the edge beam due to the loads, $V_b \sin \pi x/l$ and $S_b \cos \pi x/l$, and the weight of the edge beam taken as

$\left(\dfrac{4}{\pi}\right)q\sin\dfrac{\pi x}{l}$, where q is the weight of the edge beam per foot and $\left(\dfrac{4}{\pi}\right)q\sin\dfrac{\pi x}{l}$, represents the first term of the series expansion of q. For the sinusoidal loads $(V_b - 4q/\pi)\sin \pi x/l$, we have

$$EI\frac{d^4y}{dx^4} = \left(V_b - \frac{4q}{\pi}\right)\sin\frac{\pi x}{l} \tag{9-71a}$$

Upon successive integration, we obtain

$$EI\frac{d^3y}{dx^3} = -\left(V_b - \frac{4q}{\pi}\right)\frac{l}{\pi}\cos\frac{\pi x}{l} + C_1 \tag{9-71b}$$

$$EI\frac{d^2y}{dx^2} = -\left(V_b - \frac{4q}{\pi}\right)\left(\frac{l}{\pi}\right)^2\sin\frac{\pi x}{l} + C_1 x + C_2 \tag{9-71c}$$

But at $x=0$, $d^2y/dx^2=0$; thus $C_2=0$. Integrating again, we obtain

$$EI\frac{dy}{dx} = +\left(V_b - \frac{4q}{\pi}\right)\left(\frac{l}{\pi}\right)^3\cos\frac{\pi x}{l} + \frac{C_1 x^2}{2} + C_3 \tag{9-71d}$$

$$EIy = +\left(V_b - \frac{4q}{\pi}\right)\left(\frac{l}{\pi}\right)^4\sin\frac{\pi x}{l} + \frac{C_1 x^3}{6} + C_3 x + C_4 \tag{9-71e}$$

At $x=0$, $y=0$ gives $C_4=0$. At $x=l$, $d^2y/dx^2=0$ gives $C_1=0$. Thus the deflection is (y positive up)

$$y = +\frac{1}{EI}\left(V_b - \frac{4q}{\pi}\right)\left(\frac{l}{\pi}\right)^4\sin\frac{\pi x}{l}$$

For a beam section b wide by d deep, this becomes

$$y = +0.12319\frac{l^4}{bd^3E}\left(V_b - \frac{4q}{\pi}\right)\sin\frac{\pi x}{l} \tag{9-72}$$

The bending moment in the edge beam M is

$$EI\frac{d^2y}{dx^2} = -M = -\left(V_b - \frac{4q}{\pi}\right)\left(\frac{l}{\pi}\right)^2\sin\frac{\pi x}{l}$$

from which

$$M = \left(V_b - \frac{4q}{\pi}\right)\left(\frac{l}{\pi}\right)^2\sin\frac{\pi x}{l} \tag{9-73}$$

The corresponding bending stresses are

$$f = \pm\frac{6M}{bd^2} = \pm\left(V_b - \frac{4q}{\pi}\right)\left(\frac{6}{\pi^2}\right)\left(\frac{l}{d}\right)^2\frac{1}{b}\sin\frac{\pi x}{l} \tag{9-74}$$

From the shear loads $S_b\cos \pi x/L$, we obtain (see Fig. 9.33) the resultant thrust T

$$T = \int_0^x S_b\cos\frac{\pi x}{l}\,dx = S_b\frac{l}{\pi}\sin\frac{\pi x}{l} \tag{9-75}$$

The moment due to T is $M = Td/2$. The corresponding bending stresses are

$$f = \mp \frac{6Td}{2bd^2} = \mp \frac{3T}{bd}$$

The total stress on the top fiber becomes

$$f = T\left[-\frac{1}{bd}-\frac{3}{bd}\right] = -S_b\left(\frac{4l}{bd\pi}\right) \sin \frac{\pi x}{l}$$

$$f = -1.2732S_b\left(\frac{l}{bd}\right) \sin \frac{\pi x}{l} \qquad (9\text{-}76)$$

and on the bottom fiber

$$f = T\left[-\frac{1}{bd}+\frac{3}{bd}\right] = +S_b\left(\frac{2l}{bd\pi}\right) \sin \frac{\pi x}{l}$$

$$f = 0.6366S_b\left(\frac{l}{bd}\right) \sin \frac{\pi x}{l} \qquad (9\text{-}77)$$

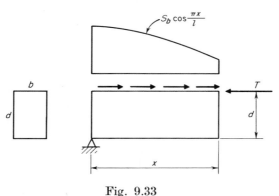

Fig. 9.33

The deflection produced by the moment $Td/2$ becomes, after successive integration of $EI\,\dfrac{d^2y}{dx^2} = -\dfrac{Td}{2}$, ($y$ is positive up)

$$y = -S_b\,\frac{6}{\pi^3}\,\frac{l^3}{bd^2E} \sin \frac{\pi x}{l} \qquad (9\text{-}78)$$

STEP 5: Now combine steps 1 through 4 to obtain the longitudinal stress, N_x/h, at the edge of the shell and the vertical deflection of the edge of the shell, and equate these to the top fiber stress and deflection of the edge beam. Thus, for the shell edge at $x = l/2$,

$$\frac{N_x}{h} = \left(\frac{l}{r}\right)^2 \frac{1}{h}\left[(-512.84+28{,}069.2)+31.74V_b+1.552S_b\right] \sin \frac{\pi x}{l} \qquad (9\text{-}79a)$$

For the beam top edge,

$$f = \left[+\left(V_b-\frac{4q}{\pi}\right)\left(\frac{6}{\pi^2}\right)\left(\frac{l}{d}\right)^2\frac{1}{b}-1.2732S_b\left(\frac{l}{bd}\right)\right]\sin\frac{\pi x}{l} \qquad (9\text{-}79b)$$

Equating the two, we obtain

$$\frac{1}{h}\left(\frac{l}{r}\right)^2[+27{,}556.4+31.74V_b+1.552S_b]$$

$$=\left[\left(V_b-\frac{4q}{\pi}\right)\left(\frac{6}{\pi^2}\right)\left(\frac{l}{d}\right)^2\frac{1}{b}-1.2732S_b\left(\frac{l}{bd}\right)\right] \qquad (9\text{-}79)$$

For the shell edge, the vertical deflection is

$$\Delta_V = \frac{l^4}{r^3hE}[+300.5+135{,}864+259.6V_b+3.968S_b]\sin\frac{\pi x}{l} \qquad (9\text{-}80a)$$

For the beam,

$$\Delta_V = \left[-0.12319\frac{l^4}{bd^3E}\left(V_b-\frac{4q}{\pi}\right)+S_b\frac{6}{\pi^3}\frac{l^3}{bd^2E}\right]\sin\frac{\pi x}{l} \qquad (9\text{-}80b)$$

Equating the two, we have

$$\frac{l^4}{r^3hE}[+136{,}164+259.6V_b+3.968S_b]$$

$$=\left[0.12319\frac{l^4}{bd^3E}\left(\frac{4q}{\pi}-V_b\right)+0.19351\frac{l^3}{bd^2E}S_b\right] \qquad (9\text{-}80)$$

Equations (9-79) and (9-80) are rearranged as follows and solved simultaneously for V_b and S_b. Using $q=720$ lb/ft, $b=1$ ft, $d=5$ ft, we have

$$27{,}556.4+31.74V_b+1.552S_b = \frac{h}{b}\left(\frac{r}{d}\right)^2\left[\left(V_b-\frac{4}{\pi}q\right)\frac{6}{\pi^2}-1.2732\left(\frac{d}{l}\right)S_b\right]$$

$$= \frac{0.25}{1}\left(\frac{50}{5}\right)^2\left[0.60793V_b-558.08-1.2732\left(\frac{5}{130}\right)S_b\right]$$

$$= 15.1983V_b-13952.03-1.2242S_b$$

or

$$16.54V_b+2.776S_b = -41{,}508$$

$$+136{,}164+259.6V_b+3.968S_b = \frac{h}{b}\left(\frac{r}{d}\right)^3\left[0.12319\left(\frac{4}{\pi}q-V_b\right)+(0.19351)\left(\frac{d}{l}\right)S_b\right]$$

$$= 0.25\left(\frac{50}{5}\right)^3\left[0.12319\times918-0.12319V_b+\frac{0.19351}{26}S_b\right]$$

$$= -30.80V_b+1.8607S_b+28{,}272.0$$

or

$$290.4V_b+2.1073S_b = -107{,}892$$

The values of V_b and S_b obtained from the solution of the above simultaneous equations are

$$V_b = -274.95 \text{ lb/ft}$$

$$S_b = -13{,}314 \text{ lb/ft}$$

Then from Equation (9-79a), the stress in the shell edge at $x = l/2$ is

$$\frac{N_x}{h} = \frac{(2.6)^2}{0.25}[27{,}556.4 - 31.4 \times 274.95 - 1.552 \times 13{,}314.4] = -49{,}602 \text{ lb/ft}^2$$

$$= -344.4 \text{ lb/in.}^2$$

For a check, the stress in the top edge of the beam is computed using Equation (9-79b) at $x = l/2$

$$f = \left[(-274.95 - 918)\frac{6}{\pi^2} \times 676 + 1.2732 \times 26 \times 13{,}314.4\right]$$

$$= -49{,}602 \text{ lb/ft}^2 = -343.8 \text{ lb/in.}^2$$

The small discrepancy in the two values of stress is due to extreme sensitivity of results to small errors. Although a calculating machine was used in arriving at all of the above results, these small errors result from the fact that some of the tabular coefficients used are given to four significant figures only.

The stress in the bottom edge of the beam at $x = l/2$ is, from Equations (9-74) and (9-77),

$$f = \left[-\left(V_b - \frac{4q}{\pi}\right)\left(\frac{6}{\pi^2}\right)\left(\frac{l}{d}\right)^2\frac{1}{b} + \frac{1}{b}(0.6366)S_b\left(\frac{l}{d}\right)\right]$$

$$= +269{,}881 \text{ lb/ft}^2 = +1874 \text{ lb/in.}^2$$

It is of interest to compare these results with the results of the elementary beam analysis of Art. 9-19, (see the following tabulation),

	Elementary Beam Theory lb/in.^{2}	Manual lb/in.^{2}	$\dfrac{\text{Beam}}{\text{Manual}} \times 100\%$ %
Stress in top fiber of beam	+316	− 344	− 92
Stress in bottom fiber of beam	+918	+1874	49

STEP 6: The final stresses and deflections of any point on the shell can now be determined by combining the membrane stress (or deflection) and the stress (or deflection) due to the shell boundary forces (line forces). This is accomplished by means of tabular coefficients. The computation for various points is shown in Table 9.2.

The vertical distance from the bottom of shell (see y on Fig. 9.34) is $y = r(\cos \phi' - \cos \phi_k)$, and

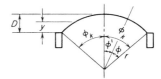

Fig. 9.34

$$y_{\max} = D = r(1 - \cos \phi_k)$$

Then

$$\frac{y}{D} = \frac{\cos \phi' - \cos \phi_k}{1 - \cos \phi_k} \qquad (9\text{-}81)$$

TABLE 9.2

(a) $N_\phi = T_\phi$ at $x = l/2$

Row		Multipliers for r/l = 0.4	35°	20°	10°	0°
1	Uniform	$4/\pi \times 20 \times 50 \times$ coeff* =	−1273	−1188	−1043	−853
2	Dead	$4/\pi \times 36 \times 50 \times$ coeff* =	−2290	−2210	−2080	−1875
3	VL	$(1567 − 275) \times$ coeff† =	−1027	−2840	−2105	+741
4	HL	$+2238 \times$ coeff† =	+93	+2590	+3440	+1837
5	SL	$(3661 − 13{,}314) \times$ coeff† =	+611	+381	−520	0
6	Σ		−4072	−3267	−2308	−150

(c) $N_z = T_z$ at $x = l/2$

Row		Multipliers for r/l = 0.4	35°	20°	10°	0°
1	Uniform	$4/\pi \times 20 \times 50 \times 2.6^2 \times$ coeff*	−2620	−2260	−1680	−895
2	Dead	$4/\pi \times 36 \times 50 \times 2.6^2 \times$ coeff*	−3140	−3060	−2850	−2570
3	VL	$1292 \times 2.6^2 \times$ coeff†	+60000	−54200	−99500	+299000
4	HL	$2238 \times 2.6^2 \times$ coeff†	−74700	+33400	+80300	−202500
5	SL	$−9653 \times 2.6^2 \times$ coeff†	+9430	+6450	−20900	−107000
6	Σ		−11080	−19670	−24630	−13965

(b) $N_{z\phi} = S$ at $x = 0$

Row		Multiplier for r/l = 0.4	35°	20°	10°	0°
1	Uniform	$4/\pi \times 20 \times 50 \times 2.6 \times$ coeff*	0	−1075	−1650	−2020
2	Dead	$4/\pi \times 36 \times 50 \times 2.6 \times$ coeff*	0	−1340	−2190	−2960
3	VL	$1292 \times 2.6 \times$ coeff†	0	+5410	−12380	0
4	HL	$2238 \times 2.6 \times$ coeff†	0	−11060	+3850	0
5	SL	$−9653 \times 2.6 \times$ coeff†	0	+2630	+1880	−9280
6	Σ		0	−5435	−10490	−14260

(d) M_ϕ at $x = l/2$

Row		Multiplier for r/l = 0.4	35°	20°	10°	0°
3	VL	$1292 \times 50 \times$ coeff†	−11850	−10650	−6480	0
4	HL	$2238 \times 50 \times$ coeff†	+9380	+9650	+6960	0
5	SL	$−9653 \times 50 \times$ coeff†	+1545	+820	+48	
6	Σ		−925	−180	−47	0

+12400

For r/l = 0.385, coeffs. interpolated

* Indicates tabular value from Manual Table 1B.
† Indicates tabular value from Manual Table 2A.

The longitudinal stress N_x/h and the stress $N_{x\phi}$ are plotted against y/D on Fig. 9.35.

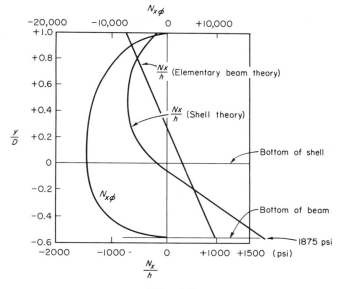

Fig. 9.35

The plotted results indicate spotty agreement between results obtained from elementary beam theory and the Manual tables. Also, it should be noted that the maximum $N_{x\phi}$ occurs where N_x is zero. For larger values of l/r (say greater than three) the N_x stresses obtained from the Manual tables agree closely with the straight-line elementary theory distribution.

9-30 Summary—cylindrical shells

A complete presentation of cylindrical shell theory and solutions should include multiple shell roofs with or without edge beams, shells continuous over several supports, shells with prestressed edge beams, etc. The reader can find suitable illustrative problems of the above types in Gibson and Cooper and in the ASCE Manual. The same general technique is used to solve these other problems following Manual procedure. The procedure is to find the solution of the simply supported shell and apply compatibility of stress and deformation equations to the boundary. This is seen to be very similar to the superposition techniques used in solving indeterminate beam and frame problems.[20]

[20] See also, *Design of Barrel Shell Roofs*, Portland Cement Association, 1954.

9-31   Shells of revolution

Thus far we have dealt only with cylindrical shells. A dome type of shell structure can be considered formed by revolving a curve about some axis. Thus a sphere is formed by revolving a circle about a diameter. For an approximate analysis of shells of revolution, it will be assumed that a membrane state of stress predominates within the shell. Then secondary stresses of limited penetration act near the shell boundaries so as to satisfy the boundary conditions. The final solution will consist of the primary membrane stresses corrected for the boundary disturbances which in general affect only the portion of the shell immediately adjacent to the boundary.

9-32   Shells of revolution—membrane theory

Assuming symmetrical loads (no shear on sections), the problem becomes independent of the horizontal angle of revolution θ (see Fig. 9.36a). The forces acting upon an element of the shell are shown

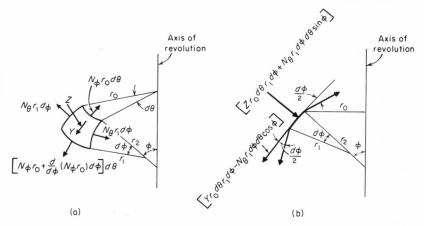

Fig. 9.36

in Fig. 9.36, where Z and Y are the radial and tangential load components. For equilibrium in the Y direction, we have (see Fig. 9.36b)

$$-N_\phi r_0 d\theta \cos \frac{d\phi}{2} + \left[N_\phi r_0 + \frac{d}{d\phi} (N_\phi r_0) d\phi \right] d\theta \cos \frac{d\phi}{2}$$
$$- N_\theta r_1 d\phi \, d\theta \cos \phi + Y r_0 d\theta r_1 d\phi = 0 \quad (9\text{-}82a)$$

Simplifying and using $\cos \dfrac{d\phi}{2} = 1$, we obtain

$$\frac{d}{d\phi} (N_\phi r_0) - N_\theta r_1 \cos \phi + Y r_0 r_1 = 0 \quad\quad\quad (9\text{-}82)$$

In the Z direction, using $\sin \dfrac{d\phi}{2} \doteq \dfrac{d\phi}{2}$, we obtain

$$Zr_0 d\theta \; r_1 d\phi + N_\phi r_0 d\theta \frac{d\phi}{2} + \left[N_\phi r_0 + \frac{d}{d\phi} \, (N_\phi r_0) d\phi \right] d\theta \frac{d\phi}{2}$$
$$+ N_\theta r_1 d\phi \; d\theta \sin \phi = 0 \quad (9\text{-}83a)$$

If differentials of higher order are dropped and we simplify, we obtain

$$N_\phi r_0 + N_\theta r_1 \sin \phi = - Z r_0 r_1 \quad (9\text{-}83b)$$

Since $r_0 = r_2 \sin \phi$, we obtain upon substitution in Equation (9-83b)

$$\frac{N_\phi}{r_1} + \frac{N_\theta}{r_2} = - Z \quad (9\text{-}83)$$

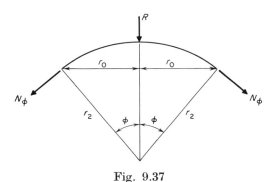

Fig. 9.37

Consider now the equilibrium of the shell above a section cut by a horizontal plane (Fig. 9.37). Let R be the resultant of all the symmetric loads above the cutting plane. Then for equilibrium,

$$2\pi r_0 N_\phi \sin \phi + R = 0 \quad (9\text{-}84a)$$

or

$$N_\phi = - \frac{R}{2\pi r_0 \sin \phi} \quad (9\text{-}84b)$$

or

$$N_\phi = - \frac{R}{2\pi r_2 \sin^2 \phi} \quad (9\text{-}84)$$

Equations (9-82), (9-83), (9-84), suffice for finding the membrane stresses in a shell of revolution.

9-33 Spherical dome—dead load membrane stresses

Let q_D be the weight per square foot of a symmetric portion of a spherical dome of constant thickness and radius a (Fig. 9.38). The weight of an element of area is $q_D r_0 a d\theta d\phi$. The weight of an annular

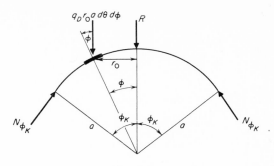

Fig. 9.38

ring of width $ad\phi$ is $2\pi q_D r_0 ad\phi$. Using $r_0 = a \sin \phi$, the total weight of the shell becomes

$$R = 2\pi q_D a^2 \int_0^{\phi_k} \sin \phi d\phi = 2\pi q_D a^2 (1 - \cos \phi_k)$$

Then from Equation (9-84),

$$N_{\phi_k} = -\frac{2\pi q_D a^2 (1 - \cos \phi_k)}{2\pi a \sin^2 \phi_k} = -\frac{q_D a}{1 + \cos \phi_k} \qquad (9\text{-}85)$$

where the minus sign indicates a compressive stress shown on Fig. 9.38.
The stress N_ϕ, for an intermediate value of ϕ is obviously

$$N_\phi = -\frac{q_D a}{1 + \cos \phi} \qquad (9\text{-}85a)$$

From Equation (9-83),

$$N_\theta = -Za - N_\phi$$

or

$$N_\theta = -q_D a \cos \phi + \frac{q_D a}{1 + \cos \phi}$$

or

$$N_\theta = +q_D a \left(\frac{\sin^2 \phi - \cos \phi}{1 + \cos \phi} \right) \qquad (9\text{-}86)$$

When ϕ has such a value that $(\sin^2 \phi - \cos \phi) = 0$, then N_θ will be zero. This value is seen to be $\phi_1 = 51°\text{--}50'$. Thus for values of ϕ less than $51°\text{--}50'$, the hoop stresses, N_θ, are compressive, and for values of ϕ greater than $51°\text{--}50'$, the hoop stresses, N_θ, are tensile. Of course, at the boundary we must be able to develop stresses N_{ϕ_k} where

$$N_{\phi_k} = -\frac{q_D a}{1 + \cos \phi_k}$$

9-34   Spherical dome—uniform load membrane stresses

The spherical dome of radius a, loaded with a uniform load of q_u lb/ft^2 of horizontal projection is shown in Fig. 9.39.   Here R is given by

$$R = q_u \pi r_0{}^2 = \pi q_u a^2 \sin^2 \phi$$

From Equation (9-84),

$$N_\phi = -\frac{\pi q_u a^2 \sin^2 \phi}{2 \pi a \sin^2 \phi}$$

or

$$N_\phi = -\tfrac{1}{2} q_u a \qquad\qquad (9\text{-}87)$$

Thus we see that N_ϕ is constant throughout the shell.   From Equation (9-83),

$$N_\theta = Za - N_\phi = -q_u a \cos^2 \phi + \frac{q_u a}{2}$$

or

$$N_\theta = +q_u a [\tfrac{1}{2} - \cos^2 \phi] \qquad\qquad (9\text{-}88)$$

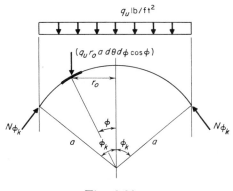

Fig. 9.39

As before, $N_\theta = 0$, when $\cos^2 \phi_1 = \tfrac{1}{2}$, or $\cos \phi_1 = 1/\sqrt{2} = \sqrt{2}/2$, from which $\phi_1 = 45°$.   Therefore when ϕ is less than 45°, the hoop stress N_θ is compressive, and when ϕ is greater than 45°, the hoop stress is tensile.

In order to have a membrane state of stress under uniform load, it will be necessary to develop boundary stresses $N_{\phi k}$ given by

$$N_{\phi k} = -\tfrac{1}{2} q_u a$$

9-35   Membrane displacements of spherical shells

The radial displacement, w, and the meridional displacement in the Y direction, v, corresponding to a membrane state of stress are given as follows for a spherical shell (for derivations see Timoshenko [21]). The tangential displacement along a parallel (at right angles to Y) is zero if we have symmetric loading.

$$w = v \cot \phi - \frac{a}{Eh} [N_\theta - \nu N_\phi] \qquad (9\text{-}89)$$

$$\frac{dv}{d\phi} - v \cot \phi = \frac{a}{Eh} (1+\nu)[N_\phi - N_\theta] \qquad (9\text{-}90)$$

where h = shell thickness, E = modulus of elasticity, a = radius of spherical shell, and ν = Poisson's ratio.

The solution of Equation (9-90) gives, for a uniformly loaded shell,

$$v = C \sin \phi + \frac{q_u a^2(1+\nu)}{Eh} \sin \phi \cos \phi \qquad (9\text{-}91)$$

where C is a constant to be determined from the boundary conditions. For a hemispherical shell subject to uniform load, the boundary condition is

$$\text{at } \phi = \frac{\pi}{2}, \quad v = 0$$

This gives $C = 0$ and

$$v = \frac{q_u a^2(1+\nu)}{Eh} \sin \phi \cos \phi \qquad (9\text{-}91\text{a})$$

The radial displacement can be determined from Equation (9-89) when v is known.

For the hemisphere, this becomes

$$w = \frac{q_u a^2(1+\nu)}{Eh} \cos^2 \phi - \frac{q_u a^2}{Eh} [\tfrac{1}{2}(1+\nu) - \cos^2 \phi] \qquad (9\text{-}92)$$

At the boundary, $\phi = \pi/2$,

$$w_0 = -\frac{q_u a^2}{2Eh} (1+\nu)$$

The shell rotation α_0 at the boundary is

$$\alpha_0 = \frac{dw}{ds}\Big|_{\phi=\pi/2} = \left[\frac{1}{a}\frac{dw}{d\phi} + \frac{1}{\phi}\frac{dw}{dr}\right]_{\phi=\pi/2} \qquad (9\text{-}93\text{a})$$

[21] S. Timoshenko, *Theory of Plates and Shells*, Engineering Societies Monographs, McGraw-Hill Book Company, New York, 1940, p. 370.

But at $\phi = \pi/2$, $dw/dr = 0$; hence

$$\alpha_0 = \frac{1}{a} \frac{dw}{d\phi}\bigg|_{\phi=\pi/2}$$

$$= -\frac{q_u a}{Eh}(1+\nu) 2 \sin\phi \cos\phi - \frac{q_u a}{Eh} 2 \sin\phi \cos\phi = 0 \quad (9\text{-}93b)$$

9-36 Hemispherical shells—built-in supports

The reactions and stresses at the built-in edge of a hemispherical shell loaded by a uniform load will be found by an approximate superposition solution (see Fig. 9.40). The procedure is as follows:

1. Find the membrane reactions and displacements.

2. Reduce the membrane displacements to zero by applying horizontal and moment reactions Q_0 and M_0.

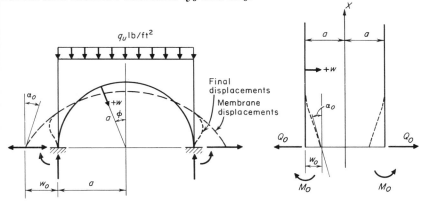

(a) Hemispherical shell   (b) Infinite cylinder

Fig. 9.40

3. To find the effect of Q_0 and M_0 on the shell, approximate the solution by using the solution of the infinite cylinder previously obtained (see Art. 9-25 and Fig. 9.40b).

4. Because the boundary disturbances caused by Q_0 and M_0 will be of limited penetration, the final displacements in the hemispherical shell will be the membrane displacements corrected locally at the boundary for the effects of Q_0 and M_0.

We had for the infinite cylinder

$$w = \frac{e^{-\beta x}}{2\beta^3 D}[\beta M_0(\sin\beta x - \cos\beta x) - Q_0 \cos\beta x] \quad (9\text{-}94)$$

$$\alpha = \frac{dw}{dx} = \frac{e^{-\beta x}}{2\beta^3 D}[2\beta M_0 \cos\beta x + Q_0(\cos\beta x + \sin\beta x)] \quad (9\text{-}95)$$

Then at the boundary of the hemisphere ($x = 0$),

$$w_0 = -\frac{1}{2\beta^3 D} [\beta M_0 + Q_0] \qquad (9\text{-}94a)$$

$$\alpha_0 = \frac{1}{2\beta^3 D} [2\beta M_0 + Q_0] \qquad (9\text{-}94b)$$

Adding these to the membrane displacements obtained in Art. 9-35, we have

$$\frac{q_u a^2}{2Eh} (1+\nu) - \frac{1}{2\beta^3 D} [\beta M_0 + Q_0] = 0 \qquad (9\text{-}95a)$$

$$\frac{1}{2\beta^3 D} [2\beta M_0 + Q_0] = 0 \qquad (9\text{-}95b)$$

Solving for M_0 and Q_0 and using $\beta = \dfrac{\sqrt[4]{3(1-\nu^2)}}{\sqrt{ah}}$ we have

$$Q_0 = -\frac{\sqrt{1+\nu}}{2\sqrt[4]{3}} \sqrt{\frac{1+\nu}{1-\nu}} q_u \sqrt{ah} \qquad (9\text{-}96)$$

$$M_0 = \frac{\sqrt{3}}{12} \sqrt{\frac{1+\nu}{1-\nu}} q_u ah \qquad (9\text{-}97)$$

The stresses adjacent to the built-in edge will no longer be membrane stresses but will be the sum of the membrane stresses and the effects due to Q_0 and M_0. For the moment at a section within the infinite cylinder,

$$M = -D\frac{d^2 w}{dx^2} = M_0 e^{-\beta x} [\cos \beta x - \sin \beta x] \qquad (9\text{-}98)$$

The maximum value of M is found by equating the derivative of Equation (9-98) to zero.

$$\frac{dM}{d(\beta x)} = M_0 e^{-\beta x}(-2\cos \beta x) = 0$$

But $\cos \beta x = 0$ for $\beta x = n\frac{\pi}{2}$, where n is any odd integer. Thus for $\beta x = \pi/2$,

$$M_1 = -M_0 e^{-\pi/2} = -0.208 M_0$$

and for $\beta x = 3\pi/2$,

$$M_3 = M_0 e^{-3\pi/2} = 0.0091 M_0$$

Hence, it is seen that for $\beta x = \pi/2$ the moment is quite small and practically vanishes for $\beta x = 3\pi/2$.

To determine the depth of penetration, solve for x, as follows:

$$x = \frac{n\pi}{2\beta} = \frac{n\pi}{2} \frac{\sqrt{ah}}{\sqrt[4]{3(1-\nu^2)}} \doteq n\pi \frac{\sqrt{ah}}{2.64}$$

for $n = 1$ $\qquad\qquad\qquad$ $x = 1.19\sqrt{ah}$

for $n = 3$ $\qquad\qquad\qquad$ $x = 5.57\sqrt{ah}$

As stated above, if we calculate the moment in the cylinder a distance $x = 1.19\sqrt{ah}$ from the edge at which M_0 and Q_0 are applied, the effects of M_0 and Q_0 have practically been dissipated. Thus for a dome of 50-ft radius and 3-in. thickness, at a distance of $x = 1.19\sqrt{50 \times 0.25} = 3.95$ ft from the built-in edge, the moment will have a value of $-0.208M_0$. It seems likely that domes can be safely designed by a procedure of this kind.

9-37 Conclusion

The techniques presented in this chapter have been extended to other shell problems, including composite shells such as cylindrical shells enclosed at the ends by spherical segments, a half sphere supported by a cylinder, spherical shells supported by columns, etc. Some references are given[22] covering shell solutions of this type.

There are other methods in use, especially those which are based upon a double curvature structural shape and the assumption that this shape lends itself particularly to membrane states of stress and hence leads to a simplified form of analysis.[23]

From the point of view of the practicing engineer, it is, of course, desirable that a safe, economical method of shell design be available which is relatively simple and does not require lengthy computations or analysis. Such methods are perhaps available for certain specialized shapes, but for the general structure it would seem to be necessary to resort to one of the more involved and lengthy methods such as described in this chapter. However, many questions concerning the accuracy of these methods are still unanswered.

[22] M. G. Salvadori, "Shell versus Arch Action in Barrel Shells," *Proceedings*, ASCE, Separate No. 653, March, 1955.

M. G. Salvadori, "Stresses and Displacements in Thin Shells Composed of Cylindrical and Spherical Segments," *Proceedings*, ASCE, Separate No. 293, October 1953.

M. G. Salvadori and A. D. Ateshoglou, "Ribless Cylindrical Shells," *Journal of the American Concrete Institute*, 1955.

[23] Some of these methods are discussed in *Proceedings of a Conference on Thin Concrete Shells*," M.I.T., June 1954. Others are discussed in a paper by Alfred L. Parme, "Hyperbolic Paraboloids and Other Shells of Double Curvature," *Proceedings*, ASCE, Paper 1057, September 1956.

Problems

1. A simply supported square plate of constant thickness is loaded uniformly over half its area (see figure). By finite differences, determine the approximate deflections and moments within the plate. Use $h=a/4$, thus dividing the plate into 16 squares.

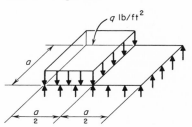

2. A plate of length $2a$ and width a is simply supported on two opposite edges and in the middle parallel to these edges. The other edges of the plate are free. By finite differences determine the moments and deflections produced by a uniformly distributed load of q lb/ft². Use $h=a/4$.

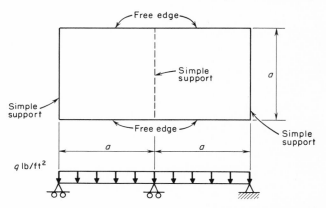

3. Given a long, reinforced concrete cylindrical shell simply supported on a span of 200 ft, radius $r=50$ ft, $\phi_k=35°$, shell thickness $h=3$ in., live load $p_u=20$ lb/ft² of horizontal projection:

   (a) Find the membrane stresses and the accompanying line loads and edge deflection.
   (b) Using the ASCE Manual, find the effects of applied line loads at the edges.
   (c) For an edge beam 16 in. wide by 60 in. deep, find the effects due to interaction with the shell.
   (d) Compare the results of adding steps (a), (b), and (c) with those obtained by the elementary beam theory.

Use the ASCE Manual in obtaining the above solutions.

4. Given an intermediate, reinforced concrete cylindrical shell simply supported on a span of 50 ft, other dimensions same as problem 3, repeat steps (a), (b), (c). Will the edge beam still be necessary in this case?

5. Given a short, reinforced concrete cylindrical shell simply supported on a span of 20 ft, the other dimensions the same as for problem 3; repeat steps (a), (b), and (c). Is the edge beam necessary for this case?

6. For problem 4, determine the effects of interaction of the shell with supporting arches if the connection between the shell and the arch is considered built-in.

7. A building 150 ft × 100 ft is roofed by six cylindrical concrete shells of the dimensions of problem 4 excepting ϕ_k, which must be computed. Three supporting arches are 50 ft apart (see figure). Edge beams line the exterior longitudinal edges of the exterior shells. The interior edges are integral with one another. Find the stresses within the shells due to dead load and live load of 20 lb/ft^2 of horizontal projection. Use the ASCE Manual tables to obtain the solution.

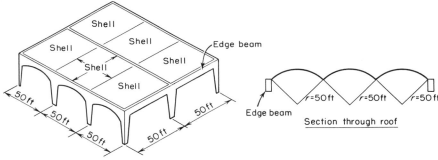

8. Find the membrane dead load stresses in a reinforced concrete spherical dome of 100-ft radius, 50-ft rise, 5-in. thickness.

9. Find the membrane stresses in the dome of problem 8 produced by a live load of 20 lb/ft^2 of horizontal projection.

Chapter 10

TEMPERATURE STRESSES IN COMPLEX STRUCTURES

10-1 Introduction

In this chapter we consider the stresses that temperature changes can introduce into complex structures and structural components. With airplanes and missiles reaching higher and higher speeds, temperature effects on material properties and temperature stresses are becoming increasingly important factors in airplane and missile structural analysis. Also, several unexplained ship structural failures possibly were caused or at least influenced by temperature effects. Nuclear power plants also introduce many structural temperature problems, and an acquaintance with temperature stresses is essential to work in the nuclear engineering field.

In view of the foregoing, it becomes necessary that the structural designer be capable of handling temperature stress analysis. The civil engineer has been dealing with temperature effects in a very elementary and approximate form in his design of trusses, arches, and similar structures. The basic procedure in use in these methods will be discussed in connection with a simplified problem (see Art. 10-2). However, the major portion of this chapter will present the more complex analysis of a structural member (possibly of different materials) subjected to variable temperature distributions. A procedure will be given for systematically determining the temperature stresses in this type of structure. It is felt that wide applications of this method can be made to civil engineering structures, as well as to marine, aircraft, and nuclear structures.

10-2 Temperature effects

The complete analysis of a temperature effect problem consists essentially of two parts:

1. The determination of the temperature distribution in the structure.

2. The determination of the stresses in the structure due to such temperature distribution.

The complete analysis of part 1 may be very complicated. It generally will be a time dependent (transient) phenomenon. This is a more difficult analysis than the "steady state" condition, which assumes that the temperatures do not vary with time (although the temperature may vary from place to place in the structure). The temperature distribution analysis is beyond the scope of this text, but its methods can be found in textbooks on heat transfer.[1]

It is well known that temperature changes tend to cause elongations or shortenings of all materials, the unit deformation for a one-dimensional object being

$$\epsilon_t = \alpha\Delta t \qquad (10\text{-}1)$$

where ϵ_t = unit elongation, α = temperature coefficient of expansion, in./in./°F, and Δt = change in temperature. If these strains are prevented or restrained in any way, they lead to induced stresses in the structure. In this respect temperature stresses are fundamentally different from ordinary stresses, in that

(a) Ordinary stresses are caused by external loadings.
(b) Temperature stresses are caused by external deformations.

To illustrate the simplest type of temperature stress analysis, we consider the following problem:

Example: A bar of length l, modulus of elasticity E, as shown in Fig. 10.1, is built in at its ends and is in equilibrium at room temperature t_0. The bar is then heated to a temperature t. Find the stress in the bar.

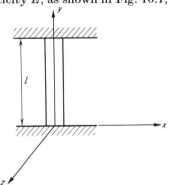

Solution: If the bar were free, it would expand an amount

$$\epsilon_y = \alpha(t - t_0) \qquad (10\text{-}2)$$

However, the wall prevents this unit elongation, i.e., it introduces stresses σ_y which will cause an equal and opposite unit deformation, or

$$\sigma_y = -(\alpha)(t - t_0)E \qquad (10\text{-}3)$$

Fig. 10.1

This is the temperature-induced stress. Although very much simplified, the above is essentially the type of temperature solution which is applied in the ordinary civil engineering analysis. It is a superposition procedure, the thermal effects being explained by simple application of Equation (10-1).

---

[1] See, for example, Max Jakob, *Heat Transfer*, John Wiley and Sons, Inc., 1949.

10-3   **The thermal analysis of irregular type structures**

In this article a procedure will be described which is suitable for temperature stress analysis of more complicated structures, such as marine ship hulls, airplane wings, nuclear reactor components, and similar members. The basic theory is well known and has been known for some time. Jasper[2] summarized the theory and set up a computational procedure for any given problem. The present discussion is based generally upon his treatment.[3]

As background for the explanation, some elementary notions of elasticity theory will be reviewed. It will be recalled that in all problems in elasticity (i.e., structural analysis), not only must the equilibrium equations ($\sum F = 0$, $\sum M = 0$) be satisfied, but also the boundary conditions and, in addition, the deformations or strains must be compatible. This last requirement is simply that the strains must be finite, single valued and continuous throughout the structure.

The above requirements restrict the number of possible solutions to a given problem, and in fact, insure uniqueness of solutions to problems in elasticity.

The significance of the compatibility conditions (and their physical interpretation insofar as uniqueness of solutions is concerned) in the approximate analysis of temperature stresses can be emphasized by considering the following example.

The hollow box section, of length l, free at its ends, is of uniform thickness as shown in Fig. 10.2. The box is initially at constant temperature t_0. Assume that the longitudinal fiber shown shaded is raised to a temperature $t_1 > t_0$, the remainder of the box remaining at temperature t_0.

This temperature rise tends to cause an elongation $\alpha(t_1 - t_0)l$ of the fiber and, if the fiber could elongate this amount, conditions would be as shown in Fig. 10.3, and the stress in the corner fiber (and all other fibers in the box) would be zero.

However, the conditions of Fig. 10.3 cannot be permitted since they violate the compatibility condition which requires continuity of deformation. In effect, there is a discontinuous deformation of the body, a condition that cannot be allowed. If we could permit a discontinuous deformation such as that shown, then an infinite number of solutions could be obtained—each corresponding to a different permitted amount of discontinuity in deflection. That is, the problem would not have a unique solution.

[2] Norman H. Jasper, *Temperature-Induced Stresses in Beams and Ships*, David W. Taylor Model Basin, Report 937, June 1955.

[3] Samuel Levy, "Thermal Stresses and Deformations in Beams," *Aeronautical Engineering Review*, October 1956, describes a somewhat similar procedure.

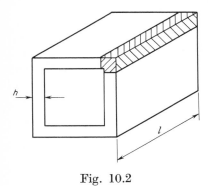

Fig. 10.2

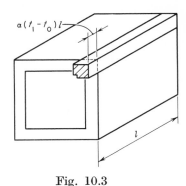

$a(t_1 - t_0)l$

Fig. 10.3

What actually does happen is that the entire cross section deforms and stresses are set up across the entire cross section which satisfy the equilibrium equations and boundary conditions everywhere,[4] as well as the compatibility conditions.

In applying the approximate method of analysis which follows, use is made of the following known, compatible deformations,

(a) The deformation of a cross section corresponding to a uniform stress distribution on the cross section is a compatible one.

(b) The deformation due to pure bending (the usual assumption that plane sections before bending remain plane after bending) is a compatible engineering deformation.

We illustrate how use is made of these known compatible deformations by considering the illustrative problem previously discussed (see Fig. 10.4).

Example: Let x, y, z axes be as shown in Fig. 10.4, y and z being principal axes.

t_0 = initial temperature of entire box.
t_1 = temperature to which corner fiber is raised.
A = cross sectional area of entire box.
A_1 = cross sectional area of corner fiber.
The ends of the box are free.

---

[4] Actually, the boundary conditions in our approximate method of analysis which follows are not exactly satisfied along the free edges. The free ends are free of stress. In our solution, there will be stresses whose resultants are zero on the free ends, but the stresses will not be zero. However, there is a well known St. Venant Principle of Elasticity which states that, in this case, although the boundary conditions are not satisfied exactly on the end faces, the stress distribution on sections away from the ends are essentially the same as though the boundary conditions were exactly satisfied.

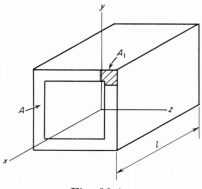

Fig. 10.4

Solution: The solution is obtained in the following steps:

I. Assume the ends of the box are fixed against longitudinal movement before t_1 is applied. Because of this a stress σ' is set up in the area A_1 with

$$\sigma' = -\alpha E(t_1 - t_0) \qquad (10\text{-}4)$$

and therefore there is a force acting on the cross section given by

$$F_1 = \sigma' A_1 \qquad (10\text{-}5)$$

All strains are compatible as of this point.

II. Because of the boundary conditions, the net force on all cross sections must be zero. To satisfy this requirement we introduce a force $F_2 = \sigma'' A$, equal and opposite to F_1, with σ'' equal to a uniformly distributed stress over the entire cross section. This is a strain compatible stress system.

III. However, the system of stresses σ' and σ'' on any cross section are equivalent to moments M_y about the Y axis, and moments M_z about the Z axis. Because of the boundary conditions, there can be no moments M_y or M_z, and we satisfy this requirement by adding the ordinary straight-line variation of stresses about the Y and Z axes such that we have moments just equal and opposite to the moments M_y and M_z due to σ' and σ''. Call these added stresses σ''' and σ''''. Both moment systems are strain compatible systems.

IV. We now have on any cross section,

(a) Stress at any point equal to
$$\sigma = \sigma' + \sigma'' + \sigma''' + \sigma''''$$

(b) $\sum F_x = 0$

(c) $\sum M_y = 0$

(d) $\sum M_z = 0$

(e) Compatible strains.

The stresses obtained represent a solution to the problem in all planes (except those in the neighborhood of the end planes).

In some cases the cross section may contain elements of different materials. If this is so, the same procedure may be used as outlined above. It is only necessary that "equivalent areas" be used instead of actual areas. The equivalent area is the actual area multiplied by the ratio of moduli of elasticity of the materials in question. This is the standard engineering method for handling structural components consisting of different materials.[5]

To illustrate all of the above, including the discussion of different materials, a problem will be solved in detail. All steps will be shown. After this is done, the general formulas will be given, and a tabular form suitable for solutions will be set up.

10-4 Illustrative problem

Example: Determine the stresses in the box structure shown in Fig. 10.5. The top side between the vertical walls is aluminum. The remainder is steel. Thickness is $\frac{1}{2}$ in. constant all around. Initial temperature was 100°C everywhere. Final corner temperatures are shown in Fig. 10.5.

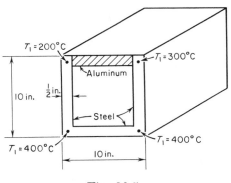

Fig. 10.5

The temperature variation from corner to corner is linear. The box is free at its ends.

$$\left.\begin{array}{l} E_a = 10{,}000{,}000 \text{ lb/in.}^2 \\ E_s = 30{,}000{,}000 \text{ lb/in.}^2 \\ \alpha_a = 0.000023 \text{ in./in./°C} \\ \alpha_s = 0.0000123 \text{ in./in./°C} \end{array}\right\} \begin{array}{l} \text{subscript } a = \text{aluminum} \\ \text{subscript } s = \text{steel} \end{array} \qquad (10\text{-}6)$$

Solution: The cross section is approximated by the "lumped area" section shown in Fig. 10.6. Also shown are the average temperatures for each lumped area. (If desired, the actual section can, of course, be approximated by a greater number of lumped stringers. This will, in general, lead to a more accurate solution. However, in this case we are

[5] See, for example, S. Timoshenko and G. H. MacCullough, *Elements of Strength of Materials*, D. Van Nostrand Company, Princeton, N.J., 3rd Ed., 1949.

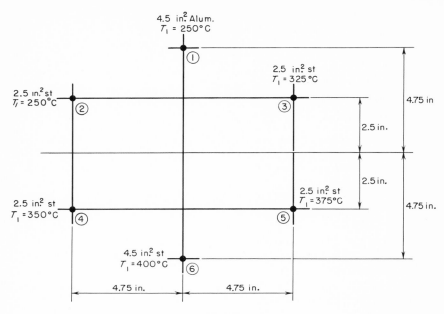

Fig. 10.6

primarily interested in developing the theory and procedure. Therefore a minimum number of stringer areas was chosen.)

The equivalent cross section and the centroidal axes of this equivalent cross section are shown in Fig. 10.7. The equivalent steel cross section is obtained by multiplying each aluminum area by E_a/E_s. Also shown is the Δt for each area.

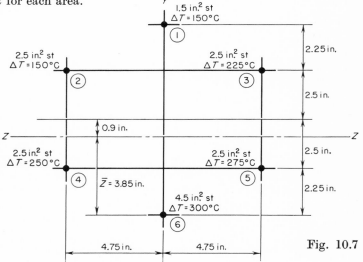

Fig. 10.7

Y-Y and Z-Z are centroidal axes of the transformed section.   To obtain Z, take moments, as follows

$$Z = \frac{5(2.25)+5(7.25)+1.5(9.5)}{5+5+1.5+4.5} = 3.85 \text{ in.}$$

Then,

$$I_{ZZ} = 1.5(5.65)^2+5(3.4)^2+5(1.6)^2+4.5(3.85)^2 = 185.4 \text{ in.}^4$$

and

$$I_{YY} = 2(5)(4.75)^2 = 225 \text{ in.}^4$$

These are moments of inertias about the principal axes.   The equivalent total $A_s = 16$ in.^{2}.

The step numbering which follows conforms to that given in Art. 10-3.

STEP I.   Determination of the stresses and forces assuming the beam is restrained against longitudinal movement.   Using Equations (10-4) and (10-5), these are

$$\sigma'_1 = -0.000023(150)(30,000,000) = -103,500 \text{ lb/in.}^2$$
$$F_1 = 1.50\sigma'_1 = -155.5 \text{ kip}$$
$$\sigma'_2 = -0.0000123(150)(30,000,000) = -55,000 \text{ lb/in.}^2$$
$$F_2 = 2.5\sigma'_2 = -138.8 \text{ kip}$$
$$\sigma'_3 = -0.0000123(225)(30,000,000) = -83,000 \text{ lb/in.}^2$$
$$F_3 = 2.5\sigma'_3 = -207.5 \text{ kip}$$
$$\sigma'_4 = -0.0000123(250)(30,000,000) = -92,500 \text{ lb/in.}^2$$
$$F_4 = 2.5\sigma'_4 = -232.0 \text{ kip}$$
$$\sigma'_5 = -0.0000123(275)(30,000,000) = -102,000 \text{ lb/in.}^2$$
$$F_5 = 2.5\sigma'_5 = -255.0 \text{ kip}$$
$$\sigma'_6 = -0.0000123(300)(30,000,000) = -111,000 \text{ lb/in.}^2$$
$$F_6 = 4.5\sigma'_6 = -500.0 \text{ kip}$$

$$\text{Total } F = -1488.8 \text{ kip}$$

STEP II.   Therefore, the required balancing stress, in order that

$$\sum F = 0 \tag{10-7}$$

is given by
$$\sigma'' = \frac{F}{A} = \frac{1488.8}{16} = +93,000 \text{ lb/in.}^2 \tag{10-8}$$

and the stresses due to the combination of the above are as shown in Fig. 10.8.   Also shown in this figure are the assumed directions of positive moment about the Y and Z axes.

STEP III.   Then, due to the stresses shown

$$M_z = +10.5(1.5)(5.65)-38.0(2.5)(3.4)-(10)(2.5)(3.4)+0.5(2.5)(1.6)$$
$$= -664 \text{ kip-in.} \tag{10-9}$$

$$M_y = (10.0-9.0-38.0-0.5)(2.5)(4.75)$$
$$= -445 \text{ kip-in.} \tag{10-10}$$

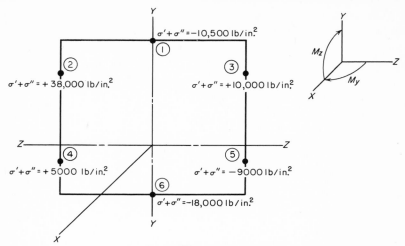

Fig. 10.8

To balance $\sum M_z = 0$, we must add

$$\sigma_1''' = -\frac{664(5.65)}{185.4} = -20,100 \text{ lb/in.}^2$$

$$\sigma_2''' = \sigma_3''' = -\frac{664(3.4)}{185.4} = -12,100 \text{ lb/in.}^2$$

$$\sigma_4''' = \sigma_5''' = +\frac{664(1.6)}{185.4} = +5700 \text{ lb/in.}^2$$

$$\sigma_6''' = +\frac{664(3.85)}{185.4} = +13,800 \text{ lb/in.}^2$$

$$(10\text{-}11)$$

and to balance $\sum M_y = 0$, we must add

$$\sigma_1'''' = \sigma_6'''' = 0$$

$$\sigma_2'''' = -\sigma_3'''' = -\frac{445(4.75)}{225} = -9400 \text{ lb/in.}^2$$

$$\sigma_4'''' = -\sigma_5'''' = -\frac{445(4.75)}{225} = -9400 \text{ lb/in.}^2$$

$$(10\text{-}12)$$

STEP IV. The final results are shown in the following tabular form

Stringer	σ', lb/in.^{2}	σ'', lb/in.^{2}	σ''', lb/in.^{2}	σ'''', lb/in.^{2}	Final $\sigma =$ $\sigma' + \sigma'' + \sigma''' +$ σ'''' lb/in.^{2}	σ Corrected for Modulus, lb/in.^{2}
1	-103500	$+93000$	-20100	0	-30600	-10200
2	$-\ 55000$	$+93000$	-12100	-9400	$+16500$	$+16500$
3	$-\ 83000$	$+93000$	-12100	$+9400$	$+\ 7300$	$+\ 7300$
4	$-\ 92500$	$+93000$	$+\ 5700$	-9400	$-\ 3200$	$-\ 3200$
5	-102000	$+93000$	$+\ 5700$	$+9400$	$+\ 6100$	$+\ 6100$
6	-111000	$+93000$	$+13800$	0	$-\ 4200$	$-\ 4200$

10-5   The general equations for thermal stress analysis

The solution of the previous section can be formalized and the general equations for the method may be obtained as follows:

STEP I.   Temperature stress σ' in any longitudinal fiber (or concentrated area) assuming the ends are fixed against translation

$$\left.\begin{aligned}\sigma' &= -\alpha E(t_1-t_0)\\ &= -\alpha E\Delta t\end{aligned}\right\} \tag{10-13}$$

STEP II.   Stress σ'' required to give balance of forces in the x direction, i.e.,

$$\sum F_x = 0 \tag{10-14}$$

$$\sigma''\!\int\!dA - \int\!\alpha E\Delta t\,dA = 0 \tag{10-15}$$

or

$$\sigma'' = \frac{1}{A}\int\alpha E\Delta t\,dA \tag{10-16}$$

STEP IIIa.   Stress σ''' required to balance moments about the z axis, i.e.,

$$\sum M_z = 0 \tag{10-17}$$

$$\int(\sigma'+\sigma''+\sigma'''+\sigma'''')y\,dA = 0 \tag{10-18}$$

(σ'''' is the stress of Step IIIb)

or

$$\frac{\sigma'''}{y} = \text{constant} = \left[\frac{-\sigma''\int y\,dA - \int\sigma'y\,dA - \int\sigma''''y\,dA}{\int y^2\,dA}\right] \tag{10-19}$$

STEP IIIb.   Similarly, the stress σ'''' required to balance moments about the y axis, i.e.,

$$\sum M_y = 0 \tag{10-20}$$

$$\int(\sigma'+\sigma''+\sigma'''+\sigma'''')z\,dA = 0 \tag{10-21}$$

or

$$\frac{\sigma''''}{z} = \text{constant} = \left[\frac{-\sigma''\int z\,dA - \int\sigma'z\,dA - \int\sigma''z\,dA}{\int z^2\,dA}\right] \tag{10-22}$$

Now, if z and y are the principal centroidal axes,

$$\int z\,dA = \int y\,dA = \int\sigma'''y\,dA = \int\sigma''z\,dA = 0 \tag{10-23}$$

so that

$$\sigma''' = -\frac{y}{I_z}\int\alpha E\Delta t y\,dA \tag{10-24}$$

$$\sigma'''' = -\frac{z}{I_y}\int\alpha E\Delta t z\,dA \tag{10-25}$$

STEP IV.   The final resultant stress is given by

$$\sigma = \sigma'+\sigma''+\sigma'''+\sigma'''' \tag{10-26}$$

or

$$\sigma = -\alpha E\Delta t+\frac{1}{A}\int\alpha E\Delta t\,dA -\frac{y}{I_z}\int\alpha E\Delta t y\,dA -\frac{z}{I_y}\int\alpha E\Delta t z\,dA \tag{10-27}$$

If the beam cross section contains elements of different materials, simply compute the equivalent one-material beam by using the ratio of moduli of elasticities as was done in the illustrative problem. If, in addition, the actual cross section is replaced by a lumped-area section, then the general equation corresponding to (10-27) (using subscripts a for "actual material" and e for "equivalent material", the $\sum$ being taken over all area elements) is:

$$\sigma_{\text{true}} = \left[-E_e\alpha_a\Delta t + \frac{\sum E_a\alpha_a\Delta t A_a}{\sum A_e} - \frac{y}{I_{z_e}}\sum \alpha_a E_a\Delta t y A_e - \frac{z}{I_{y_e}}\sum \alpha_a E_a\Delta t z A_e \right] \frac{E_a}{E_e} \qquad (10\text{-}28)$$

10-6 Tabular form for thermal stress computation

The solution of Equation (10-28) may be obtained in the tabular form which follows.

TABULAR FORM FOR DETERMINING TEMPERATURE STRESSES

Subscript a is for "actual material"

Subscript e is for "equivalent material"

1	2	3	4	5	6	7	8	9	10	11	12	13	14	15	16	17	18	19
Area Number	E_a	E_e	α_a	Δt	A_a	A_e	y from prin. axis	z from prin. axis	7×8^2	7×9^2	$-3 \times 4 \times 5 = \sigma_1$	12×6	$\dfrac{\sum 13}{\sum 7} = \sigma_2$	$12 \times 7 \times 8$	$\dfrac{(\sum 15) \times 8}{\sum 10} = \sigma_3$	$12 \times 7 \times 9$	$\dfrac{(\sum 17) \times 9}{\sum 11} = \sigma_4$	$\sigma_{\text{true}} = (12+14+16+18) \times \dfrac{2}{3}$
						$\sum A_e =$			$\sum = I_{z_e}$	$\sum = I_{y_e}$								

It is assumed that prior to filling in this table,

(a) The actual cross section has been replaced by an equivalent one-material cross section.

(b) The one-material cross section has been replaced by a lumped area cross section.

(c) The principal axes, moments of inertia about the principal axes, and other section properties have been obtained for the cross section of (b).

Problems

1. A typical airplane wing spar-skin unit is shown in Fig. 10.9. Material is aluminum. The temperature due to high-speed flight varies with time until a steady-state condition is reached. A typical temperature distribution at a time $t = 10$ minutes after beginning of flight is shown on the figure. Determine the stresses corresponding to this temperature distribution. The structure and temperature distribution are symmetrical about both center lines.

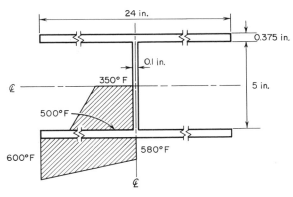

Fig. 10.9

2. A simplified ship cross section is shown in Fig. 10.10. Also shown is an approximate temperature (t) distribution, in which the temperatures shown are above the equilibrium values. Determine the stresses in the structure. The structure and temperature distribution are symmetrical about the center line.

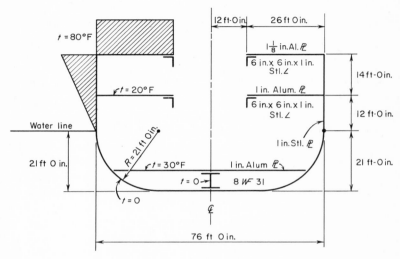

Fig. 10.10

Chapter 11

ELECTRONIC COMPUTER SOLUTIONS
OF STRUCTURAL PROBLEMS

11-1 Introduction

It was shown in Chapter 2 that the solution of multiply redundant structures requires solving simultaneous equations, the number of simultaneous equations being just equal to the number of redundants. For structures which have two or three redundants, numerical iterative methods or desk calculator machines can be used. However, the modern complex structure frequently contains many more redundants, and in these cases the calculation becomes a superhuman task, requiring many months of human labor—labor subject to the inherent shortcomings of human beings which produce errors, omissions, and the like.

The invention and development of the high-speed electronic computer has now made it possible to solve many simultaneous equations in a reasonable time. An example has been cited[1] in which a structure with 106 redundants was solved initially in about 12 hours, and each additional loading condition was solved in an additional $1\frac{1}{2}$ hours of computing time. This same problem could probably never have been solved using human labor with automatic desk calculators.

The solution to structural problems using the electronic computer is really a two-part problem. The problem must first be set up and formulated in a way to permit an electronic computer solution. This part of the problem lies within the scope of the structural engineer's work. The second part of the problem requires coding, or programing, and setting up the card system for the actual machine operation. This generally calls for the services of a specially trained operator, familiar with the particular computer being used. This person is often a mathematician in the field of applied mathematics, trained (usually under direction of the computer manufacturer) to set up the coding and card system for special kinds of problems. His programing can

---

[1] J. S. Archer, "Digital Computation for Stiffness Matrix Analyses," *Journal of the Structural Division, Proceedings of the American Society of Civil Engineers*, Oct. 1958. The present chapter is much indebted to this article.

be applied to any similar future problem and is stored in a "library" and brought out and used when needed.

The successful solution to the highly indeterminate structural problem is thus a joint effort and the two parties are equally important. Our topic is the first portion of the project as described above. After descriptions in very general terms of the two types of electronic computers in common use—the analog and the digital—we present the elementary theory of matrix algebra which is the basis of one of the computer operations. Application to structural problems will then be described in fairly general terms. Then the steps in the solution of a typical problem will be detailed; and finally, a typical problem will be solved.

11-2   The two usual types of electronic computers

There are two types of electronic computers in ordinary use:

1. The analog computer, which deals with physical variables.
2. The digital computer, which deals with numbers.

There are also converters that make it possible to convert from analog to digital computer, but we shall not discuss these here.

The electronic analog computer, developed during World War II, is used primarily for solving complex dynamic problems. It simulates the actual physical problem by noting the analogy between the differential equations of the actual problem and the differential equations of electronic network systems. All measured quantities are electronic; but because of the analogy, these can readily be converted to the actual required quantities. The analog computer makes it possible to solve both linear and non-linear differential equations, and typical applications have been made in practically all engineering and scientific fields. The indeterminate structure, however, can best be solved with the digital computer, to be described next.

The digital computer works directly with numbers. The electronic digital computer is fundamentally like all other digitial computers (e.g., the abacus, the desk calculator) in that it performs a limited number of very simple tasks, viz.:

1. To read a number.
2. To write a number.
3. To change the sign of a number.
4. Tc change the decimal point of a number.
5. To add two numbers.

Subtraction is a combination of operations (3) and (5); multiplication of (4) and (5); division of (3), (4), and (5). The difference between the electronic digital computer and the non-electronic digital computer is simply that whereas the non-electronic computer may take a second or more to complete a given operation, the electronic computer will complete this same operation in milliseconds or microseconds. Thus a problem which requires many thousands of applications of very simple elementary steps will take years of calculation with a desk computer, but only hours with an electric computer.

Many types of electronic digital computers are in use, and more are being constructed. The "memory systems" and storage units are constantly being improved. Card programing systems as well as paper and magnetic systems are in use.

The structural problem can be programed in such a way that all the many steps involved in the solution are handled by the computer. Thus the stiffness factors (EI/L) can be obtained, all intermediate balance-of-force and moment equations can be solved, and the simultaneous equations can also be solved. In fact, the programing can be so arranged that the basic input data are all that is required to be determined by the human operator—the final answer, moments in inch pounds and shears in pounds, being recorded and put out by the computer.

Beyond any question, the electronic high-speed computer has become a part of ordinary everyday engineering procedure, and its use is bound to increase as time goes on. It is essential for the modern structural engineer to have some understanding of procedures used in programing for this equipment.[2]

11-3 Introductory matrix algebra[3]

In structural applications, one of the steps in the solution requires that the electronic digital computer solve a matrix equation. Some understanding of matrix algebra is required to appreciate fully the applications that are possible in structural analyses. Fortunately the matrix operations involved are quite elementary. These will

---

[2] Structural engineering applications of electronic digital computers are dealt with in the following:

E. Czermak, "Rigid Frame Analysis with the Aid of Digital Computers," *Journal of the Structural Division, American Society of Civil Engineers*, Sept. 1958.

H. U. Schuerch, "Vibration Mode Analyses for Delta Wing Structure," Convair, San Diego, *Memo* DG-G-100, 12-18-51.

S. Levy, "Structural Analysis and Influence Coefficients for Delta Wings," *Journal of Aeronautical Sciences*, Vol. 20, No. 7, July 1953.

G. Best and M. P. Keating, "A Stiffness Matrix Method of Delta Wing Stress Analyses," Convair, Fort Worth, SRG-16, 9-8-53.

[3] A very brief introductory treatment of matrix algebra will be found in *An Introduction to Matrix Tensor Methods in Theoretical and Applied Mechanics* by S. F. Borg, published by J. W. Edwards, Ann Arbor, Mich., 1956.

now be described. An understanding of the few simple relations that follow is all that is necessary for the matrix applications to the structural engineering part of computer programing.

A rectangular array of m rows and n columns of numbers is called a matrix. We designate a matrix by a capital letter and show it in its expanded form as follows (a typical 2×4 matrix—i.e., two rows and four columns):

$$A = \begin{pmatrix} a_{11} & a_{12} & a_{13} & a_{14} \\ a_{21} & a_{22} & a_{23} & a_{33} \end{pmatrix} \tag{11-1}$$

In the expression above, a_{ij} represents an element of the matrix. Note that the subscripts carry a positional significance. That is, the first subscript represents the row position of the element and the second subscript represents the column position.

A matrix is not a determinant. As a reminder of this, the enclosing bars are shown curved and not straight, as is usual for a determinant.

A matrix may be a column matrix:

$$B = \begin{pmatrix} b_{11} \\ b_{21} \\ b_{31} \end{pmatrix} \tag{11-2}$$

or a row matrix:

$$C = \begin{pmatrix} c_{11} & c_{12} & c_{13} \end{pmatrix} \tag{11-3}$$

A matrix is a square matrix if it has the same number of rows as columns:

$$D = \begin{pmatrix} d_{11} & d_{12} \\ d_{21} & d_{22} \end{pmatrix} \tag{11-4}$$

A square matrix is symmetrical if $a_{ij} = a_{ji}$. Thus in Equation (11-4), D will be a symmetrical matrix if $d_{12} = d_{21}$.

The transpose D^* of a matrix D is obtained by interchanging the rows and columns of D. Thus if, as before,

$$D = \begin{pmatrix} d_{11} & d_{12} \\ d_{21} & d_{22} \end{pmatrix} \tag{11-5}$$

then

$$D^* = \begin{pmatrix} d_{11} & d_{21} \\ d_{12} & d_{22} \end{pmatrix} \tag{11-6}$$

The determinant of a square matrix is equal to the determinant of its elements. Thus, again referring to the matrix D of equation (11-5),

$$\det D = \begin{vmatrix} d_{11} & d_{12} \\ d_{21} & d_{22} \end{vmatrix} = d_{11}d_{22} - d_{12}d_{21}$$

The cofactor matrix of any square matrix A with n rows and columns (denoted by co A) is the matrix obtained by replacing each element of A by its cofactor, the cofactor of a_{pq} being the product of the determinant of the matrix with $n-1$ rows and columns, obtained by erasing the p-th row and q-th column of A, by $(-1)^{p+q}$. Thus, again referring to matrix D of Equation (11-5), we have

$$\text{co } D = \begin{pmatrix} d_{22} & -d_{21} \\ -d_{12} & d_{11} \end{pmatrix} \tag{11-8}$$

The product of two matrices, AB, may be obtained if B possesses as many rows as A possesses columns. Then

$$C = AB \tag{11-9}$$

in which C is the matrix equal to the product of A and B, and the element c_{jk} is the sum of the product of each element of the k-th column of B by the corresponding element of the j-th row of A. For example, if

$$A = \begin{pmatrix} 2 & 1 \\ 3 & 4 \end{pmatrix} \tag{11-10a}$$

and

$$B = \begin{pmatrix} 6 \\ 3 \end{pmatrix} \tag{11-10b}$$

then

$$C = \begin{pmatrix} 2 & 1 \\ 3 & 4 \end{pmatrix}\begin{pmatrix} 6 \\ 3 \end{pmatrix} = \begin{pmatrix} 2 \times 6 + 1 \times 3 \\ 3 \times 6 + 4 \times 3 \end{pmatrix} = \begin{pmatrix} 15 \\ 30 \end{pmatrix} \tag{11-10c}$$

If A is any square matrix of n columns and rows, then the inverse matrix, denoted by A^{-1}, is a matrix such that

$$AA^{-1} = 1 \tag{11-11}$$

and A^{-1} is given by

$$A^{-1} = \frac{(\text{co } A)^*}{\det A} \tag{11-12}$$

The short treatment above covers all the matrix algebra theory needed for many applications in structural analyses.

11-4 The matrix formulation of structural problems

In Art. 1-24 it is shown that the following load-deflection relation may be given for the general structure,

$$\left.\begin{aligned} y_1 &= a_{11}P_1 + a_{12}P_2 + \cdots a_{1j}P_j + \cdots a_{1n}P_n \\ y_2 &= a_{21}P_1 + a_{22}P_2 + \cdots a_{2j}P_j + \cdots a_{2n}P_n \\ y_j &= a_{j1}P_1 + a_{j2}P_2 + \cdots a_{jj}P_j + \cdots a_{jn}P_n \end{aligned}\right\} \tag{11-13}$$

which, in matrix notation, is, for deflections at the n points of loading,

$$\begin{pmatrix} y_1 \\ y_2 \\ \vdots \\ y_n \end{pmatrix} = \begin{pmatrix} a_{11} & a_{12} \cdots a_{1j} \cdots a_{1n} \\ a_{21} & a_{22} \cdots a_{2j} \cdots a_{2n} \\ \vdots & \vdots \quad \vdots \quad \vdots \\ a_{n1} & a_{n2} \cdots a_{nj} \cdots a_{nn} \end{pmatrix} \begin{pmatrix} P_1 \\ P_2 \\ \vdots \\ P_n \end{pmatrix} \qquad (11\text{-}14a)$$

or

$$Y = AP \qquad\qquad (11\text{-}14b)$$

Note that A is a symmetrical matrix (see Art. 1–24).

The elements a_{ij} are called *flexibility influence coefficients* and are defined in the following way:

> a_{ij} is the deflection of point i due to a unit load at point j, all other points being assumed unloaded.

The calculation of these coefficients is very lengthy and laborious. For this reason Equation (11-13) is not used directly in the digital computer solution of the problem.

However, Equation (11-13) may be thought of as solved for the P's in terms of the deflections y. Then

$$\left.\begin{aligned} P_1 &= s_{11}y_1 + s_{12}y_2 + \cdots s_{1n}y_n \\ P_2 &= s_{21}y_1 + s_{22}y_2 + \cdots s_{2n}y_n \\ &\vdots \\ P_n &= s_{n1}y_1 + s_{n2}y_2 + \cdots s_{nn}y_n \end{aligned}\right\} \qquad (11\text{-}15)$$

which is, in matrix notation

$$\begin{pmatrix} P_1 \\ P_2 \\ \vdots \\ P_n \end{pmatrix} = \begin{pmatrix} s_{11} & s_{12} \cdots s_{1n} \\ s_{21} & s_{22} \cdots s_{2n} \\ s_{n1} & s_{n2} \cdots s_{nn} \end{pmatrix} \begin{pmatrix} y_1 \\ y_2 \\ \vdots \\ y_n \end{pmatrix} \qquad (11\text{-}16a)$$

or

$$P = SY \qquad\qquad (11\text{-}16b)$$

In the above equations, s_{ij} are the *stiffness coefficients* and are defined as follows:

> s_{ij} is the load developed at point i due to a unit deflection at point j, all other points being assumed fixed.

The computation for s_{ij} is relatively simple. Then since

$$P = SY \qquad\qquad (11\text{-}16b)$$

it follows that by multiplying both sides of Equation (11-16b) by the matrix A, we obtain

$$AP = ASY \qquad (11\text{-}17)$$

which—see Equations (11-14b) and (11-11)—means that

$$AS = 1 \qquad (11\text{-}18)$$

or

$$\left.\begin{aligned} A &= S^{-1} \\ &= \frac{(\text{co } S)^*}{\det S} \end{aligned}\right\} \qquad (11\text{-}19)$$

Note that S will be also be a symmetrical matrix, since A is symmetrical.

In applying the matrix technique just described to the structural engineering problem, one proceeds as follows.

1. Assume unknown deflections (angular rotations, horizontal linear and vertical linear) at all support points that can have deflections and at all loaded interior points. This includes assumed sidesway deflections in rigid frames. There will be n unknown deflections.

2. We do *not* assume deflections at points that cannot deflect. Thus a hinged end can have only an angular deflection, not a linear one. A built-in end cannot have an angular or linear deflection. This assumption is necessary, since otherwise the determinants of the flexibility and stiffness matrices will be zero and the inverse of the matrix will be undefined.

3. Assume that a load is acting at each reaction corresponding to the assumed deflection—moment for angular deflection, force for linear deflection. At intermediate points, due to sidesway or actual loading, also assume loads are acting; but these will be zero or will have known values. There will be n loads, all of which are known.

4. Compute the stiffness coefficients S of Equation (11-16a). This may be programed and computed by the machine. These will be the elements of an $n \times n$ symmetrical matrix.

5. Determine the inverse of S, Equation (11-19). This is A, the flexibility matrix—see Equation (11-14b). The inversion is performed by the computer and will result in an $n \times n$ symmetrical matrix.

6. Now using Equation (11-14b), determine the deflections of the n points assumed in step 1. This is performed by the computer.

7. Knowing all the deflections and using the simple elastic relations governing moments, shears, and deflections of simple bars, determine the moments and shears at all key points in the structure. This is performed by the computer.

11-5   Illustrative problem

We shall illustrate this procedure by referring to a specific problem which was solved on a computer.[4]

Example: A rigid frame and loading are shown in Fig. 11.1.   Determine the shears and moments at the ends of the members.

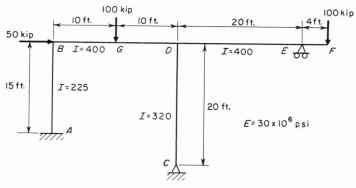

Fig. 11.1

Solution : The solution will be given in a series of steps labeled to conform to the detailed procedure of the preceding article.

1. We assume unknown deflections (linear and angular) as shown in Fig. 11.2.   There are nine unknown deflections in this problem.

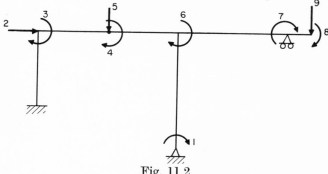

Fig. 11.2

2. Note that at the built-in end there are no assumed unknown deflections and at the hinge supports there are only unknown rotations.

3. There are therefore nine loads assumed to be acting on the structure. All of these loads are known.

---

[4] The illustrative problem which follows was used by J. S. Archer in his paper, "Digital Computation for Stiffness Matrix Analyses," Paper No. 1814, *Journal of the Structural Division, Proceedings of the American Society of Civil Engineers,* Oct. 1958. Tables 11.1, 11.2, 11.3, and 11.4 are reprinted from this article.

4. We next determine the elements s_{ij} of the stiffness matrix, in which s_{ij}, it will be recalled, is the load developed at point i due to a unit deflection at point j, all other points being assumed fixed. Thus for example, s_{61} = moment at point 6 due to a unit rotation at joint 1, all other joints assumed fixed. This is given by Fig. 11.3.

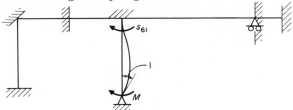

Fig. 11.3

$$s_{61} = \frac{M}{2} \qquad (11\text{-}20)$$

where

$$\frac{Ml}{4EI} = 1 \qquad (11\text{-}21)$$

as may easily be verified by conjugate beam.
Hence

$$s_{61} = \frac{4EI}{2l}$$

$$= \frac{4}{2} \frac{(30 \times 10^6)(320)}{(20)(12)}$$

$$s_{61} = 0.8 \times 10^8 \qquad (11\text{-}22)$$

The other terms are obtained in a similar manner. All of these may be programed and computed by the machine as part of the over-all operation.

The stiffness matrix is then as shown in Table 11.1. Note that this is a 9×9 symmetrical matrix.

TABLE 11.1

1	2	3	4	5	6	7	8	9
16×10^9	$-.1 \times 10^7$	0	0	0	$.8 \times 10^8$	0	0	0
$-.1 \times 10^7$	$.22 \times 10^5$	$-.125 \times 10^7$	0	0	$-.1 \times 10^7$	0	0	0
0	$-.125 \times 10^7$	$.55 \times 10^9$	$.2 \times 10^9$	$-.5 \times 10^7$	0	0	0	0
0	0	$.2 \times 10^9$	$.8 \times 10^9$	0	$.2 \times 10^9$	0	0	0
0	0	$-.5 \times 10^7$	0	$.16 \times 10^6$	$.5 \times 10^7$	0	0	0
$.8 \times 10^8$	$-.1 \times 10^7$	0	$.2 \times 10^9$	$.5 \times 10^7$	$.76 \times 10^9$	$.1 \times 10^9$	0	0
0	0	0	0	0	$.1 \times 10^9$	$.12 \times 10^{10}$	$.5 \times 10^9$	$-.3125 \times 10^8$
0	0	0	0	0	0	$.5 \times 10^9$	$.1 \times 10^{10}$	$-.3125 \times 10^8$
0	0	0	0	0	0	$-.3125 \times 10^8$	$-.3125 \times 10^8$	$.1302 \times 10^7$

5. The flexibility matrix A is now obtained by inversion. This is a machine operation and may be programed without difficulty. The flexibility matrix is shown in Table 11.2.

TABLE 11.2

1	2	3	4	5	6	7	8	9
$.1005 \times 10^{-7}$	$.5312 \times 10^{-6}$	$.2172 \times 10^{-8}$	$-.3027 \times 10^{-9}$	$.9397 \times 10^{-7}$	$-.9608 \times 10^{-9}$	$.4804 \times 10^{-9}$	$.4804 \times 10^{-9}$	$.2306 \times 10^{-7}$
$.5312 \times 10^{-6}$	$.8725 \times 10^{-4}$	$.3035 \times 10^{-6}$	$-.8294 \times 10^{-7}$	$.8259 \times 10^{-5}$	$.2824 \times 10^{-7}$	$-.1412 \times 10^{-7}$	$-.1412 \times 10^{-7}$	$-.6776 \times 10^{-6}$
$.2172 \times 10^{-8}$	$.3035 \times 10^{-6}$	$.4098 \times 10^{-8}$	$.8873 \times 10^{-9}$	$.1394 \times 10^{-6}$	$-.5490 \times 10^{-9}$	$.2745 \times 10^{-9}$	$.2745 \times 10^{-9}$	$.1318 \times 10^{-7}$
$-.3027 \times 10^{-9}$	$-.8294 \times 10^{-7}$	$-.8873 \times 10^{-9}$	$.1580 \times 10^{-8}$	$-.1368 \times 10^{-7}$	$-.4314 \times 10^{-9}$	$.2157 \times 10^{-9}$	$.2157 \times 10^{-9}$	$.1035 \times 10^{-7}$
$.9397 \times 10^{-7}$	$.8259 \times 10^{-5}$	$.1394 \times 10^{-6}$	$-.1368 \times 10^{-7}$	$-.8471 \times 10^{-7}$	$.2275 \times 10^{-8}$	$.4235 \times 10^{-7}$	$.4235 \times 10^{-7}$	$.2033 \times 10^{-5}$
$-.9608 \times 10^{-9}$	$.2824 \times 10^{-7}$	$-.5490 \times 10^{-9}$	$-.4314 \times 10^{-9}$	$-.8471 \times 10^{-7}$	$.2275 \times 10^{-8}$	$-.1137 \times 10^{-8}$	$-.1137 \times 10^{-8}$	$-.5459 \times 10^{-7}$
$.4804 \times 10^{-9}$	$-.1412 \times 10^{-7}$	$.2745 \times 10^{-9}$	$.2157 \times 10^{-9}$	$.4235 \times 10^{-7}$	$-.1137 \times 10^{-8}$	$.5569 \times 10^{-8}$	$.5569 \times 10^{-8}$	$.2673 \times 10^{-6}$
$.4804 \times 10^{-9}$	$-.1412 \times 10^{-7}$	$.2745 \times 10^{-9}$	$.2157 \times 10^{-9}$	$.4235 \times 10^{-7}$	$-.1137 \times 10^{-8}$	$.5569 \times 10^{-8}$	$.9569 \times 10^{-8}$	$.3633 \times 10^{-6}$
$.2306 \times 10^{-7}$	$-.6776 \times 10^{-6}$	$.1318 \times 10^{-7}$	$.1035 \times 10^{-7}$	$.2033 \times 10^{-5}$	$-.5459 \times 10^{-7}$	$.2673 \times 10^{-6}$	$.3633 \times 10^{-6}$	$.1590 \times 10^{-4}$

6. The matrix equation (11-14b),

$$Y = AP \tag{11-14b}$$

may now be solved by the computer for the deflections, since A and P are known. The results of this machine computation are shown in Table 11.3.

TABLE 11.3

Coordinate	Deflection	Coordinate	Deflection
1	.0383 rad.	6	−.0125 rad.
2	5.120 in.	7	.0303 rad.
3	.0304 rad.	8	.0399 rad.
4	−.00448 rad.	9	1.760 in.
5	1.889 in.		

7. It is now possible to obtain, by use of the simple structure elastic relations, the shears and moments at all points in the structure. For example, M_{AB} is determined as follows.

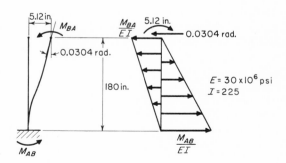

Fig. 11.4

Fig. 11.4 shows the portion of the deflected structure AB. The deflections at B are given in Table 11.3.   Also shown is the conjugate beam for this portion of the structure.   Referring to the conjugate beam,

$$\frac{(M_{AB} - M_{BA})(180)}{2(30 \times 10^6)(225)} = 0.0304$$

and

$$\frac{M_{AB}}{(225)(30 \times 10^6)} \left(\frac{180}{2}\right)\left(\frac{2}{3}\right)\left(180\right) = 5.12 + \frac{M_{BA}}{(225)(30 \times 10^6)}\left(\frac{180}{2}\right)\left(\frac{1}{3}\right)\left(180\right)$$

Solving these simultaneously, we obtain

$$M_{AB} = 0.4118 \times 10^7 \text{ in. lb}$$

The other moments and shears are obtained in similar ways, using the computer machine properly programed for the particular load desired.   The final results are shown in Table 11.4, which represents the solution to the problem.

TABLE 11.4

Member	Moment (l.e.), in. ~ lb	Shear, lb	Moment (r.e.), in. ~ lb
AB	.4118 × 10⁷	− 33,074	− .1835 × 10⁷
BG	− .1835 × 10⁷	− 27,603	− .5148 × 10⁷
GD	− .5148 × 10⁷	72,397	.3540 × 10⁷
DE	− .5224 × 10⁶	22,176	.4800 × 10⁷
EF	.4800 × 10⁷	− 100,000	0
CD	0	− 16,126	− .4062 × 10⁷

11-6   Conclusion

In the preceding sections we discussed one special type of computer solution to a structural problem.   There are other types of solutions possible, corresponding to other formulations of the problem and hence other programing.   For example, it is possible to solve the problem above by formulating the structural equations in the form of the slope deflection equations of Chapter 3.   All of the steps shown in Art. 3–4 can be programed and handled directly by the computer.   The computer would then solve for the unknown end slopes and deflections θ and ψ, using the necessary shear balance and other compatibility equations.   The final end moments and shears will be automatically determined by the machine.

Which formulation is used depends upon the problem, the machine that is available, and possibly the preferences of the engineer and the mathematician setting up the program.[5]

[5] A recent text describing general techniques in all phases of electronic computer work is F. L. Alt's *Electronic Digital Computors*, Academic Press, Inc., New York, 1958.

INDEX

Date Due